D1479264

A FIELD GUIDE TO THE
# Coral Reef Fishes
## of the Indian and West Pacific Oceans

A FIELD GUIDE TO THE

# Coral Reef Fishes

of the Indian and West Pacific Oceans

## R. H. Carcasson

COLLINS
St James's Place, London

William Collins Sons & Co Ltd
London · Glasgow · Sydney · Auckland
Toronto · Johannesburg

FOR BEE

First published 1977
© R. H. Carcasson 1977

ISBN 0 00 219664 6

Made and Printed in Great Britain by
William Collins Sons & Co Ltd Glasgow

# Acknowledgements

This book could not have been completed without the assistance and facilities afforded by the following persons and institutions.

The Green Island Aquarium, Great Barrier Reef, Queensland
The Port Moresby Aquarium, Papua-New Guinea
Dr Ian S. R. Munro of C.S.I.R.O., Cronulla, Australia
The Director and Trustees of the National Museum, Nairobi, Kenya
The Director and staff of the Kenya National Parks
Dr Murray Newman of the Vancouver Public Aquarium
Mr Vic Oke of the Cairns Oceanarium, Queensland
Mr G. Palmer of the Ichthyology Department, British Museum
Mr Peter Phillips of Mombasa, Kenya
Mr Peter Saw of Malindi, Kenya
The Sea Life Park Aquarium, Oahu, Hawaii
Mrs M. M. Smith, director of the J. L. B. Smith Institute of Ichthyology, Rhodes University, Grahamstown, South Africa
Mr Harold Stork of the Aquarium, Suva, Fiji
Miss R. Tauber of Kikambala, Kenya
The Public Aquarium, Singapore
Mr Spencer Tinker of the Waikiki Aquarium, Honolulu, Hawaii
Mr E. G. White, aquarium overseer, Zoological Gardens, Colombo, Ceylon

A multitude of fishermen and market-masters from one end of the Indo-Pacific to the other, who put up with my photographic activities with unfailing good humour, and finally my wife, who held a flash gun until her arm ached, carried unmanageable bits of equipment in a variety of improbable places, deciphered my handwriting and typed much of the manuscript.

# Contents

# CONTENTS

# Introduction

The purpose of this book is to enable the amateur naturalist and the enquiring traveller to recognise the commoner inshore fishes which he is likely to see when snorkelling or scuba diving and to identify what he sees in the local fish market, or what he may catch on his line when angling from a pier or a small boat. The area is the tropical Indo-Pacific, a vast region extending from the Red Sea and the east coast of Africa to southern Japan, the Hawaiian islands in the north-east and to the Tuamotu Archipelago in the south Pacific.

In recent years the hobby of keeping tropical marine fishes in home aquaria has become increasingly popular and it is hoped that these pages will assist aquarists as well as dealers and exporters of tropical fishes to identify the majority of Indo-Pacific aquarium fishes.

A great deal has been written about marine fishes, but the older classical works are generally unobtainable and difficult to use, and much of the more recent semi-popular literature consists of general introductions, or of collections of beautiful photographs with little explanatory text. Most recent scientific works are surveys of the fish fauna of restricted areas, or monographs of single families. There are no general works on Indo-Pacific fishes.

Fishes are the most abundant of vertebrates and some 25,000 to 30,000 species have been described. No check-list of the Indo-Pacific fishes has been published, but it is probable that the number of species is in the region of 6-7,000.

In this book some 1,800 species have been described, the majority being shallow water inshore fishes (coral reef fishes); species of deep water and of open offshore waters (pelagic) have been given more cursory treatment. In such difficult groups as the Blennies, Gobies and smaller Scorpaenids only the commoner and more conspicuous members have been selected for detailed description.

The colour plates have been painted by the author from his photos of live or recently live fishes. Additional coloured illustrations would have been desirable, but could not be included without making the book impossibly expensive. Some important species have not been figured in colour because no live model has been available. Species which can be identified from characters other than colour have been drawn in black and white.

Much research remains to be done on Indo-Pacific fishes and there is little agreement on their classification. The classifications and systematic sequences adopted by different specialists vary considerably and the system followed in this book is a modified version of that used by Ian S. R. Munro (*Fishes of New Guinea*, 1967).

Many of the more common fishes have been described more than once under different names, from different areas, in different works, usually, but not always, by different authors. This confusion has been due to the fact that many species vary considerably according to age and sex and that the true relationship of such forms had not been recognised by early authors. In the case of widespread species, authors working in one area and unfamiliar with the literature relating to the fauna of other areas, have re-described as new, species which had already been described from elsewhere. In theory the oldest published name is the only one that has validity, all subsequent names being invalid synonyms. In practice however, it is often impossible to ascertain the oldest name, because some old (and not so old) descriptions are so inadequate, that they cannot be applied to the appropriate species with any degree of confidence. Another source of confusion is due to the structural uniformity of certain groups of fishes which can only be distinguished by colour or pattern, characters which are lost in preserved specimens and thus not available to workers in distant institutions. The live colours of many species have never been described in the scientific literature and such species can only be identified from structural characters which cannot be seen in the field, but require handling of the specimen.

The only identification key used in this book is a very simple illustrated key to the orders and to the more important families. Identification keys, such as those used in most scientific works, would be of little use in a book of this nature. Keys to the genera are useless because scientists do not agree on the generic characters of fishes; keys to the species cannot be used by the average amateur, because they often have to be based on structural characters which cannot be seen without handling the specimen.

No common names have been coined in this book; only those in common use and those used in well known standard works have been mentioned. Common names vary so much from place to place and from person to person, that anyone with more than a passing interest in marine fishes will be well advised to learn the Latin names and use them.

### THE INDO-PACIFIC REGION

This book deals primarily with the coral reef fishes of the Indian Ocean and of the western Pacific. Reef building corals occur in shallow warm waters only, between 30 degrees of latitude, north and south. In the Indo-Pacific the most northerly reefs are situated in the Gulf of Aqaba, in the northern Red Sea, in southern Japan and in the Hawaiian islands; the most southerly are off Lourenço Marques (Mozambique), at Lord Howe Island (off eastern Australia) and in the Tubuai islands. East of a line drawn from the island of Hawaii to the Marquesas and to Gambier Island there is a vast stretch of deep water devoid of islands and of coral reefs, which is and has been a barrier to the passage of most inshore fishes. Beyond 30 degrees of latitude in either hemisphere the water is too cold for the development of coral reefs and the fauna loses its tropical character.

The comparatively small area of warm water in the eastern Pacific, off Central America, has derived most of its fauna from the Caribbean, before the formation of the Isthmus of Panama. The tropical eastern Pacific, together with the Caribbean and the tropical Atlantic, forms a distinctive zoogeographic unit known as the Atlanto-East Pacific Region.

The tropical Indo-Pacific, also called the Indo-West Pacific Region, and the Atlanto-East Pacific Region have completely different faunas and only an insignificant proportion of pelagic species are common to both areas. The Indo-Pacific, thanks to its immense expanse and diversity, is much richer in species than the Atlanto-East Pacific and, in fact, has the richest marine fauna in the world.

A surprisingly high proportion of Indo-Pacific species occur throughout the area; the Central Indo-Pacific, consisting roughly of the Malay Archipelago, the Philippines and New Guinea, has a richer fauna than any other part of the Region and has probably been the principal evolutionary centre from which the entire Indo-Pacific has been populated. As one moves away from this area, the fauna becomes progressively impoverished; nevertheless there are many species endemic to the Indian Ocean, to the south-west Pacific and to Japanese waters which to some extent compensate for the loss of Central Indo-Pacific species.

There are two outlying parts of the Region which have developed a distinctive character: the Hawaiian Archipelago, thanks to its isolation, lacks several typical Indo-Pacific families such as the Clownfishes and many genera and species, but has developed an important endemic element. The Red Sea, because of its high salinity and possibly for other reasons which are not clearly understood, also has a number of endemic forms.

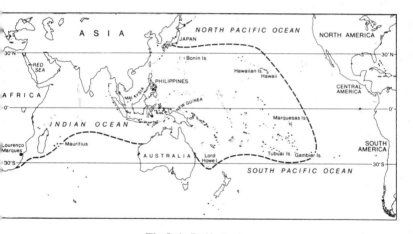

The Indo-Pacific Region

## HOW TO USE THIS BOOK

If you cannot place a fish in its appropriate order or family, follow the key and then examine the plates. Having found the family, read the descriptions until you find the species you want. If it is a reasonably common and well known inshore species, it will be in the book; if not, you will have to consult more specialised literature. Always read the paragraph at the beginning of the family and subfamily, as it often contains information which is applicable to all or most members of the group and which may not be repeated under the specific headings.

The immensely rich Indo-Pacific fauna is poorly known. Many species have been inadequately described and some are known from the original type specimens only. The geographic range of a great many species still remains to be determined and some highly productive areas have been hardly explored. There are probably still hundreds of species awaiting discovery and description.

Anyone interested in coral fishes in almost any capacity, will inevitably uncover new knowledge, whether it be unknown live colours, extension of known ranges, unsuspected details of behaviour, unknown ecological associations, or even new species. Any such specimens, photos or information should be sent to the nearest fisheries officer or large museum without delay.

## OBSERVING UNDERWATER LIFE

Although diving with an aqualung or a floating compressor (Aquanaut) are most exciting experiences, the majority of the more colourful reef fishes can usually be seen at their best near the surface, with the aid of a mask and breathing tube (snorkel). This is a fascinating pastime which requires no expensive equipment, entails virtually no risks and which can be enjoyed by almost anyone. When snorkelling it is advisable to have a companion in case of accident, and one should bear in mind that Portuguese men o'war can be dangerous in some areas. One should never touch anything with one's bare hands and one should keep one's feet off the bottom as much as possible. There are many creatures capable of inflicting very painful stings and most of them are practically invisible when lying on the bottom. When walking on a coral reef one should always wear stout footwear.

Many tropical fish are very toxic and no fish should be eaten without consulting the local people.

Finally I would appeal to the reader not to use a harpoon gun. Fish learn very quickly to avoid areas where harpoon guns are being used and many of the more beautiful and accessible reefs are almost deserted as a result. Please leave something for those who will come after you.

## PLACE NAMES

Since this book was written some place names have been changed, notably Ceylon has become Sri Lanka.

# Glossary

**Acute**  Sharp, pointed
**Adipose**  Fatty
**Anal**  Pertaining to the anus, or vent; anal fin, or pertaining to the anal fin
**Antrorse**  Directed forward
**Apical**  At the tip (apex)
**Asymmetrical**  Without symmetry, lop-sided
**Axil**  Area where a paired fin is attached to the body
**Axillary**  Pertaining to the axil

**Barbel**  Elongated fleshy tentacle, generally under the chin
**Basal**  At or near the base
**Bifid**  Split in two
**Bifurcated**  Forked

**Calcified**  Containing much calcium carbonate in its composition
**Canine** (teeth)  Prominent conical teeth, like those of dogs
**Caniniform**  Shaped like a canine
**Carapace**  A hard shell or box encasing the body
**Cartilaginous**  Made of cartilage or gristle
**Caudal**  Pertaining to the tail
**Cephalic**  Pertaining to the head
**Circumtropical**  Occurring in all tropical waters
**Cirrus** (pl. **cirri**)  Small unbranched barbels
**Coalesced**  Grown together
**Compressed**  Flattened laterally
**Confluent**  Joined together
**Conspecific**  Belonging to the same species
**Crescentic**  Shaped like a crescent
**Crenulate**  With slightly scalloped margin
**Ctenoid** (scale)  With spiny hind margin
**Cusp**  Protuberance of a tooth
**Cycloid** (scale)  With smooth hind margin

**Deciduous** (scale)  Easily shed
**Denticle**  Small tooth-like structure
**Depressed**  Flattened from top to bottom

**Dermal**  Pertaining to the skin
**Dimorphism**  Of two different forms (generally meaning colour patterns)
**Distal**  Furthest from the point of attachment
**Diurnal**  Active in the daytime
**Dorsal**  Pertaining to the back; dorsal fin

**Emarginate** (tail)  With slightly hollowed margin
**Entire**  With smooth margin
**Erectile**  Capable of being raised
**Estuarine**  Pertaining to the mouth of rivers

**Falcate**  Sickle-shaped

**Gill arch**  The bony structure which supports the gills
**Gill raker**  Bony projections along the front edge of the gill arch
**Granular**  A surface of small hard lumps

**Herbivorous**  Feeding on vegetable matter
**Hyaline**  Transparent

**Illicium**  An isolated modified dorsal ray or spine used as a fishing lure
**Inframarginal**  Inside or below the margin
**Interdorsal**  Between the two dorsal fins
**Interorbital**  Between the eyes
**Isthmus**  The fleshy projection which separates the two gills under the throat

**Jugular**  Pertaining to the throat

**Lateral line**  A sensory organ consisting of lateral series of small raised tubes
**Littoral**  Pertaining to shallow inshore waters
**Lunate** (tail)  Shaped like a crescent moon

**Median**  In the middle
**Mesial**  Pertaining to the middle
**Mid-lateral**  Pertaining to the middle of the sides

15

**Nape** Back of the head, upper neck

**Nasal** Pertaining to the nose or nostrils

**Nictitating membrane** An inner transparent eyelid which helps to keep the eye clean

**Nuchal** Pertaining to the nape

**Ocellus** (pl. **ocelli**) An eye-like spot, usually surrounded by a different coloured ring

**Ocular** Pertaining to the eyes

**Opercular** Pertaining to the operculum

**Operculum** One of the bones of the head which protects the gill chamber

**Orbicular** Round

**Orbital** Pertaining to the bones surrounding the eyes

**Ossified** Changed to bone

**Oviparous** Producing eggs which hatch after being laid

**Ovo-viviparous** Producing eggs which hatch inside the body of the mother

**Papilla** A small fleshy projection of the skin

**Pectoral** Pertaining to the breast; the pectoral fins

**Peduncle** (caudal) Basal support of the tail

**Pelagic** Living in the open sea

**Peripheral** At the external boundary

**Posteroventral** Pertaining to the lower posterior area

**Posterodorsal** Pertaining to the upper posterior area

**Prehensile** Adapted for holding

**Preoperculum** The front part of the gill cover

**Preorbital** A bone of the skull situated in front and below the eye; in front of the eye

**Procumbent** Horizontal and pointing forward

**Protractile** Capable of forward extension

**Protrusible** Capable of forward extension

**Proximal** Nearest to the point of attachment

**Ray** A flexible structure supporting the membrane of a fin

**Reticulation, Reticulated** Net-like

**Rhomboidal** Diamond-shaped

**Rostrum** Beak or projecting snout

**Rudimentary** A very weakly developed structure

**Scute** A large shield-like scale, usually with a prominent ridge or keel

**Serrated** With saw-like teeth

**Seta** Bristle

**Setiform** Bristle-like

**Soft dorsal** Portion of dorsal fin supported by flexible rays

**Spine** A rigid structure supporting the membrane of a fin; a sharp projecting point

**Spinous dorsal** Anterior part of dorsal fin, supported by spines

**Spiracle** A respiratory opening behind the eye in sharks and rays

**Subapical** Inside the apex, short of the apex

**Subbasal** Immediately beyond the base

**Subcutaneous** Under the skin

**Submarginal** Immediately inside the margin

**Suboperculum** A bone beneath the operculum, part of the gill cover

**Subspecies** A local population which shows constant differences from other populations of the same species

**Subspecific** Pertaining to a subspecies

**Supra-orbital** Above the eye

**Supra-pectoral** Above the pectoral fin, or its axil

**Suture** The line along which two bones are immovably connected

**Trifid** Divided into three parts by two clefts

**Truncate** (tail) Abruptly cut off

**Tubercle** A small hard protuberance

**Type** The original specimens from which a species or subspecies has been described

**Typical** Similar to the type

**Urogenital** Pertaining to the kidneys and reproductive organs

**Vent** External opening of the alimentary system, anus

**Ventral** Pertaining to the lower surface

**Ventrals** Paired abdominal or pelvic fins

**Vermiculation** A pattern of fine, wavy, worm-like lines

**Vestigial** Small remnant of an organ or structure which is in the process of being lost

**Villous, Villiform** (teeth) Small, with the appearance of velvet

**Viviparous** Producing living young from within the body of the mother

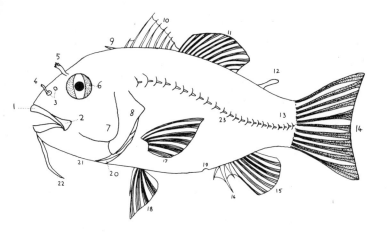

Parts of a modern bony fish

| | |
|---|---|
| 1 premaxilla | 13 caudal peduncle |
| 2 maxilla | 14 caudal fin or tail |
| 3 nostrils | 15 anal fin |
| 4 nasal tentacle | 16 anal spines |
| 5 supraorbital tentacle | 17 pectoral fin |
| 6 adipose eyelid | 18 ventral or pelvic fin |
| 7 preoperculum | 19 anus or vent |
| 8 operculum | 20 branchiostegal rays |
| 9 procumbent spine | 21 isthmus |
| 10 first or spinous dorsal fin | 22 barbel |
| 11 second or soft dorsal fin | 23 lateral line |
| 12 adipose fin | |

Standard length is measured from the tip of the snout to the base of the caudal fin.

# Abbreviations and Symbols

## Fin counts

D = Dorsal fin     P = Pectoral fin
A = Anal fin      V = Ventral fin

Above letters followed by Arabic numerals = number of flexible rays.

Above letters followed by Roman numerals in capitals = number of fin spines.

Above letters followed by Roman numerals in lower case = number of small incipient spines.

An oblique stroke (/) between Arabic and Roman numerals means that the fin is continuous.

Semicolon (;) between Arabic and Roman numerals means that the first and second dorsal fins are separate.

## Scale counts

Sc = Number of scales in the longest horizontal series.

L1 = Number of scales along the lateral line.

tr = Number of horizontal scale rows.

Oblique stroke (/): Number before stroke represents scale rows above the lateral line; number after the stroke represents scale rows below lateral line.

## Sex symbols

♂ = male;      ♀ = female

## Nomenclature

All fishes have two Latin names in italics (binomial system); the first, always with an initial capital, is the name of the genus, or group of related species to which the fish belongs; the second name (always with a lower case initial) is the name of the species. When there is a third name, as in *Coris gaimardi africanus, africanus* is a subspecies of *Coris gaimardi*; *Coris gaimardi gaimardi* is the typical subspecies, i.e. the first to have been described.

Names of persons following the binomial or trinomial formula (not in italics) are the names of the authors of the description and the year is the year of publication. When the author's name is in brackets, it means that the species was originally placed in a genus other than the one in which it appears in this work. Some authors' names have been abbreviated thus:

Bloch & Sneider = B. & S.      Linnaeus = L.
Cuvier & Valenciennes = C. & V.      Müller & Henle = M. & H.
Hamilton-Buchanan = H.-B.      Quoy & Gaimard = Q. & G.
Jordan & Everman = J. & E.      Smith & Radcliffe = S. & R.
Jordan & Snyder = J. & S.      Temminck & Schlegel = T. & S.

## Abbreviations of some areas where common names are used

A = Australia      Q = Queensland
H = Hawaii      S = Seychelles
M = Mauritius      S.A. = South Africa

# Key to Orders, Suborders and principal Percoid Families

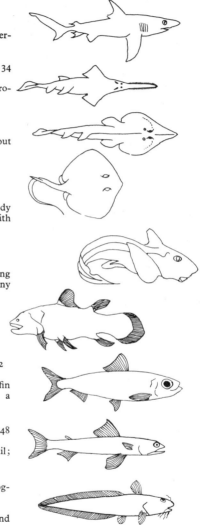

**LAMNIFORMES** (Selachii) p. 29
Sharks
Scales absent; gill-openings lateral (generally 5 slits); mouth inferior

**PRISTIFORMES** (Pristiophorae) p. 34
Saw-fishes
Scales absent; gill-slits ventral; snout prolonged; ventral fins free

**RHINOBATIFORMES** p. 35
Shark Rays, Fiddler Rays, Sand Sharks
Scales absent; gill-slits ventral; snout normal; ventral fins free

**MYLIOBATIFORMES** (Rajae, Batoidei) p. 36
Rays
Scales absent; gill-slits ventral; body flattened, disc-like; pectoral fins fused with body

**CHIMAERAE** p. 41
Ghost Sharks, Chimaeras
Scales absent; body elongated; tail tapering or whip-like; gill-slits concealed as in bony fishes

**CROSSOPTERYGII** p. 41
Coelacanth
Scales large; paired fins limb-like

**ISOSPONDYLI** (Clupeiformes) p. 42
Herrings, Anchovies, Sardines, Tarpons
Silvery; scales small to moderate; no fin spines; a single dorsal fin, sometimes a small adipose fin near tail

**MYCTOPHIFORMES** (Iniomi) p. 48
Lizardfish, Bombay Ducks
No fin spines; a small adipose fin near tail; not silvery; scales large; mouth large

**SILUROIDIFORMES** (Nematognathi) p. 50
Catfishes
Scales absent; fin spines present; mouth and snout armed with fleshy barbels

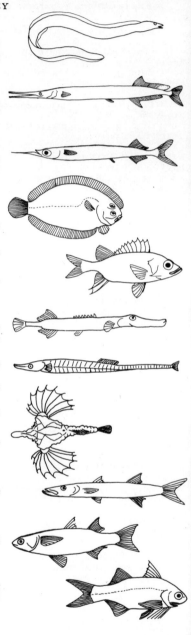

**ANGUILLIFORMES** (Apodes) p. 52
Eels, Morays, Congers
Extremely elongated; gill-openings small;
paired fins absent or reduced; scales minute
or absent

**SCOMBERESOCOIDEI** p. 62
Needle-fish, Long Toms, Alligator Gar
Very elongated, silvery; scales small; fin
spines absent; single dorsal fin; both jaws
elongated and pointed

**EXOCOETOIDEI** p. 62
Half-beaks and Flyingfish
Silvery; scales large; a single dorsal fin;
no fin spines; upper jaw cut off, lower
pointed (Half-beaks)

**PLEURONECTIFORMES**
(Heterosomata) p. 64
Flatfishes, Soles, Flounders
Asymmetrical, very flattened; both eyes
on one side

**BERYCIFORMES**    (Berycomorphi,
Berycoidei) p. 69
Knight-fishes and Squirrel-fishes
Silvery and red; scales large; eyes very
large; fin spines present

**AULOSTOMOIDEI** p. 75
Razorfish, Flutemouth, Cornetfish
Snout prolonged, mouth tubular, very
small; not encased in bony rings; scales
absent

**SYNGNATHOIDEI** (Lophobranchii)
p. 77 Sea-horses, Pipefishes
Snout tubular; body encased in bony rings;
pectoral fins small

**PEGASIFORMES**    (Hypostomides)
p. 81
Sea Moths
Snout long, pointed; body encased by bony
rings; pectoral fins very large

**SPHYRAENOIDEI** p. 82
Barracuda, Sea-pike
Large, silvery; scales small; lateral line
present; 2 widely spaced dorsal fins

**MUGILOIDEI** p. 83
Gray Mullet and Silversides
Silvery; scales large; lateral line absent;
2 widely spaced dorsal fins

**POLYNEMIFORMES** p. 86
Threadfins, Tasselfish
Scales large; lateral line present; lower
pectoral rays free, prolonged; 2 well
separated dorsal fins

**SCOMBROIDEI** p. 87
Tuna, Mackerel, Marlin, Sailfish
Body streamlined, silvery; 2 well separated
dorsal fins; several isolated finlets from
dorsal and anal fins to tail

**STROMATEOIDEI** p. 90
Pelagic fishes associated with jellyfish

**PERCOIDEI** (Typical perch-like fishes)
**Carangidae** p. 91
Trevally, Jacks, Scad, Darts, Runners etc.
Large, compressed, silvery; scales in-
conspicuous; a series of large keeled scutes
along posterior lateral line

**Menidae** p. 98
Moonfish
Extremely thin and compressed; triangular
in profile

**Leiognathidae** p. 99
Ponyfish, Slimys
Silvery; scales small, concealed; compressed and elevated; a single dorsal fin with
anterior spines

**Apogonidae** p. 100
Cardinalfishes
Small, brightly coloured; 2 dorsal fins; eyes
large, scales large

**Kuhliidae** (Duleidae) p. 106
Flagtails
Silvery, tail usually with black bands; a
deep notch between spinous and soft dorsals;
scales large; 2 opercular spines

**Latidae** p. 107
Barramundi, Giant Perch, Sand-bass
Silvery, scales large; back elevated, head
depressed; a narrow gap between dorsal
fins
**Serranidae** p. 108
Rock-cod, Groupers, Coral-trout
Not silvery; scales small or concealed;
single dorsal, slightly notched; pectorals
rounded; mouth large; 2-3 opercular spines

**Pseudoplesiopidae** p. 118
False Roundheads
Lateral line incomplete; dorsal fin elevated,
without notch, dorsal spines weak; scales
large

**Plesiopidae** p. 119
Roundheads, Longfins
Lateral line interrupted; dorsal fin without
notch; spines normal; ventral fins elongated; scales large

**Priacanthidae** p. 120
Bullseyes
Bright red; scales small; lateral line normal;
eyes very large; dorsal, anal and ventral
fins very large

**Lobotidae** p. 120
Triple Tail, Jumping Cod, Flasher
Compressed and deep-bodied; lateral line
normal; scales large; dorsal and anal fins
extended backwards

**Lutjanidae** p. 121
Snappers, Sea-perch, Hussars
Lateral line normal; dorsal fin continuous;
fin spines well developed; scales small or
moderate; tail truncate or forked (rounded
in juvenile Plectorhynchinae)

**Theraponidae** p. 136
Grunters
Silvery with black bands or spots; a strong
opercular spine; dorsal fin deeply notched

**Sparidae** p. 137
Silver Bream, Sea-bream, Porgies
Red or silvery, deep-bodied and compressed; dorsal high, slightly notched;
scales large; lateral line complete with
enlarged scales at its origin; pectorals long
and pointed

**Gerridae** p. 138
Silver-biddies
Small and silvery; scales large; lateral line
complete; first dorsal spines often prolonged; base of dorsal and anal fins scaly

**Mullidae** p. 140
Red Mullet, Goatfish
Generally red or yellow; 2 widely spaced
dorsal fins; 2 barbels under chin

**Sciaenidae** p. 143
Croakers, Drummers
Single deeply notched dorsal fin, spinous
part much shorter than soft part; tail wedge-
shaped; 2 flat opercular spines; anal fin
short based

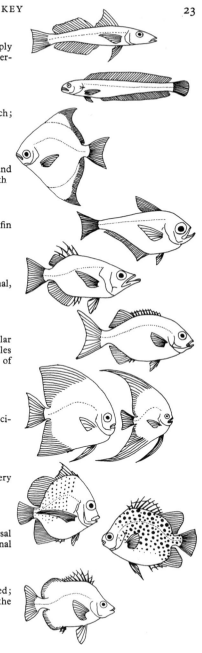

**Sillaginidae** p. 144
Whiting, Smelts
Slender, silvery; dorsal very deeply notched; anal long based; one small opercular spine

**Malacanthidae** p. 145
Blanquillos
Anal and dorsal very long, without notch; scales small; a strong opercular spine

**Monodactylidae** p. 146
Silver Batfish, Kite-fish
Silvery, elevated and compressed; anal and dorsal fin without notch, of equal length

**Pempheridae** p. 146
Sweepers
Compressed, with large eyes; dorsal fin placed forward, much shorter than anal

**Toxotidae** p. 147
Archerfish, Riflefish
Small, silvery; dorsal shorter than anal, inserted near tail

**Kyphosidae** p. 147
Drummers, Rudderfish
Silvery, smoothly oval; 1-2 blunt opercular spines; dorsal slightly notched; scales moderate; tail emarginate, high; base of vertical fins scaly

**Platacidae** p. 148
Batfish, Leaf-fish
Extremely compressed and elevated, especially juveniles

**Drepanidae** p. 149
Sicklefish, Spotted Batfish
Compressed and elevated; pectorals very long, sickle-shaped

**Scatophagidae** p. 149
Scats, Butterfish
Deep-bodied, very compressed; dorsal deeply notched; scales very small; 4 anal spines

**Scorpididae** p. 150
Small, silvery, elevated and compressed; black bands longitudinal; similar to the Chaetodontidae, but scales smaller

**Chaetodontidae** p. 150
Butterflyfish, Coralfish, Angelfish
Small, brightly coloured, compressed; base
of dorsal and anal fins scaly; Angelfishes
have strong spine at lower angle of preoperculum; scales large

**Histiopteridae** p. 166
Boarfish
Very compressed; scales small; rayed portion of dorsal fin extremely elevated; paired
fins large

**Amphiprionidae** p. 166
Clownfish, Anemone-fish
Small and brightly coloured; scales very
small; always associated with large sea
anemones

**Pomacentridae** p. 170
Damselfish, Sergeant-majors, Pullers, Hum-
bugs
Small and brightly coloured; scales large

**Labridae** p. 183
Wrasses, Tusk-fish
Small to moderate, brightly coloured;
extremely varied in appearance; scales
moderate to large; teeth sharp and prominent; lips fleshy

**Scaridae** p. 204
Parrotfishes
Medium to large, very colourful; scales very
large; teeth fused into a blunt beak

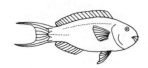

**Cirrhitidae** p. 211
Hawkfishes
Small, colours generally dull; scales
moderate; lower pectoral rays unbranched,
protruding beyond fin; a prominent fringe
behind nostril

**Cheilodactylidae** p. 213
Morwongs
Medium-sized, compressed; body elevated
at dorsal origin; anterior dorsal spines
elevated; marked with alternate dark and
pale oblique bands

**Opistognathidae** p. 213
Smilers, Jaw-fishes
Moderate size, head very large; scales small;
lateral line high, often incomplete

**Parapercidae** p. 214
Grubfish, Weevers
Small, slender, dull-coloured; spinous
dorsal lower and much shorter than soft
dorsal; anal fin without spines

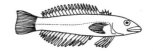

**Trichonotidae** p. 215
Sand-eels, Hairfins
Small, extremely slender and elongated;
fins very high

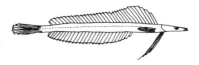

**BLENNIOIDEI** p. 216
Blennies and allies
Small, elongated, compressed; generally
scale-less, or if scaly, with 3 dorsal fins;
mouth inferior; ventrals reduced, inserted
forwards

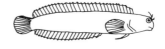

**OPHIDIOIDEI** p. 226
Pearl-fishes, Messmate-fishes and Eel-pouts
Ribbon-like, tail tapering; no fin spines;
ventrals reduced or absent; some species
with barbels on chin and snout (*Brotulidae*)

**CALLIONYMOIDEI** p. 227
Dragonets, Mandarin-fishes
Small; 2 dorsal fins; ventrals very large,
placed ahead of pectorals; no scales

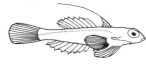

**SIGANOIDEI** p. 230
Spinefeet, Rabbitfishes
Small to moderate, compressed; no visible
scales; ventral fins 2 sharp spines separated
by 3 rays

## ACANTHUROIDEI p. 232

Tangs, Surgeon-fishes, Unicorns, Moorish Idol
Compressed, small to moderate; no scales; one or more large spines or plates on caudal
peduncle (Acanthuridae); if caudal spines absent, dorsal spines extremely prolonged
Zanclidae); sometimes a prominent horn above snout (*Naso*)

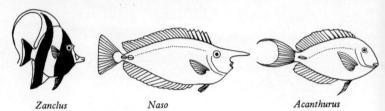

*Zanclus*              *Naso*                          *Acanthurus*

## GOBIOIDEI p. 239

Gobies, Mud-skippers, Gudgeons
Small; head large and blunt; mouth large;
ventrals fused into a disc or inserted very
close together

## COTTOIDEI (Cataphracti) p. 246

Dragonfish, Waspfish, Stonefish, Gurnards, Flatheads
Small to moderate; head encased in bony armour; bony ridges and spines and dermal
appendages often present; extremely varied in shape and appearance

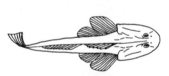

**Platycephalidae** p. 247

**Dactylopteridae** p. 249

**Tetrarogidae** p. 250

**Scorpaenidae** p. 251

## ECHENEIFORMES (Discocephali)

p. 260 Remoras, Suckerfish, Sharksuckers
Slender fishes with a large sucking disc on
top of head

**BALISTOIDEI** p. 261
Triggerfishes, Filefishes, Tripod-fishes
Deep-bodied and compressed, often brightly
coloured; spinous dorsal fin reduced;
ventral fins absent

**OSTRACIOIDEI** (Ostracodermi) p. 269
Boxfishes, Cowfishes, Trunkfishes
Small; encased in bony carapace; teeth
fused into a blunt beak; spinous dorsal and
ventral fins lacking

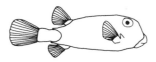

**TETRODONTOIDEI** p. 272
Puffers, Porcupinefishes
Scales absent, sometimes replaced by fixed
or erectile spines; spinous dorsal and ventral
fins absent; mouth a blunt beak; capable of
inflating themselves

**XENOPTERYGII** p. 279
Clingfishes
Small, scale-less; a large ventral sucking
disc between ventral fins

**BATRACHOIDIFORMES**
(Haplodoci) p. 279
Frogfishes
Small, elongated; scales absent; numerous
dermal appendages; similar to some
Blennies, but spinous dorsal fin very short
and low

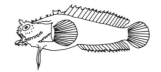

**LOPHIIFORMES** (Pediculati) p. 280
Anglerfishes, Sargassum-fishes
Small to moderate; scales absent; shape
varied and grotesque, generally more or less
globular; first dorsal spine modified into a
fishing pole and lure; mouth very large

# Class ELASMOBRANCHII (Chondrichthyes)

## Sharks, Rays, Ghost-sharks

An ancient group of primitive fishes with cartilaginous skeleton. Unlike the true bony fishes, they have no overlapping scales, but the skin is covered by variously shaped, usually minute bony plates (denticles) which give it the characteristic sandpaper-like texture (shagreen). There are no sutures in the skull and the skeleton is never ossified. The gills are not covered by an operculum and the males have paired copulatory organs. Reproduction may be viviparous or oviparous; in the oviparous species the egg case is usually squarish and produced into four tendrils which help to anchor it to algae or corals. Many species have a nictitating membrane, which is an eyelid attached to the skin below the eye. The teeth, which are modified dermal denticles, are not fixed in sockets, but attached to a band of tissue which grows forward, the teeth at the rear becoming erect and functional as they move forward to replace the older worn teeth at the front which are then shed.

## Subclass PLAGIOSTOMI (Euselachii)

### Sharks and Rays

In these fishes the upper jaw is not fixed to the skull and a breathing hole (spiracle) is usually present behind the eye.

## Order LAMNIFORMES (Selachii)

### Sharks

Medium-sized to very large fishes which occur in all seas, though most numerous in the shallow coastal waters of the tropics. Some of the smaller species are bottom dwelling scavengers or feed on molluscs and other invertebrates, but most are active and voracious predators. Usually cigar-shaped with two dorsal and one anal fin; pectorals placed ventrally, not fused with body. Fins without calcified rays. Five lateral slit-like gill openings. Skin covered with small denticles, rough.

Family ORECTOLOBIDAE
## Catsharks, Carpetsharks, Wobbegongs (A), Endormi (S)
Small to medium-sized sluggish bottom dwelling sharks of shallow coastal
waters. Generally harmless to man, some are fair eating. They are nocturnal
and feed on invertebrates and small fishes. Spiracle present, nictitating membrane absent, teeth small and compressed; often strikingly marked. Many
species in the tropical Indo-Pacific, a few in the Atlantic.

## 1. ORECTOLOBUS ORNATUS (De Vis) 1883
Banded Wobbegong, Banded Carpetshark
210 cm. Brown, banded and mottled with black; known to be dangerous when
cornered. Ovo-viviparous. Usually among weed-covered rocks. Australia and
New Guinea.

## 2. ORECTOLOBUS OGILBYI Regan 1909
Tasselled Wobbegong
360 cm. Possibly dangerous. Armed with numerous dermal appendages on
upper lip, between angle of mouth and first gill-slit and on chin. Light sandy,
decorated with dark brown rings with dark centres; 5 faint dark cross bands
on body and 4 on tail. North Queensland and Torres Straits.

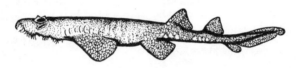

Tasselled Wobbegong

ALLIED SPECIES:
**3. ORECTOLOBUS WARDI** Whitley 40 cm. Yellowish with 3 dark dorsal spots
and 3 black rings on tail. North Queensland and N. Territory. Rare.
**4. O. MACULATUS** (Bonnaterre) 300 cm. Brown above with pale rings on head,
back and fins. Teeth large, fang-like, probably dangerous. Australia.

## 5. EUCROSSORHINUS DASYPOGON (Bleeker) 1867
Tasselled Wobbegong
360 cm. Dangerous. Dermal appendages of mouth and head numerous and
branched. Brown, decorated with a pattern of closely spaced white spots. New
Guinea and Indonesia.

## 6. GINGLYMOSTOMA FERRUGINEUM (Lesson) 1830
Tawny Shark
240 cm. Harmless. Lacks dermal appendages; tawny, unmarked. Oviparous.
East Africa to Indonesia and New Guinea.

ALLIED SPECIES:
**7. GINGLYMOSTOMA BREVICAUDATUM** (Günther) 80 cm. Tail shorter
and broader than in *G. ferrugineum,* fins more rounded. Uniform brown. Western
Indian Ocean.

## 8. HEMISCYLLIUM OCELLATUM (Bonnaterre) 1788
Epauletted Shark

80 cm. Very elongated and slender. Brown above, whitish below, marked with irregular brown blotches; a prominent, pale-edged round black eye-spot above pectoral base. Oviparous. Almost blind, clumsy and slow, found amongst coral. India to Indonesia, New Guinea and Queensland.

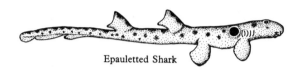

Epauletted Shark

ALLIED SPECIES:

**9. HEMISCYLLIUM FREYCINETI** (Q. & G.) Black supra-pectoral ocelli not ringed with white. East Indies and Melanesia.

**10. H. TRISPECULARE** Richardson 60 cm. Supra-pectoral ocelli imperfect, body covered by small black dots. Australia.

**11. H. PUNCTATUM** (M. & H.) 100 cm. Supra-pectoral ocelli absent, body banded in young, sometimes spotted. Queensland, E. Indies, Philippines, Taiwan.

## 12. STEGOSTOMA FASCIATUM (Pennant) 1769
Zebra Shark, Leopard Shark, Monkey Mouth

335 cm. Harmless; 2nd dorsal very small and tail very long; a prominent dorsal ridge. Brown with bold light spots and bars; feeds on crustacea and molluscs. East Africa to the W. Pacific.

Zebra Shark

OTHER SPECIES:

**13. NEBRIUS CONCOLOR** Rüppell 300 cm. Uniform brown, tail long, pointed, prominently notched near apex. Red Sea, E. Africa, Ceylon, E. Indies. Rare.

*Nebrius concolor*

**14. CHILOSCYLLIUM PLAGIOSUM** (Bennett) 70 cm. Body with dorsal ridge, fins and tail rounded. Ten dark cross-bands and numerous small white or blue spots. South and E. Africa to E. Indies.

**15. C. GRISEUM** (M. & H.) 60 cm. Body with dorsal ridge. 10–12 cross-bands, unspotted. South and E. Africa to E. Indies.

**16. C. INDICUM** (Günther) 50 cm. Three dorsal ridges; numerous small dark spots. South and E. Africa to E. Indies.

Family RHINCHODONTIDAE
Comprises a single living species which is the largest known fish.

**17. RHINCHODON TYPUS** (Smith) 1829
Whale Shark
14 m. Harmless giants found in all tropical waters. Adapted to feed on plankton and small fishes. Spiracle present, gill openings very wide, teeth small and weak.

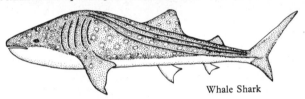

Whale Shark

Family SPHYRNIDAE **Hammerhead Sharks**
Fast and fierce man-eating sharks of all warm and temperate waters. Front of head flattened and expanded laterally in characteristic hammerhead shape. Ovo-viviparous. Feed on other fishes.

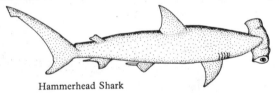

Hammerhead Shark

Family CARCHARHINIDAE (GALEIDAE) **Typical Sharks**
Moderate to very large, active, predatory sharks. Nictitating membrane well developed. Spiracle present in some species. Base of 1st dorsal fin anterior to ventrals. Many Indo-Pacific species. The dangerous man-eating Tiger Shark (*Galeocerda cuvieri* Le Sueur) and the whaler sharks (*Eulamia* sp. and *Carcharhinus* sp.) belong to this family.

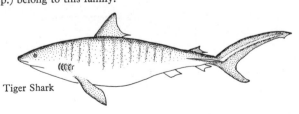

Tiger Shark

## Family ISURIDAE **Porbeagles, Mackerel Sharks**

Large, surface swimming sharks of all seas. Fast, stoutly built, torpedo-shaped.
A lateral keel usually present on each side of caudal peduncle. No nictitating
membrane, spiracle small. First dorsal large, 2nd dorsal and anal small. The
dangerous Blue Pointer, or Mako (*Isurus glaucus* (M. & H.)) and the equally
dangerous White Shark, or White Pointer (*Carcharodon carcharias* (L.)) belong
to this family.

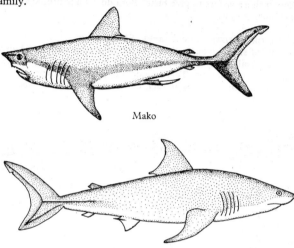

Mako

White Shark

## Family ALOPIIDAE **Thresher Sharks**

Tail very long and slender, pectorals very long. A single species (*Alopias
vulpinus* (Bonnaterre)) found in all warm waters. Up to 540 cm, harmless to
man. Thresher Sharks use their long tails to drive schools of small fish towards
their mouths.

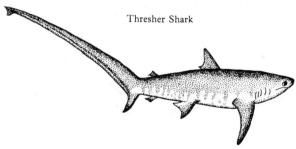

Thresher Shark

Family TRIAKIDAE **Smooth Dog Sharks**
Small, inoffensive sharks of shallow coastal waters. Slender, tail less than ¼ of
total length. Teeth small, rounded, or 3-4-cusped. Several Indo-Pacific species.

Family SQUALIDAE **Spiny Dogfishes, Spiny Sharks**
Numerous, mostly small species of deep water. Viviparous. The females come
into shallow inshore waters to give birth. Both dorsal fins preceded by a strong,
stout spine, anal absent.

Family SCYLIORHINIDAE **Lazy Sharks, Skaamoogs**
A small family of small sluggish sharks found in coastal waters and also in deep
oceanic waters. Tail hardly bent upwards, unnotched at base. Spiracles present,
nictitating membrane absent. Teeth moderate, generally tricuspid. Oviparous,
eggs rectangular with a tendril at each corner, attached to weeds. Inoffensive
scavengers.

*Scyliorhinus capensis*

## Order **PRISTIFORMES** (Pristiophorae)

Family PRISTIOPHORIDAE **Saw-fishes**
Transitional between the sharks and rays. Body shape elongated as in the
sharks, but gill slits ventral, not lateral, pectorals fused to head. Head flattened,
snout produced into a long flattened bony rod armed with a single series of
teeth on each side. The saw is used to slash schools of small fish in order to stun
them and kill them and also to grub for invertebrates on the bottom. Saw-fishes
occur in shallow coastal waters in all warm seas, some species ascending rivers.
Moderate to very large (10 m), the larger species dangerous to man.
*Pristis microdon* Latham and *P. zisjron* Bleeker are wide ranging Indo-Pacific
species.

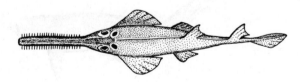

*Pristis zisjron*

## Order **RHINOBATIFORMES**

Family RHINOBATIDAE
**Shark Rays, Fiddler Rays, Sand Sharks, Shovel-nose Rays**
Similar to the Pristiformes, but lack the saw-like projection of the head. Skin smooth, sometimes armed with thorn-like warts along back and round the eyes. Five ventral gill openings. Spiracle large and close to the eye; snout dorso-ventrally compressed, shovel-like. Numerous rows of small teeth forming a pavement-like band. Many species in shallow coastal waters of all warm seas, usually bottom dwellers feeding on molluscs and crustacea. Ovo-viviparous. Excellent eating.

**18. RHYNCHOBATUS DJIDDENSIS** (Forskål) 1775
White-spotted Shovel-nose Ray; Violon (S)
300 cm and up to 250 kg. A row of tubercles on mid-line of back, two short rows on each shoulder and a row above each eye. Two folds behind each spiracle. Sandy brown with white spots or ocelli; sometimes a large black scapular spot. Shallow, sandy estuaries. Red Sea, E. Africa, India, Ceylon, Seychelles, Madagascar, Indonesia, Philippines, Queensland and W. Pacific.

**19. RHINA ANCYLOSTOMUS** Bloch & Schneider 1801
Bow-mouthed Angelfish; Short-nosed Mudskate (Q)
270 cm, 140 kg. Head and shoulders armed with large bony tubercles. Dull brown, usually spotted with white and sometimes decorated with black lines on body and fins. East Africa, Seychelles, India, Indonesia, Philippines, Melanesia, Queensland.

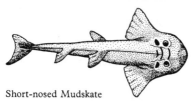

Short-nosed Mudskate

**20. RHINOBATOS ARMATUS** (Gray) 1834
Shovel-nose Ray
210 cm. Nostrils very long oblique slits. Light brown or olive above, paler below; pectorals and ventrals yellowish. Shallow coastal waters, occasionally ascending rivers to breed. India, Indonesia, Philippines, Queensland.

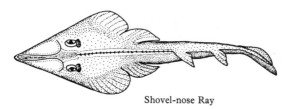

Shovel-nose Ray

ALLIED SPECIES:

**21. RHINOBATOS BLOCHI** M. & H. 120 cm. Skin smooth snout, blunt. Western Indian Ocean.

**22. R. BATILLUM** (Whitley) 210 cm. Flat coarse denticles around eyes, on back and on anterior margins of pectorals. Central Indo-Pacific.

**23. R. OBTUSUS** M. & H. 90 cm. Snout pointed. Small spine-like denticles on back and shoulders. One skinny projection behind spiracle. East Africa to E. Indies.

**24. R. ANNULATUS** M. & H. 135 cm. Denticles very small, skin smooth to touch; two skinny projections behind spiracle. East and S. Africa.

**25. R. SCHLEGELI** M. & H. 125 cm. Smooth except for single row of spines along back. Two skinny projections behind spiracle. East Africa to W. Pacific.

## Order **MYLIOBATIFORMES** (Rajae, Batoidei)

### Rays and Skates

Very flattened disc-like fishes. Pectorals completely fused with body, forming lateral flap-like extensions of the trunk. Tail whip-like, or terminating in a single small lobe. 5 ventral gill openings. Spiracles well developed. Mouth ventral; teeth of both jaws small, compacted to form grinding plates. Rays feed on molluscs and crabs on the bottom, often concealing themselves in the sand or mud, with only the eyes and spiracles exposed. Skin smooth, sometimes armed with a few large tubercles on back. Numerous species in all shallow coastal waters.

### Family UROLOPHIDAE **Short-tailed Stingrays**

Species few. Small rays with rounded or slightly angular disc. Tail short, terminating in a single rounded lobe. A single saw-edged spine at base of tail; the spine is covered by poisonous mucus and can inflict extremely painful wounds.

### 26. UROLOPHUS ARMATUS Müller & Henle 1841

Black-spotted Stingray

18 cm. Snout prominent and pointed. A strong tubercle on each shoulder. Brown with numerous round black spots above, pale with dark margins below. Very shallow coastal waters in the C. Indo-Pacific.

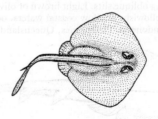

Black-spotted Stingray

Family DASYATIDAE **Stingrays**
A large family of tropical and subtropical rays. Tail whip-like, sometimes very
long, usually with one or more poisonous spines at the base. Dorsal and ventral
fins absent.

### 27. TAENYURA LYMMA (Forskål) 1775
Lesser Fantail Ray, Ribbontail Ray, Blue-spotted Lagoon Ray
240 cm. A few flattened tubercles on shoulders and back. Tail thick, longer than
disc, armed with 2 spines. Brown with large round blue spots on disc and a
blue stripe on each side of tail. Sandy areas among coral reefs. Very common
throughout the Indo-Pacific region, excluding Hawaii.

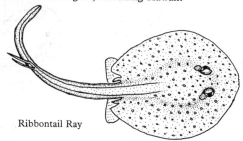

Ribbontail Ray

### 28. HIMANTURA GRANULATA (Macleay) 1883
Mangrove Ray, Macleay's Coachwhip Ray
90 cm in length. Tail slender, 1½ times as long as disc. A single caudal spine.
Skin granular on shoulders and along back to base of spine. Upperside brown to
grey with faint dark crescents along margins, underside white with brown
blotches and margins. Common among mangroves in Queensland, N. Australia,
New Guinea and the Solomon islands.

### 29. HIMANTURA UARNAK (Forskål) 1775
Coachwhip Ray, Long-tailed Ray, Raie bouclée (S)
150 cm across disc, 100 kg. Disc kite-shaped, snout pointed. Tail slender,
twice as long as disc, armed with a single large spine. One or two large tubercles
on the back. Colour above sandy to very dark brown with a few black spots,
paler at margin, white below. Tail black with about 35 encircling light bluish
grey rings. Tidal sands and mudflats. Dangerous, should be handled with
extreme care. Common throughout the area, from the Red Sea and E. Africa to
Indonesia, Melanesia and Queensland, but apparently not in Hawaii.

### 30. DASYATIS SEPHEN (Forskål) 1775
=PASTINACHUS SEPHEN
Cow-tail Ray, Fantail Ray
180 cm across disc which is squarish, wider than long. Spiracles large, twice
size of eye. Young individuals smooth, developing small granules on top of disc
and tail and a few large tubercles on back when older. Tail twice length of disc,
with black cutaneous fold below. One large caudal spine. Grey to black above,
white below. Dangerous, as it can use its caudal spine even when held between
the eyes. Shallow tidal flats from the Red Sea and E. Africa to the E. Indies,
Australia and the W. Pacific.

### 31. DASYATIS KUHLII (Müller & Henle) 1841
### =AMPHOTISTIUS KUHLII
Blue-spotted Stingray
35 cm across disc which is kite-shaped. Spiracle much larger than eye. Tail thick, slightly longer than disc, with one or two spines. Skin smooth with a few large tubercles on back. Adults light brown with faintly dark-ringed blue spots. Tail blackish. Very common in sandy patches among coral. Red Sea and E. Africa to the E. Indies, Australia and the W. Pacific, but not in Hawaii.

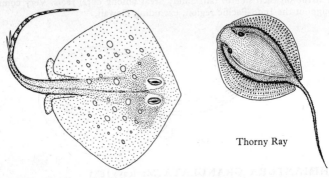

Thorny Ray

Blue-spotted Stingray

ALLIED SPECIES:
### 32. DASYATIS FAVUS (Annandale) 180 cm wide. Tail 1½ times length of disc. Marked with close-set irregular rings all over. Indian Ocean.
### 33. D. HAWAIIENSIS Jenkins 120 cm wide. A fleshy fold above and below tail. Hawaii.
### 34. D. LATA (Garman) 90 cm wide. Tail with a fleshy keel below. Hawaii.

### 35. UROGYMNUS AFRICANUS (Bloch & Schneider) 1801
Thorny Ray
60 cm wide. Disc regularly ovoid, longer than wide, covered by close-set blunt spines. Tail slender, slightly longer than disc, spineless. Upperside greenish or brownish, tubercles whitish or yellowish. South and E. Africa to the E. Indies and Australia.

### Family MYLIOBATIDAE (AETOBATIDAE) Eagle-rays, Bull-rays
Numerous species of large rays, found in all warm seas. Head raised well above disc. Eyes large, lateral. Disc much wider than long with prominently falcate tips. Lower front of head expanded into a thick fleshy flap used for scooping up molluscs and other invertebrates. Tail very long and whip-like, without caudal lobe, but with a small dorsal fin at base and often armed with one or more spines. Teeth large and blunt, adapted for crushing molluscs. More pelagic in their habits than most rays. When not feeding or resting on the bottom they swim near the surface flapping their pectoral fins with extreme grace, rather like a bird flying in slow motion.

## 36. AETOBATUS NARINARI (Euphrasen) 1790
## =STOASODON NARINARI

Duck-billed Ray, Spotted Eagle Ray, Bonnet Skate (A), Raie chauve-souris (S)
135 cm across, 330 cm long. Skin smooth; a single strong caudal spine. Dark
grey or dark green above, with evenly spaced rounded blue-white spots with
diffuse edges all over. Eyes yellow. Feeds on oysters and clams, often in small
schools which can do much damage to oyster-banks. The female is viviparous
and is said to leap out of the water to release her young. Common throughout the
entire tropical Indo-Pacific, including Hawaii.

Spotted Eagle Ray

## 37. RHINOPTERA JAVANICA Müller & Henle 1841

Cow-nosed Ray, Flapray
90 cm wide. Disc more than twice as broad as long. Ventral fins very short, tail
long and slender. Uniform brown above, white below. Rare. East Africa and
Seychelles to India, Indonesia, Philippines and China. Occasionally found in
Australia.

Family MOBULIDAE
### Devil-rays, Manta Rays, Diables de Mer (S)

Few species found in all warm waters. Surface dwelling oceanic fishes of great
size. Harmless to man, they feed on small fishes and crustacea which are swept
into the mouth with the aid of a pair of cephalic fins placed in front of the head.
The pantropical *Manta birostris* (Walbaum) 1792 may measure 7 m across the
disc and weigh 2 tons. These giant fishes swim with extreme grace and occasionally leap out of the water and fall back with a spectacular splash and a thun-
derous clap, a sight which can make even the most seasoned naturalist doubt
his sobriety.

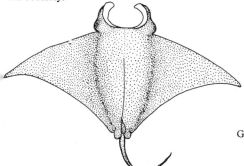

Giant Manta (*Manta birostris*)

Family TORPEDINIDAE **Electric Rays, Numb-fishes, Cramp-fishes**
A small family of sluggish bottom dwelling rays which can give a powerful
electric shock. Disc almost round, ventrals very large, united, tail thick and
very short. Dorsal fins, caudal and anal present. Spiracles large, fringed, behind
eye. Electric organs below skin, between head and each pectoral. Some species
live at great depth and are blind and some of the larger ones attain 150 cm
across the disc. Most electric rays live in very shallow water, usually buried in
the sand or mud of the bottom. The electric organs are presumably used to
paralyse and capture any small creature which accidentally touches them and
possibly as a defence from predators; nevertheless the larger sharks frequently
feed on electric rays.

### 38. TORPEDO FUSCOMACULATA Peters 1853
Electric Ray, Raie trembleur (S)
45 cm across disc. Two small dorsal fins. Yellowish brown, irregularly marked
with dark blotches. Shallow coastal waters in the W. Indian Ocean.

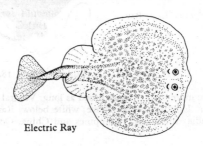

Electric Ray

### 39. HYPNARCE SUBNIGRA (Dumeril) 1852
Cramp-fish, Numb-fish
60 cm across disc. Two dorsal fins. Dark reddish brown above, white below.
Occurs in Australian waters, from tidal flats to 100 m.

ALLIED SPECIES:
**40. NARCINE BRUNNEA** (Annandale) 20 cm. 2 dorsal fins; uniform brown.
India, Ceylon, Maldives.
**41. N. TIMLEI** (B. & S.) 30 cm. 2 dorsal fins; light brown with large round dark
spots. Tropical Indian Ocean, but not so far recorded from E. Africa.
**42. NARKE DIPTERYGIA** (B. & S.) 1 dorsal fin; disc almost round; brown,
clouded with blackish. Tropical Indian Ocean.

## Subclass HOLOCEPHALI

### Order CHIMAERAE

#### Ghost Sharks, Chimaeras

Few species in deep waters in all oceans. They differ from the Plagiostomi in having the upper jaw fused to the skull. Elongated body with smooth skin, spiracles absent. Teeth fused into three bony plates, two in upper jaw, one in lower jaw. Probably relics of great antiquity. Three families: Chimaeridae, Callorhynchidae, Rhinochimaeridae. Fig., p. 19.

## Class TELEOSTOMI (Osteichthyes, Pisces)

#### Bony Fishes

Fishes with bony skeleton. This class comprises the vast majority of living fishes. It may be divided into three subclasses:
1. *Choanichthyes*, which includes the Coelacanth and the Lungfishes.
2. *Neopterygii* (=*Actinopterygii*), the modern bony fishes.
3. *Palaeopterygii*, a few primitive relict species, mostly of fresh water.

## Subclass CHOANICHTHYES

### Order CROSSOPTERYGII (Coelacanthini)

#### Coelacanth Fishes

A curious group of primitive fishes, the great majority of which lived from 300 to 70 million years ago and of which only one species, discovered in 1938, is known to survive today. In this group the fins and tail are fringed fleshy lobes and the skeleton is only very weakly ossified. Four families, all but one extinct.

Family LATIMERIDAE **Coelacanth**
This family is based on the single known surviving species.

**43. LATIMERIA CHALUMNAE** Smith 1939          Fig., p. 19.
Large deep water fishes (up to 120 cm) found near the Comoro Islands, in the Mozambique Channel. The first known specimen was taken near E. London, in S. Africa.

## Subclass NEOPTERYGII (Actinopterygii)

Fishes with completely ossified skeleton and fins supported by bony spines and rays. Spiracles and nictitating membrane absent. Males lack external copulatory organs and fertilisation is generally external, reproduction oviparous. The gills are protected by a bony operculum. Most species are covered by overlapping scales which are sometimes greatly reduced, absent, or modified into bony plates or rings. A lateral line (a sensory organ the function of which is not fully understood) is present in many species.

Although there are fossil forms dating back to the mid-Triassic, the Neopterygii are the dominant group of living fishes, numbering some 20 to 25,000 species.

## Order ISOSPONDYLI (Clupeiformes)

### Herring-like fishes

Small to medium-sized fishes characterised by having a single dorsal fin and lacking spines in all fins.

### Suborder Clupeoidei

### Typical Herring-like fishes

Small coastal fishes usually found in large schools. Many species are of seasonal occurrence and of considerable economic importance. Some inhabit estuaries and a few are permanent residents of fresh waters. Common in all seas.

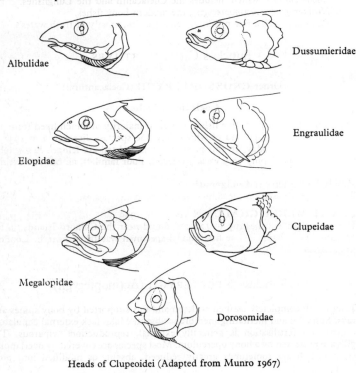

Heads of Clupeoidei (Adapted from Munro 1967)

Family ALEPOCEPHALIDAE **Black-heads, Naked-heads**
Small to medium-sized fishes inhabiting great oceanic depths. Some have light
producing organs (photophores).

Family ALBULIDAE **Bonefish**
Based on a single species found in all tropical waters.

**44. ALBULA VULPES** (Linnaeus) 1758
Bonefish, Ladyfish, Tarpon, O'io (H), Banane (S)
90 cm. D 15–17; A 8; L 1 65–77; tr 8/12. A beautiful cigar-shaped silvery
fish with yellowish fins and snout, sometimes with faint longitudinal lines above
lateral line. Excellent sport, but poor eating.

Bonefish

Family ELOPIDAE (including MEGALOPIDAE)
**Tarpons, Ox-eye Herring, Giant Herring, Ten-pounders**
Few medium to large species found in all warm waters. Compressed, elongated.
Scales cycloid, lateral line and adipose fin present. Head naked. Coastal waters,
entering estuaries and rivers.

**45. ELOPS SAURUS** Linnaeus 1758
Banana-fish (Q), Springer, Cape Salmon (S. Africa), Ten-pounder. Bony fish
(America), Giant Herring, Saumon (S)
120 cm; D 20–25; A 13–17; l 100–120;   tr 12/17. Silvery, bluish above, fins
yellowish. Good sport, poor eating. All warm seas.

ALLIED SPECIES:
**46. ELOPS HAWAIENSIS** Regan 60 cm. Silvery; the only species found in Hawaii.
Hawaii and W. Pacific.

**47. MEGALOPS CYPRINOIDES** (Broussonet) 1782
Tarpon, Ox-eye Herring (Q), Bastard Mullet (S. Africa), Alose, Lubine (S)
150 cm; D 17–20; A 24–31; L 1 36–40; tr 5–6/6–8. Olive above, silvery below,
fins yellowish. Harbours and estuaries, ascending rivers. Common throughout
the tropical Indo-Pacific.

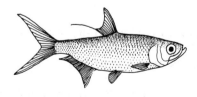

Tarpon

Family DOROSOMIDAE **Gizzard-shads, Bony-bream**
Herring-like scavengers of muddy bottoms, usually close inshore, but some
species inhabit fresh waters. Oval, moderately compressed. Belly often armed
with bony scutes. Adipose lid present, lateral line and teeth lacking. Sometimes
congregate in enormous shoals. Poor eating.

## 48. NEMATOLOSA COME (Richardson) 1844–48
Hairback Herring, Gizzard-shad
22 cm; D 17–18; A 22–23; Sc 42–46; tr 15–17. Silvery, green above, with
darker streaks along upper scale rows. A diffuse blackish blotch on shoulder.
Bays and harbours, from E. Africa to the E. Indies and W. Pacific.

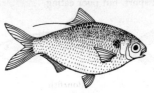

Gizzard-shad

## 49. ANODONTOSTOMA CHACUNDA (H.-B.) 20 cm. Similar to 48,
but dorsal fin does not end in long free filament. Central Indo-Pacific.

Family ENGRAULIDAE (including STOLEPHORIDAE) **Anchovies**
Small silvery fishes which often congregate in immense shoals in shallow coastal
waters and are given to seasonal movements. Flesh strong tasting; usually salted
or sun-dried, of considerable economic importance. Slender fishes with prominent snout, adipose lid, large cycloid scales, ventral scutes and forked tail.
Lateral line absent. All warm seas. The species are numerous, similar and
confusing and cannot be identified with certainty except by an expert. The ones
listed below are among the more important.

## 50. THRISSOCLES SETIROSTRIS (Broussonet) 1782 Indian Ocean to
W. Pacific.

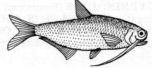

*Thrissocles setirostris*

## 51. THRISSOCLES PURAVA (H.-B.) 1822 Indian Ocean and C. Indo-
Pacific.

## 52. THRISSOCLES MALABARICUS (Bloch) 1801 Indian Ocean and
C. Indo-Pacific.

## 53. THRISSINA BAELAMA (Forskål) 1775 Red Sea and E. Africa to W.
Pacific.

**54. STOLEPHORUS INDICUS** (van Hasselt) 1823 Indian Ocean to C. Indo-Pacific.

**55. STOLEPHORUS PURPUREUS** Fowler 1900 C. Indo-Pacific, W. Pacific, Hawaii.

**56. STOLEPHORUS ZOLLINGERI** (Bleeker) 1849 C. Indo-Pacific, W. Pacific.

**57. STOLEPHORUS DEVISI** (Whitley) 1940 Central Indo-Pacific.

**58. STOLEPHORUS BATAVIENSIS** Hardenberg 1933 Central Indo-Pacific.

*Stolephorus bataviensis*

**59. STOLEPHORUS TRI** (Bleeker) 1852 Central Indo-Pacific.

**60. STOLEPHORUS HETEROLOBUS** Rüppell 1835 Red Sea, E. Africa, C. Indo-Pacific, W. Pacific.

**61. STOLEPHORUS COMMERSONI** Lacépède 1803 Central Indo-Pacific, W. Pacific.

**62. SCUTENGRAULIS HAMILTONI** (Gray) 1834 Indian Ocean, W. Pacific.

**63. SCUTENGRAULIS KAUMALENSIS** (Bleeker) 1849 Central Indo-Pacific.

**64. COILIA DUSSUMIERI** C. & V. 1848 Indian Ocean, C. Indo-Pacific.

**65. AMENTUM CARPENTARIAE** (De Vis) 1882 Central Indo-Pacific, Queensland.

Family DUSSUMIERIIDAE **Round Herrings, Sprats**
Small silvery herring-like fishes which occur in large shoals in open coastal waters. Cigar-shaped, with large cycloid scales. Ventral scales normal; lateral line absent, tail forked. Important as food for larger, economic fishes. Larger species good eating. Species similar and difficult to identify.

**66. DUSSUMIERIA ACUTA** C. & V. 1847 Central Indo-Pacific.

**67. DUSSUMIERIA HASSELTI** Bleeker 1851 Central Indo-Pacific, W. Pacific.

*Dussumieria hasselti*

**68. SPRATELLOIDES DELICATULUS** (Bennett) 1831 Indian Ocean, C. Indo-Pacific, W. Pacific, Hawaii.

**69. SPRATELLOIDES JAPONICUS** (Houttuyn) 1782 Indian Ocean, C. Indo-Pacific, W. Pacific.

**70. ETRUMEUS MICROPUS** (Schlegel) 1846 Western Pacific, Hawaii.

Family CLUPEIDAE **Herrings, Sardines, Pilchards**
Small migratory fishes which congregate in enormous shoals in shallow coastal waters. Elongated and laterally compressed. Lateral line absent, scales large, thin, cycloid, deciduous. Belly with keeled scutes. Lower part of operculum with an angular emargination. Anal much longer than dorsal. Teeth small and weak. Flesh excellent, economic importance considerable. Many species in all seas, very similar and difficult to identify.

**71. KOWALA COVAL** (C. & V.) 1829 Indian Ocean, C. Indo-Pacific.

**72. KOWALA MACROLEPIS** (Steindachner) 1879 Central Indo-Pacific, W. Pacific.

**73. SARDINELLA PERFORATA** (Cantor) 1849 Central Indo-Pacific.

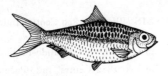
*Sardinella perforata*

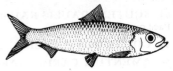
*S. melanura*

**74. SARDINELLA MELANURA** (C. & V.) 1829 Indian Ocean, C. Indo-Pacific, W. Pacific.

**75. SARDINELLA JUSSUIEUI** (Lacépède) 1803 Indian Ocean, C. Indo-Pacific, W. Pacific.

**76. AMBLYGASTER SIRM** (Walbaum) 1792 Indian Ocean, C. Indo-Pacific, W. Pacific.

**77. AMBLYGASTER CLUPEOIDES** Bleeker 1849 Central Indo-Pacific.

**78. MACRURA BREVIS** (Bleeker) 1848 Central Indo-Pacific.

**79. HARENGULA OVALIS** (Bennett) 1830 Indian Ocean, C. Indo-Pacific.

**80. PELLONA DITCHELA** C. & V. 1847 Indian Ocean, C. Indo-Pacific, W. Pacific.

## Suborder **Chanoidei**

Family CHANIDAE **Milkfish, Salmon-herring**
A single species which occurs throughout the Indo-Pacific and in the Red Sea.

### 81. CHANOS CHANOS (Forskål) 1775
Milkfish, Salmon-herring, Awa (H), Lubine (S and M)
120 cm; D 13–17; A 9–11; P 16–17; V 11–12; L 1 75–91; tr 12/9–13. Scales small, cycloid, lateral line present. Olive green above, silvery below; anal and caudal fins with dark margins. Coastal waters and estuaries. An important food fish.

Milkfish

## Suborder **Chirocentroidei**

Family CHIROCENTRIDAE **Wolf-herrings, Silkfish, Dorab, Parang**
Two large Indo-Pacific species. Very long, strap-like; scales cycloid, very small; lateral line absent. Eyes small, mouth large, oblique, both jaws armed with large fang-like canines. No abdominal scutes.

### 82. CHIROCENTRUS DORAB (Forskål) 1775
360 cm; D 16–18; A 32–35; eye with adipose lid; ventral fins very small. Blue above, silvery below, tail yellow. Good eating, but bony; large specimens dangerous. Red Sea and E. Africa to W. Pacific.

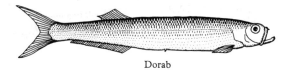

Dorab

ALLIED SPECIES:
**83. CHIROCENTRUS NUDUS** Swainson 45 cm. Differs from *C. dorab* in having 16–18 gill-rakers instead of 11. Indian Ocean, C. Indo-Pacific.

## Suborder **Stomiatoidei**

A group of highly specialised small fishes of great depths which includes the families *Idiacanthidae, Chauliodontidae, Stomiatidae, Malacosteidae, Gonostomidae* and *Sternoptychidae*.

## Order **MYCTOPHIFORMES** (Iniomi)

Small to medium fishes related to the herring-like fishes. Fins without true
spines. A small adipose fin usually present. Comprises two families of luminous
deep water species (*Myctophidae* and *Paralepidae*) and two families of inshore
fishes.

Family SYNODONTIDAE (SYNODIDAE) **Lizardfish, Grinners**
A small family of solitary bottom dwellers of shallow coastal waters. Some bury
themselves in the sand and make short dashes to capture their prey or to escape
capture. Lateral line present, mouth very large. General appearance lizard-
like, pattern and colours mottled and variable, designed to blend with weedy
bottom. Edible, but of poor quality.

**84. SYNODUS VARIEGATUS** (Lacépède) 1803
Variegated Lizardfish, Baise Dame, Lezard (M)
26 cm; D 12–13; A 8–10; L l 58–62; tr 4–6/10–11. Brown with 8–9 darker
vertical bands, sometimes broken into spots; ventrals and anal yellow, rays of
other fins spotted. Throughout the tropical Indo-Pacific, including the Red Sea
and Hawaii.

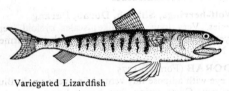

Variegated Lizardfish

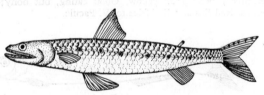

*Synodus indicus*

ALLIED SPECIES:
**85. SYNODUS INDICUS** (Day) 23 cm. Mottled olive-brown above, fins pinkish,
dorsal and tail olive. Indian Ocean.
**86. S. KAIANUS** Günther 25 cm. Rare, usually below 200 m. East Indies, W. Pacific,
Hawaii.
**87. S. BINOTATUS** Schultz 12 cm. Differs from other species by the presence of a
prominent black spot on the tip of the snout. Western Pacific, Hawaii.
**88. S. DERMATOGENYS** Fowler 40 cm. Similar to 84, but larger and with 14
dorsal rays and 63 or more L l scales. Hawaii.
**89. S. JAPONICUS** (Houttuyn) 30 cm. Similar to 84, but much rarer. Indian Ocean,
C. Indo-Pacific, W. Pacific.

**90. TRACHINOCEPHALUS MYOPS** (Bloch & Schneider) 1801
Painted Saury
32 cm. D 11-13; A 15-16; L l 54-58; tr 3/6-7. Grey brown above, silvery
yellow below; two blue stripes with brown edges on each side and a blackish
blotch on shoulder. Fins light yellow. Warm waters of all oceans.

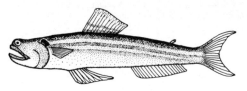

Painted Saury

**91. SAURIDA GRACILIS** Quoy & Gaimard 1824
Slender Saury, Arna sala, Vivace (M)
28 cm. D 10-11; A 9-10; L l 45-49; tr 4/6. Brown above, silvery below,
marked with irregular dark bands and spots; dark bars on fins. East Africa to
the W. Pacific, including Australia.

ALLIED SPECIES:
**92. SAURIDA TUMBIL** (Bloch) 40 cm. Fins unspotted, pectorals with 14-15 rays,
12-13 in 91. Central Indo-Pacific, W. Pacific.
**93. S. UNDOSQUAMIS** (Richardson) 43 cm. A series of regular dark spots along
lateral line; upper tail lobe spotted. East Africa, Seychelles, C. Indo-Pacific.

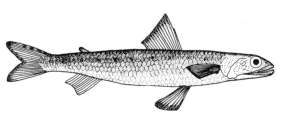

*Saurida undosquamis*

**94. XYSTODUS SAGENEUS** (Waite) 26 cm. Lilac above, with 9 thin longitudinal
lines; yellowish white on lower sides, head spotted with violet. Australia.

Family HARPODONTIDAE **Bombay Ducks**
Moderate-sized translucid fishes of muddy river-mouths. Some species are
salted and eaten with curry. Elongated, flatly compressed fishes with cycloid
scales which are absent from anterior part of body. Lateral line present; eyes
very small, near snout, mouth very large.

G.C.R.F.-D

**95. HARPODON NEHEREUS** (Hamilton-Buchanan) 1822
Bombay Duck
40 cm; D 12–14; A 13–15; L 1 40. Brown or grey, speckled with black, translucid when alive; fins dark. Melanesia and E. Indies to India.

ALLIED SPECIES:
**96. HARPODON TRANSLUCENS** Saville-Kent 70 cm. D 14–15, L 1 55; caudal and dorsal tips blackish. New Guinea and Australia.

*Harpodon translucens*

## Order **SACCOPHARYNGIFORMES**

Family EURYPHARYNGIDAE **Pelican Eels, Gulpers**
Eel-like fishes with enormous heads and mouths which inhabit great oceanic depths.

## Order **MIRIPINNIFORMES**

Family EUTAENIOPHORIDAE **Tapetails**
A small family of elongated scale-less pelagic fishes.

## Order **SILUROIDIFORMES** (Nematognathi)

A large group of carnivorous bottom feeders with naked slimy skin. Most species have very sharp pectoral and dorsal spines covered by a poisonous mucus and capable of inflicting painful wounds. Most species are permanent residents of fresh waters.

Family PLOTOSIDAE **Catfishes, Cobblers, Tandans**
Elongated catfishes with tapering tail. Lateral line represented by a series of pores. First dorsal fin short-based with strongly ossified 1st spine. Anal, caudal and 2nd dorsal forming a continuous fin. Four pairs of fleshy barbels on the snout. Many Indo-Pacific species, mostly in fresh water. The larger species are excellent eating despite repulsive appearance.

### 97. PLOTOSUS ANGUILLARIS (Bloch) 1794
### =PLOTOSUS ARAB Bleeker 1862
Striped Catfish-eel, Machoiron (S)
90 cm. Very dark brown above, much paler below. The young have two sharply
defined whitish longitudinal lines on each side. Young individuals of up to
15 cm or so occur in very tight shoals of closely packed individuals, usually
about 50, often in tidal pools, sheltering from the sun under low coral overhangs.
As they grow they lose their very conspicuous light stripes, the shoals break up
and the fishes become solitary and move into estuaries and may ascend rivers.
Red Sea and E. Africa to Queensland, Melanesia, Micronesia, Polynesia and
Japan.

Striped Catfish-eel

ALLIED SPECIES:
### 98. PLOTOSUS CANIUS H.-B. 90 cm. Without stripes at all ages. India, C. Indo-
Pacific, W. Pacific.
### 99. EURISTHMUS NUDICEPS (Günther) 32 cm. Mottled brown, fins tipped
with black. Gulf of Papua.
### 100. PARAPLOTOSUS ALBILABRIS (C. & V.) 35 cm. Uniform blackish with
white lips. East Indies, N. Australia, Queensland.

Family TACHYSURIDAE **Estuarine Catfish**
Fresh water and estuarine catfish which may be separated from the Plotosidae
by the presence of a distinct forked tail, an adipose fin and a well developed
lateral line. Three pairs of barbels. Dorsal and pectoral fins poisonous. The eggs
are incubated in the mouth of the males.

### 101. NETUMA THALASSINA (Rüppell) 1835–40
### =TACHYSURUS THALASSINUS
Giant Salmon-catfish
120 cm; D 1/7; A 15–18. Reddish brown above, silvery below. A dark spot on
adipose dorsal. Red Sea to India, Indonesia, Melanesia, N. Australia and
Queensland.

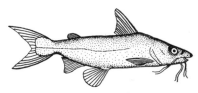

Giant Salmon-Catfish

## Order **ANGUILLIFORMES** (Apodes)

### Eels, Morays, Congers

A large group of predatory elongated snake-like fishes found in all seas. They
have no poison glands, but bites often turn septic. The larvae are transparent
ribbon-like creatures ('Leptocephalus') which live in the open sea. True eels
(Anguillidae) spend their adult lives in rivers, but return to the sea to spawn.
Some species are often mistaken for Sea-snakes, which however can always be
recognised by their compressed tails, large scales and complete lack of fins.

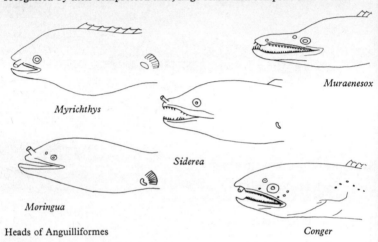

*Muraenesox*

*Myrichthys*

*Siderea*

*Moringua*

Heads of Anguilliformes                                    *Conger*

Family OPHICHTHYIDAE (including ECHELIDAE) **Snake-eels, Serpent-eels**
A large, varied group of marine eels. The tail is sharply pointed, free and used
for burrowing into sand or mud; these eels spend most of the day at the bottom,
but may be attracted to the surface by light at night. They can inflict severe
bites if handled without care. Extremely elongated, cylindrical, scale-less.
Dorsal and anal, when present, end before tip of tail. Caudal fin absent. Pectorals
absent or vestigial. Anterior nostril a tube on upper lip. Many species, some
boldly marked; usually in sandy areas among coral. Some species take shelter
in the urogenital passage of larger fishes.

### 102. **MYRICHTHYS MACULOSUS** (Cuvier) 1817
Spotted Snake-eel
90 cm. Yellowish white with 3 longitudinal rows of round brown spots. Spots
extending on fins. Coral reefs in the entire tropical Indo-Pacific, including the
Red Sea and Hawaii.

Spotted Snake-eel

## 103. MYRICHTHYS COLUBRINUS (Boddaert) 1781

90 cm. Head yellow, body red with 25 or more encircling blackish rings. Coral reefs from the Red Sea and E. Africa to the E. Indies, Philippines, Ryukyu islands, Melanesia, Micronesia and Polynesia, but not in Hawaii.

*Myrichthys colubrinus*

## 104. LEIURANUS SEMICINCTUS (Lay & Bennett) 1839
Culverin

50 cm; creamy white with 25–30 broad black bands which extend onto the dorsal, but do not encircle the belly. Coral reefs throughout the tropical Indo-Pacific, from Africa to Hawaii.

Culverin

OTHER SPECIES:

**105. LEIURANUS PHOENIXENSIS** Schultz 45 cm. Light yellowish with 25 dark dorsal saddles, the last 6–7 encircling tail. East Africa to W. Pacific.

**106. PISODONOPHIS BORO** (H.-B.) 90 cm. Pectorals well developed. Teeth granular, in several series. Uniform olive brown above, pinkish or yellowish on sides and belly. East Africa to W. Pacific.

**107. P. CANCRIVORUS** Richardson 75 cm. Pectorals well developed. Brown, paler below. Fins with dark edge, dorsal with anterior black spot. Red Sea, E. Africa, C. Indo-Pacific, Australia, China, Polynesia.

**108. ZONOPHICHTHUS MARGINATUS** Peters 45 cm. Teeth large and sharp, in single series. Pectorals present. A broad dark cross-band behind head. East Africa to E. Indies and Melanesia.

**109. CAECULA BICOLOR** (Kaup) 43 cm. Pectorals absent. Usually buried in sand, seldom seen. Dark olive above, pale yellowish below, strongly contrasting. Fiji.

**110. C. PLATYRHYNCHA** Gosline 35 cm. Lacks all fins. Stocky, triangular in section. Usually buried in sand, seldom seen. Hawaii.

**111. C. FLAVICAUDA** Snyder 45 cm. Lacks all fins. Slender, eyes large. Usually buried in sand, seldom seen. Hawaii.

**112. C. LUMBRICOIDES** Bleeker 27 cm. Pectorals absent, dorsal and anal very low, almost absent. Rare. Ceylon, E. Indies, Fiji.

**113. C. MACRODON** Bleeker 50 cm. Pectorals absent, dorsal and anal very low. Dark olive above, light yellowish olive below. East Indies and Fiji.

**114. C. KIRKI** (Günther) 35 cm. Pectorals absent. Grey-green, paler below. East Africa to India and Ceylon.

**115. CALLECHELYS MARMORATUS** (Bleeker) 60 cm. White with irregular close-set black and yellow spots. East Africa to W. Pacific.

**116. C. NEBULOSUS** Smith 50 cm. Dark grey brown, irregularly mottled with lighter markings. East Africa, Aldabra.

**117. C. STRIATUS** Smith 60 cm. Light yellow with a dark dorso-lateral band from head to tail, broadening towards tail. Dorsal white with narrow black edge. Western Indian Ocean.

**118. C. LUTEUS** Snyder 90 cm. Extremely slender, dorsal commences ahead of gill openings, pectorals absent. Rare. Hawaii.

**119. C. LONGIPINNIS** (Kner & Steindachner) 45 cm. Darker above, with fine, irregular dark spots; paler below, fins pale, pectorals absent. Polynesia.

**120. C. FILARIA** (Günther) 60 cm. Extremely slender and elongated. Pectorals absent. Dorsal starts on head. Uniform grey-brown. East Indies, Polynesia.

**121. C. PUSILLUS** (Seale) 55 cm. No pectorals. Back brown, belly, anal and dorsal paler. Fiji.

**122. C. FIJIENSIS** (Seale) 35 cm. No pectorals. Dark brown with small black spots; belly and fins paler. Fiji.

**123. JENKINSIELLA PLAYFAIRII** (Günther) 37 cm. Pectorals present. Teeth blunt and granular. A fringe of fine long barbels along upper lip. East Africa to W. Pacific.

**124. PHYLLOPHICHTHUS XENODONTUS** Gosline 45 cm. Anterior nostril with leaf-like flap. Plain greenish. Rare. East Africa to W. Pacific and Hawaii.

**125. SCHULTZIDIA JOHNSTONENSIS** Schultz & Woods 30 cm. Strongly compressed, dark above, pale below. Rare. Hawaii.

**126. MURAENICHTHYS LABIALIS** Seale 15 cm. Dorsal begins a short way behind gill opening. Rare. Western Pacific, Hawaii.

**127. M. COOKEI** Fowler 25 cm. Head broad, colour yellow. Hawaii.

**128. M. GYMNOTUS** Bleeker Dorsal fin rudimentary, begins well back, behind anus. Central Indo-Pacific to Hawaii.

**129. M. SCHULTZEI** Bleeker 15 cm. Corner of mouth well behind eye. Central Indo-Pacific to Hawaii.

**130. M. IREDALEI** Whitley 15 cm. Pectorals absent. Brown with small black dots on back. A dark patch on each side of thorax. Fins colourless. Queensland.

**131. M. MACROSTOMUS** Bleeker 23 cm. Uniform yellowish brown. Central Indo-Pacific, Fiji.

**132. M. MACROPTERUS** Bleeker 23 cm. Pale brownish with fine black dots above. East Indies, Philippines, Melanesia, Micronesia, Polynesia.

**133. M. GYMNOPTERUS** Bleeker 30 cm. Uniform brown, paler below. East Indies, Philippines, China, Polynesia, Hawaii.

**134. MICRODONOPHIS MACGREGORI** Jenkins 25 cm. Pectorals normal. Dorsal starts forward of gill openings. Uniformly coloured. Known from half a dozen specimens. Hawaii.

**135. OPHICHTHUS POLYOPHTHALMUS** Bleeker 32 cm. Probably an active predator. Teeth large and strong, eyes forward. Back and head brownish red with irregular white spots. Sides paler with reddish brown rings. Fins orange brown. Rare. East Indies, Polynesia, Hawaii.

*Ophichthus polyophthalmus*

**136. O. CEPHALOZONA** Bleeker 82 cm. Dull brown; a wide blackish cross band on nape, broadly edged with white fore and aft. Dorsal and anal blackish with white edge. Central Indo-Pacific, China, Australia, Micronesia, Polynesia.

**137. O. APICALIS** (Bennett) 50 cm. Uniform light brown. East Africa, C. Indo-Pacific.

**138. BRACHYSOMOPHIS SAUROPSIS** Schultz 50 cm. Eyes almost on tip of snout. Dorsal fin pale. Western Pacific, Hawaii.
**139. B. HENSHAWI** J. & S. 75 cm. Dorsal black with white margin. Very rare. Hawaii.
**140. ACHIROPHICHTHYS TYPUS** Bleeker 23 cm. No pectorals. Eyes large, well forward. Dark brown above, paler below. East Indies, Philippines.
**141. OPHISURUS SERPENS** (L.) 3 m. Uniform light olive green, paler below. East Africa, S. Africa, C. Indo-Pacific, Mediterranean.

### Family MURAENIDAE Moray Eels, Reef Eels

A very numerous family of large tropical marine eels. All are fierce predators and many spend much of their lives in holes in rock and coral, from which they will emerge suddenly to snap at their prey and into which they retreat when alarmed. Many species are nocturnal. Large moray eels are dangerous and may attack without provocation; divers should be careful not to poke their hands into blind crevices and holes. Edible, but of poor quality. Naked with tough skin extending over fins. Gill openings small. Dorsal and anal usually well developed and confluent with tail; pectorals absent. Snout short and blunt, mouth very wide, teeth sharp and strong, nostrils tubular. Most species are dark and dull-coloured, but some are strikingly marked.
Difficult to identify; the genus *Uropterygius* is finless, but most other genera are based on dental characters.

### 142. ECHIDNA ZEBRA (Shaw & Nodder) 1797
Zebra Moray, Congre (S)
120 cm. Black to dark chocolate with numerous well defined narrow yellow encircling rings. Coral reefs in the entire tropical Indo-Pacific, including the Red Sea and Hawaii.

Zebra Moray

### 143. ECHIDNA NEBULOSA (Ahl) 1789
Starry Moray, Cloudy Moray
75 cm. Whitish with two rows of dark star-shaped blotches enclosing one or more white spots. One of the commonest species throughout the Indo-Pacific including the Red Sea and Hawaii. Coral reefs, often in very shallow water; very active at night and attracted to light.

Starry Moray

### 144. ECHIDNA POLYZONA (Richardson) 1844

Girdled Moray

90 cm. Dark brown with 24–30 whitish rings extending onto fins. Coral reefs throughout the tropical Indo-Pacific, including the Red Sea and Hawaii.

Girdled Moray

ALLIED SPECIES:

### 145. ECHIDNA LEUCOTAENIA Schultz 52 cm. Dark brown; snout, lower jaw and margins of both fins white. Polynesia and Melanesia.

### 146. THYRSOIDEA MACRURA (Bleeker) 1864
### =EVENCHELYS MACRURA

Pompa (E. Indies)

The largest known eel, exceeding 3 m. Uniform olive brown. Not dangerous to man. Shallow coastal waters, often ascending rivers. South and E. Africa to the C. Indo-Pacific and W. Pacific. Common in Queensland.

### 147. UROPTERYGIUS CONCOLOR Rüppell 1835–40

Brown Moray

50 cm. Fins rudimentary. Uniform red-brown. Fins yellowish. Coral reefs from S. and E. Africa to the C. Indo-Pacific and W. Pacific.

### 148. UROPTERYGIUS MARMORATUS (Lacépède) 1803

Marbled Moray

90 cm. Fins rudimentary. Creamy, marbled and blotched with brown, especially on back. Anus dark blue. Wriggles into its hole tail first. Coral reefs from S. and E. Africa to the C. Indo-Pacific and the W. Pacific.

### 149. UROPTERYGIUS TIGRINUS (Lesson) 1829

120 cm. Pectorals completely absent. Tail short and anus placed a long way back. Light grey with irregular dark rounded spots and blotches. South and E. Africa, Seychelles, C. Indo-Pacific and Hawaii.

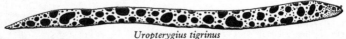

*Uropterygius tigrinus*

ALLIED SPECIES:

### 150. UROPTERYGIUS FASCIOLATUS (Regan) 30 cm. Dorsal and anal rudimentary. Numerous narrow dark undulating cross-bands, some breaking into spots. Central Indo-Pacific.

### 151. U. ALBOGUTTATUS Smith 38 cm. Dark olive brown with small white spots on head. East Africa, Seychelles to C. Indo-Pacific.

### 152. U. SEALEI Schultz 90 cm. Plain brown, rare. Western Pacific, Hawaii.

### 153. U. POLYSPILUS (Regan) 42 cm. Similar to 149, but position of anus normal. Western Pacific, Hawaii.

### 154. U. KNIGHTI (Jordan & Starks) 35 cm. Posterior half much darker than anterior, with irregular light grey markings. Shallow water less than 3 m. Western Pacific, Hawaii.

**155.** **U. INORNATUS** Gosline 20 cm. Uniform brown, usually in 6 m or more of water. Hawaii.
**156.** **U. FUSCOGUTTATUS** Schultz 30 cm. Head uniform brown, rear of body speckled with darker brown. Hawaii.
**157.** **U. SUPRAFORATUS** (Regan) 45 cm. Similar to 156, but dark mottlings extending to head. Rare. Hawaii.
**158.** **U. FIJIENSIS** Fowler & Bean 70 cm. Rich dark brown, spotted with black. Spots smaller on head, forming longitudinal lines on throat. Rare. Fiji.

## 159. ENCHELYNASSA CANINA (Quoy & Gaimard) 1824

180 cm. Uniform dark brown. A dangerous fish with a wide gape and long fang-like teeth. Central Indo-Pacific, W. Pacific, Hawaii.

*Enchelynassa canina*

OTHER SPECIES:
**160.** **PSEUDECHIDNA BRUMMERI** (Bleeker) 100 cm. Very elongated and slender. Yellow with 3 longitudinal rows of dark star-shaped blotches. A single row on dorsal. Throughout tropical Indo-Pacific.
**161.** **RABULA FUSCOMACULATA** Schultz 20 cm. Anal and dorsal beginning behind anus. Snout blunt. Mottled brown. Rare. Hawaii.

## 162. MURAENA PARDALIS Schlegel 1846

Puhi-oa, Puhi-kauhila (Hawaii)
90 cm. Nostrils enclosed by long erect red tubes. Brown, boldly marked with white and red spots and blotches. Madagascar, Mauritius, C. Indo-Pacific, Melanesia, Micronesia, Polynesia, Hawaii.

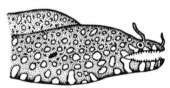

Puhi-oa

OTHER SPECIES:
**163.** **ANARCHIAS LEUCURUS** Snyder 25 cm. Head and sides of lower jaw mottled. Inner series of large teeth in upper jaw not extending behind eye. Western Pacific, Hawaii.
**164.** **A. CANTONENSIS** Schultz 20 cm. Similar to 163, but inner series of large teeth in upper jaw extending behind eye. Western Pacific, Hawaii.
**165.** **A. SEYCHELLENSIS** Smith 17 cm. Sluggish, slender, dark, faintly mottled. Seychelles.

## 166. SIDEREA PICTA (Ahl) 1789

Painted Moray, Congre (S)
75 cm. Yellowish with 4 to 6 rows of dark star-shaped blotches, the narrow interspaces irregularly speckled with dark spots. One of the commonest morays on most Indo-Pacific coral reefs. Very active at night, when it ventures into

shallow sandy pools. Throughout the Indo-Pacific, including the Red Sea, Queensland and Hawaii.

Painted Moray

ALLIED SPECIES:
**167. SIDEREA THYRSOIDEA** (Richardson) 65 cm. Uniform brown, faintly mottled with lighter areas. Red Sea, India, C. Indo-Pacific, W. Pacific, Queensland.
**168. S. GRISEA** (Lacépède) 45 cm. Grey, faintly, but closely mottled with darker grey. Conspicuous dark pores on sides of head and along first fifth of lateral line. East Africa, C. Indo-Pacific, W. Pacific.

### 169. GYMNOTHORAX MELEAGRIS (Shaw) 1795
Speckled Moray
90 cm. Black, with numerous small white or yellow spots. Gill openings black. Throughout the Indo-Pacific, including the Red Sea and Hawaii.

Speckled Moray

### 170. GYMNOTHORAX FLAVOMARGINATUS (Rüppell) 1828
Leopard Moray, Puhi-paka (H)
150 cm. Yellowish, densely speckled with dark brown spots. Gill opening in a dark spot. Throughout the Indo-Pacific, including the Red Sea and Hawaii.

### 171. GYMNOTHORAX UNDULATUS (Lacépède) 1803
Mottled Moray, Puhi-laumila (H)
180 cm. A very aggressive species. Blackish, paler below, decorated with an irregular network of narrow pale lines, denser on the head. South and E. Africa to Hawaii.

### 172 GYMNOTHORAX FAVAGINEUS Bloch & Schneider 1801
Congre mousquée (S)
180 cm. Light grey, irregularly marked with large dark rounded blotches. South and E. Africa, Seychelles and C. Indo-Pacific.

### 173. GYMNOTHORAX TESSELLATUS (Richardson) 1844
Reticulated Moray
150 cm. Dangerous. Black, covered all over with clearly defined light yellow reticulations. Often found in old wrecks. East and S. Africa to C. Indo-Pacific.

Reticulated Moray

ALLIED SPECIES:

**174. GYMNOTHORAX BUROENSIS** (Bleeker) 60 cm. Brown with diffuse blackish spots fusing to form a dark network on tail. East Africa, C. Indo-Pacific, Hawaii.

**175. G. RUPPELLI** (McClelland) 60 cm. Yellowish to brown with 15–20 encircling black rings. East Africa, C. Indo-Pacific, Hawaii.

**176. G. HEPATICUS** (Rüppell) 90 cm. Plain uniform grey-brown, margins of fins lighter. Red Sea, E. Africa to W. Pacific and Hawaii.

**177. G. CHILOSPILUS** (Bleeker) 30 cm. Brown with incomplete wavy cross-bands, a dark line behind corner of mouth and white spots on jaws. East Africa to C. Indo-Pacific.

**178. G. RICHARDSONI** (Bleeker) 90 cm. Dark brown, paler below. 24–32 irregular transverse black lines meeting and forming a partial network. Anal with narrow white margin. East Africa to W. Pacific.

**179. G. MOLUCCENSIS** (Bleeker) 45 cm. Uniform plain brown, fin margins not paler. Central Indo-Pacific, W. Pacific, Hawaii.

**180. G. MALATREMUS** Schultz 30 cm. Light grey with well defined black speckles. Western Pacific, Hawaii. Very common.

**181. G. EUROSTUS** Abbot 60 cm. Very variable, from light grey to black; spotted when young. Can only be identified with certainty from its dentition. Hawaii.

**182. G. STEINDACHNERI** J. & E. 60 cm. Snout rather long. Yellowish brown with darker markings, particularly on furrows behind lower jaw. Hawaii.

**183. G. BERNDTI** Snyder 90 cm. Extensive light patches separated by narrow dark interspaces. Rare. Hawaii.

**184. G. PETELLI** (Bleeker) 90 cm. Light grey with 18 blackish cross-bands twice as wide as interspaces, wider in middle of body. First band on nape. East Africa, C. Indo-Pacific, W. Pacific, Hawaii.

**185. G. GRACILICAUDUS** Jenkins 30 cm. Very slender. Head white, sometimes with dark blotches. Common. Western Pacific, Hawaii.

**186. G. MUCIFER** Snyder 75 cm. Dark brown with irregular white spots. Known from a single specimen. Hawaii.

**187. G. PINDAE** Smith 35 cm. Uniform olive brown, teeth serrated. East Africa.

**188. G. JAVANICUS** (Bleeker) 60 cm. Yellowish with 5–6 rows of large irregular dark spots extending to fins. Light interspaces with small dark dots. A dark area surrounding gill opening. East Africa to C. Indo-Pacific.

**189. G. MARGARITOPHORUS** (Bleeker) 90 cm. Dark yellowish grey with numerous diffuse oblique dark encircling rings as wide as interspaces. 4–5 large rounded black spots between eye and pectoral. East Africa to C. Indo-Pacific.

**190. G. MONOCHROUS** (Bleeker) 60 cm. Dorsal rather high; uniform olive-grey. East Africa to C. Indo-Pacific.

**191. G. PERMISTUS** (Smith) 60 cm. Pale yellow with large irregular black spots; light interspaces narrow, forming a bold network. Western Indian Ocean.

**192. G. PERUSTUS** (Smith) 25 cm. Uniform dark olive brown. Western Indian Ocean.

**193. G. PIKEI** (Bliss) Head blackish, body light greyish with numerous narrow wavy irregular dark cross-bands. Fin margins narrowly blackish. Mauritius.

**194. G. PUNCTATUS** (Schneider) 120 cm. Purplish brown, covered with small white spots. Flesh said to be poisonous. Indian Ocean.

**195. G. NUDIVOMER** (Günther) 100 cm. Thick-set with short blunt snout. Brown with yellowish spots which become progressively larger towards tail. South Africa, E. Africa to C. Indo-Pacific.

## 196. RHINOMURAENA AMBOINENSIS Barbour 1908
Blue Ribbon Eel

75cm. Slender, somewhat compressed eels. Dorsal fin well developed. Tubular nostrils erect, long, near tip of snout. Snout acute, eye large, pectoral rudimentary. Brilliant ultramarine blue, eye, snout and dorsal fin orange. East Indies and Philippines.

## 197. RHINOMURAENA QUAESITA Garman 1888
Black Ribbon Eel

75 cm. Similar in shape to 201. Head and anterior part of body black, posterior part of body and dorsal fin orange. A narrow whitish margin along entire length of dorsal. Philippines and Marshall islands.

## Family MORINGUIDAE **Thrush-eels**

Very slender degenerate eels of shallow coastal waters. They usually lie buried in the sand and mud of the bottom and rise to the surface at night. Naked, thread-like, round in section. Dorsal and anal very reduced, confined to and confluent with the tail. Pectorals rudimentary or absent. Snout short, anterior nostrils tubular, at tip of snout; eyes small, covered by skin.

## 198. MORINGUA BICOLOR Kaup 1856
Black-tailed Thrush-eel

75 cm. Both fins supported by bony rays anteriorly and near the tail, but vestigial in the middle. Lateral line present. Greenish brown above, yellow below; fins yellow. Central Indo-Pacific and W. Pacific.

Black-tailed Thrush-eel

ALLIED SPECIES:

**199. MORINGUA PENNI** Schultz 50 cm. Lateral line absent, dorsal origin behind anal origin. Tail truncate. Light brown, darker above. Central Indo-Pacific.

**200. M. MACROCEPHALA** (Bleeker) 70 cm. Dorsal and anal origins opposite. Tail truncate. Brown above, yellowish below. India, E. Indies, Philippines, Polynesia.

**201. M. ABBREVIATA** (Bleeker) Dorsal origin slightly behind anal. Tail rounded. Front nostril near tip of snout, with low fleshy rim. Hind nostril a large pore. East Indies, Philippines, N. Australia, Ryukyu islands, Polynesia.

**202. M. JAVANICA** (Kaup) 90 cm. Hind nostril a short tube before and below eye. Tail short, pointed. Dark sepia, paler below and on muzzle. East Indies, Philippines, Japan, Micronesia, Melanesia, Polynesia.

**203. M. MICROCHIR** Bleeker 50 cm. Anal origin well before dorsal. Tail broadly rounded. Colour uniform. East Africa to W. Pacific.

**204. M. MACROCHIR** Bleeker 45 cm. Anal origin opposite dorsal. Tail truncate. Dark dorsal colour sharply contrasted with pale sides and belly. Central Indo-Pacific, W. Pacific, Hawaii.

**205. M. LINEARIS** Gray 25 cm. Tail rounded. Pectoral rudiment very short and broad. Uniform olive brown. East Indies, S. China, Polynesia.

## Family MURAENESOCIDAE **Pike-eels**

A small family included in the Leptocephalidae by some authors. Should be handled with care because of their large, strong, sharp teeth. Excellent eating. Robust eels, cylindrical anteriorly, compressed posteriorly. Naked. Dorsal and anal fins well developed, confluent with tail. Anterior nostrils tubular. Eyes large, covered with skin. Shallow coastal waters, sometimes entering rivers.

**206. MURAENESOX CINEREUS** (Forskål) 1775
=**M. ARABICUS** Schneider
Arabian Pike-eel
150 cm. Silvery, fins broadly edged with black. Red Sea, E. and S. Africa,
Indonesia, Queensland, China, Polynesia.

Arabian Pike-eel

ALLIED SPECIES:
**207. RHECHIAS ARMIGER** Jordan 1921 Known from a single specimen from
Hawaii, possibly not referable to this family.

Family LEPTOCEPHALIDAE (CONGRIDAE) **Conger-eels**
Large powerful eels, similar to the Pike-eels, but differ in having the tongue
free and in lacking canine-like teeth. Excellent eating. Some are coastal, some
from deep water and some live in brackish or even fresh water. In the genera
*Conger* and *Ariosoma* the front nostril is tubular, but not in *Uroconger*; in
*Conger* the outer teeth are close-set, forming a cutting edge.

**208. CONGER CINEREUS** Rüppell 1828
Grey Conger-eel
100 cm. Yellowish when young; adults dark brown above, paler below. Fins
edged with black; a black spot on pectoral. Lives in cracks and crevices, coming
inshore at night. Red Sea and S. Africa to the C. Indo-Pacific, W. Pacific
and Queensland.

Grey Conger-eel

OTHER SPECIES:
**209. CONGER CONGER** (L.) 240 cm. Similar to 208, but dorsal origin above tip
of depressed pectoral, further forward in 208. Uniform grey to black. Should be handled
with care. All warm waters, including Atlantic.
**210. C. MARGINATUS** Valenciennes (White Eel, Puhi-uha) 90 cm. A dark marking
above posterior part of mouth. Common. Hawaii.
**211. C. WILSONI** (Schneider) 150 cm. Similar to 210, but dorsal origin further back,
dark mark lacking. Uncommon. Central Indo-Pacific, W. Pacific, Hawaii.
**212. UROCONGER LEPTURUS** (Richardson) 45 cm. Dorsal origin above
pectoral base. Uniform blackish to brown, fins darker. East and S. Africa to C. Indo-
Pacific.
**213. BRACHYCONGER PLATYRHYNCHUS** Norman Snout broad and flat,
anteriorly rounded. Brownish, tail with narrow light margin. Central Indo-Pacific.
**214. ARIOSOMA BOWERSI** (Jenkins) 40 cm. Silvery, burrows in sand in shallow
water; Hawaii.
**215. A. FIJIENSIS** (Ogilby) 15 cm. Dorsal well developed, commencing above
pectoral base. Uniform pale yellow. Fiji.
**216. A. ANAGO** (Schlegel) 60 cm. Brown with two dark blotches behind eyes. Dorsal
and anal edged with black, tip of tail white. East and S. Africa to C. Indo-Pacific.
**217. A. GUTTULATA** (Günther) 20 cm. Pale greyish yellow. A series of very
small black dots above lateral line and a similar series below it. Fiji.

## Order **BELONIFORMES** (Synentognathi)

A large group of silvery surface fishes. Moderately to extremely elongated. Scales cycloid. Lateral line close to ventral profile. A single dorsal fin. Pectorals high, very large in some families. Ventrals placed far back, with 6 rays. No fin spines; tail usually forked.

### Suborder **Scomberesocoidei**

Family BELONIDAE **Needle-fish, Long Toms, Alligator Gar, Aiguilles (S)**
Pelagic surface predators, often congregating in large schools. A few estuarine and fresh water forms. Excellent eating despite greenish bones. Both jaws produced into a pointed beak and armed with sharp canines to the tip. Scales small, eye large. About 25 Indo-Pacific species.

**218. STRONGYLURA STRONGYLURA** (van Hasselt) 1823
Black-spot Long Tom
45 cm; D 10–13; A 13–15; L 1 170. Lateral line not forming a keel on caudal peduncle. Brownish or yellowish green above, sides silvery, white below; rear half of body marked by a blue-edged longitudinal band. Dorsal bordered with orange, anal yellow, tail green with blackish median blotch. India, E. Indies, Philippines, Queensland.

Black-spot Long Tom

**219. TYLOSURUS INDICUS** (Le Suer) 1821
Giant Long Tom
120 cm; D 20–22; A 18–20; L 1 350. Dark green above, sides silvery, white below; dorsal, pectorals and tail yellow-green, blackish distally. Rays of front half of dorsal and middle rays of tail black. India, E. Indies, Philippines, W. Pacific.

Giant Long Tom

### Suborder **Exocoetoidei**

Scales large and thin, teeth small.

### Family HEMIRHAMPHIDAE **Half-beaks, Garfish, Aiguilles (S)**
Similar to long toms, but only lower jaw produced into a half beak. Occur in coastal waters, often in large shoals. Half-beaks feed on algae and other vegetable matter at the surface. Important food fishes despite small size and numerou

small bones. Teeth small, absent from beak. Lateral line near ventral profile. Eggs large, anchored to vegetation by means of sticky threads. About 30 Indo-Pacific species.

### 220. EULEPTORHAMPHUS VIRIDIS (Van Hasselt) 1824
Long-finned Garfish
48 cm; D 19–22; A 19–20; L 1 105–126. Blue above, silvery on sides and below. Tail and pectorals dusky. Capable of flying for 20 m out of the water. Central Indo-Pacific and W. Pacific, including Hawaii.

### 221. HEMIRHAMPHUS FAR (Forskål) 1775
Black-barred Garfish, Needle-fish, Candle-fish
50 cm; D 12–14; A 10–12. Greenish blue above, silvery on sides and below. 4 to 9 large black spots on sides. Upper lobe of tail bright yellow, lower lobe blue. Red Sea and E. Africa to India, the E. Indies, Philippines and Queensland.

Black-barred Garfish

### 222. HYPORHAMPHUS DUSSUMIERI (Cuvier & Valenciennes) 1846
37 cm; D 12–14; A 11–12; L 1 52–56; greenish blue above, each scale with a black dot. Sides silvery with a blackish line separating silver from blue areas. Dorsal and tail blackish. East and S. Africa to the C. Indo-Pacific and W. Pacific.

### Family EXOCOETIDAE Flyingfish, Poissons volants (S)
Small pelagic fishes which feed on plankton. The large pectorals and ventrals are used as wings and these fishes are capable of flying considerable distances to escape pursuing predators. Mouth symmetrical in adults, but lower jaw may be produced in the juveniles. Chin barbels present in the juveniles of some species. Eggs large, attached to floating objects by sticky threads. About 40 Indo-Pacific species, many widespread, some common to the Atlantic and Indo-Pacific.

### 223. EXOCOETUS VOLITANS Linnaeus 1758
Flyingfish
25 cm; D 13–15; A 14–15; L 1 39–43. Dark above, silvery on sides and below. Pectorals blackish at base, other fins yellowish. One of the commonest and most widespread species. Tropical Indian Ocean, Atlantic and Pacific.

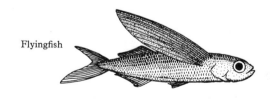

Flyingfish

**224. CYPSELURUS FURCATUS** (Mitchell) 1815
Black-tipped Flyingfish
35 cm; D 13–15; A 10; L 1 56–62. Blue above, silver on sides and below. Pectorals purplish with dark spots. Tail dusky, dorsal with a blackish spot. All warm seas.

## Order LAMPRIDIFORMES (Allotriognathi)

### Ribbonfish, Oarfish

A small group of pelagic and deep water fishes which seldom come inshore. Highly compressed body, some species very elongated, ribbon-like. Scales vestigial or absent. Lateral line present in most species. Dorsal and anal long-based, with many rays, but no spines. The order comprises the following families: *Lampridae, Trachipteridae, Lophotidae* and *Stylephoridae.*

## Order PLEURONECTIFORMES (Heterosomata)

### Flatfishes

A large group of bottom-dwelling fishes. The larvae are normally symmetrical and pelagic, but the adults are asymmetrical, with both eyes on one side (on the right, except in the left-handed Bothidae). The side on which they lie is blind and unpigmented, the side which is exposed is coloured and marked to match the background. Some species are able to change colour like a chamaeleon. Flatfishes feed on small fishes, worms, molluscs and crustacea. Oval and extremely compressed. Scales small, lateral line present, sometimes branched or duplicated. Fins without spines. Teeth small, often on blind side only. Excellent eating, the larger species being the object of important commercial fisheries.

Family PSETTODIDAE **Toothed Flounders**
A single species of wide Indo-Pacific distribution. Large teeth and shape somewhat similar to that of the northern halibut. Lack of symmetry less extreme than in other flatfish. Individuals may be right or left-handed.

**225. PSETTODES ERUMEI** (Bloch & Schneider) 1801
Queensland Halibut, Kalankan (E. Indies) Adalah
60 cm; D 49–56; A 24–44; L 1 68–67; tr 21–28/33–41. Uniformly dark brown; young specimens with four dark cross-bars. Excellent eating. South and E. Africa to W. Pacific and Queensland.

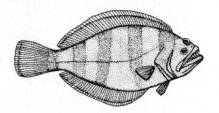

Queensland Halibut

## Family BOTHIDAE **Left-handed Flounders**

About 45 Indo-Pacific species. Small to moderate flatfishes with characteristic ocellated and mottled patterns. Most species inhabit shallow coastal waters and are excellent eating, but of little commercial importance. Oval and compressed, 'left-handed'; scales generally small, lateral line single, strongly curved anteriorly. Dorsal extends onto head; dorsal and anal free from tail which is rounded or truncate.

### 226. **TAENIOPSETTA OCELLATA** (Günther) 1880
Ocellated Flounder

12 cm; D 88–93; A 72–76; L 1 110–120. Some anterior dorsal and anal rays prolonged into free filaments, especially in the males. Scales ctenoid. Light olive brown speckled with dark brown and marked with brown-edged ocelli along dorsal and ventral profiles. Deepish water in the C. Indo-Pacific.

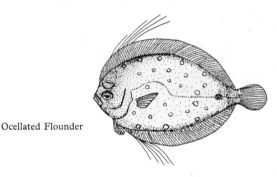

Ocellated Flounder

ALLIED SPECIES:
**227. TAENIOPSETTA RADULA** Gilbert 15 cm, deepish water. Hawaii.

### 228. **PSEUDORHOMBUS ARSIUS** (Hamilton-Buchanan) 1822
Large-toothed Flounder

35 cm; D 70–80; A 51–62; L 1 67–80. Jaws with enlarged canines anteriorly. Lateral line on both sides. Exposed (ocular) side and fins brown with dusky spots and rings. Often one to three large dark blotches surrounded by rings of white dots along lateral line. East coast of Africa to the W. Pacific. Common in Queensland.

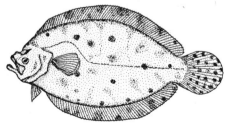

Large-toothed Flounder

ALLIED SPECIES:

**229. PSEUDORHOMBUS ELEVATUS** Ogilby 18 cm. Left pectoral longer than right one. Pale brown with 5 series of faint darker rings; 2–3 dark blotches along lateral line. Fins spotted. Persian Gulf to India, E. Indies and Queensland.

## 230. BOTHUS PANTHERINUS (Rüppell) 1828
Leopard Flounder, Paku, Ui-Ui (H)

30 cm; D 86–93; A 65–70; L 1 82–87. Second to fourth pectoral rays prolonged and reaching caudal base in males. Scales ctenoid on ocular side, cycloid on blind side. Eyelid with fleshy tentacle. Lateral line on ocular side only. Reddish brown with darker blotches and ocelli. A prominent dark spot at end of lateral line. Fins mottled. Common throughout the Indo-Pacific, including the Red Sea and Hawaii.

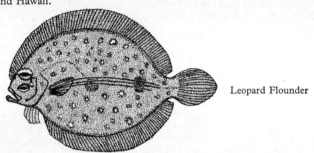

Leopard Flounder

ALLIED SPECIES:

**231. BOTHUS MANCUS** (Broussonet) 35 cm. Similar to 230, but lacks eye tentacle and has a prominent indentation above snout. East Africa, C. Indo-Pacific, W. Pacific, Hawaii.

**232. B. BLEEKERI** Steindachner. Known from a single 12 cm specimen from Hawaii.

**233. B. OVALIS** (Regan) 11 cm. One pectoral ray prolonged in ♂. Tail rounded. Grey-brown with numerous small blue or white spots surrounded by dark rings. A large round ocellus above lateral line, behind pectoral base. Central Indo-Pacific.

**234. B. MYRIASTER** T. & S. 12 cm. Very rounded. Left pectoral long and falcate. Blind side with numerous transverse lines. East Africa to W. Pacific.

**235. ARNOGLOSSUS INTERMEDIUS** Bleeker 12 cm. First dorsal ray prolonged and expanded. A small fleshy tentacle near eye. Tail rather pointed. Light brown with darker rings and blotches, especially along margins and lateral line. Seychelles to W. Pacific.

**236. A. TAPEINOSOMA** Bleeker 12 cm. Anterior dorsal rays greatly prolonged in ♂, less so in ♀. Markings much as in 235. Central Indo-Pacific.

## 237. ENGYPROSOPON GRANDISQUAMA
(Temminck & Schlegel) 1846
Spotted-tail Flounder

15 cm; D 79–89; A 59–68. Light brown, mottled with brown; fins spotted with brown, tail with two large dark spots at upper and lower margins. Seychelles to C. Indo-Pacific and Queensland.

ALLIED SPECIES:

**238. ENGYPROSOPON HAWAIIENSIS** J. & E. 10 cm. Eyes small, lips fringed with fleshy projections. Hawaii.

**239. E. XENANDRUS** Gilbert 10 cm. Eyes large, no fleshy projections. Deep water, Hawaii.

**240. E. LATIFRONS** (Regan) 12 cm. Found in 60–80 m of water. Seychelles, Maldives.

**241. E. SEYCHELLENSIS** (Regan) 8 cm. Known from type only. Seychelles.

**242. E. FIJIENSIS** Norman 8 cm. Greyish brown with many paler and darker spots and ocelli. Fins variegated. Fiji.

## Family PLEURONECTIDAE **Right-handed Flounders**

An important family in cool waters, where it comprises such species as the Halibut, Dab, Lemon Sole, Plaice and Flounder, but represented by few small species in tropical waters. Oval and compressed; scales moderate; lateral line simple; dorsal and anal free from tail; eyes on right side.

**243. BRACHYPLEURA MICROSTOMA** Günther 1880 9 cm. Deep water, Melanesia.

**244. POECILOPSETTA HAWAIIENSIS** Gilbert 1905 12 cm. Deep water, Hawaii.

**245. SAMARISCUS TRIOCELLATUS** Woods 1960 12 cm. Marked with 3 large rings; Hawaii.

**246. SAMARISCUS CORALLINUS** Gilbert 1905 12 cm. Deep water, Hawaii.

## Family SOLEIDAE **Soles**

A large family of right-handed flatfish represented in the Indo-Pacific by some forty species. Oval and compressed. Scales moderately large. Lateral line single and straight, but may be arched and branched on head. Preoperculum without free edge, embedded in the skin. Dorsal and anal free or fused with tail. Pectorals rudimentary, right larger than left. Shallow coastal waters.

**247. ACHIRUS PAVONINUS** Lacépède 1802
Peacock Sole

20 cm; D 63–71; A 49–54; L 1 84–90. Dorsal and anal free from tail, pectorals absent. Lateral line branched on blind side. Dark red-brown marked with numerous light eye spots with dark centres and enclosed by dark rings. Central Indo-Pacific from the Andaman islands to the E. Indies, Queensland and Japan.

OTHER SPECIES:

**248. HETEROMYCTERIS HARTZFELDI** (Bleeker) 12 cm. Snout strongly hooked around mouth. Purplish brown with wavy paler lines and irregular dark spots and rings. East Indies, New Guinea.

**249. ASERAGGODES PERSIMILIS** (Günther) 12 cm. Snout rounded. Pectorals absent, tail free. Brown with white or rosy black-ringed, brown-pupilled ocelli. Bismarck islands.

**250. A. MELANOSTICTUS** (Peters) 15 cm. Pectorals absent, tail free. Brown with many small black dots. Solomon islands.

**251. A. KOBENSIS** (Steindachner) 10 cm. Front of head fringed. Pectorals absent, tail free. China, Japan, Hawaii.

**252. A. MORROWI** Chab 12 cm. Snout rounded. Pectorals absent, tail free, rounded. Boldly marked with numerous dark and light ringed ocelli. East Africa, Aldabra.

### 253. AESOPIA HETERORHINOS (Bleeker) 1856
Aesop Sole, Tiger Sole
15 cm; D 88–98; A 78–87; L 1 106–120. Eyes contiguous. Snout projecting beyond edge of dorsal. Ocular nostril prolonged into a long tube. Dorsal and anal free from slightly rounded tail. Yellowish brown with numerous irregular dark cross-bands. Fins with light margins, black submarginally. East Indies, Andamans, Melanesia, N. Queensland, Micronesia, Polynesia.

### 254. DEXILLICHTHYS MUELLERI (Steindachner) 1879
Tufted Sole
20 cm; D 61–70; A 46–57; L 1 70–87; tr 28–32/33–37. Dermal fringes on snout, chin, around eyes, along lower lip and opercular edge. Tufts of filaments on ocular side, especially in middle of lateral line and near dorsal and anal bases. Tail pointed, confluent with dorsal and anal. Lateral line branched on ocular side. Light brown, filaments black. East Indies to New Guinea.

### 255. SYNAPTURA ORIENTALIS (Bloch & Schneider) 1801
Black Sole
23 cm; D 61–65; A 44–50; L 1 70–85. Dorsal and anal confluent with rounded tail. Dermal fringes around eyes and along lips and scattered filaments on ocular side. Lateral line with long transverse branches. Slate blue or blackish with narrow cross-bands and large rounded dark blotches. Muddy bays and estuaries in the E. Indian Ocean, E. Indies, China Sea, Melanesia and Queensland.

ALLIED SPECIES:
**256. SYNAPTURA VILLOSA** Weber 14 cm. Snout hooked, nostril tubular. Tail pointed. Irregular patches of dermal filaments on ocular side. Dark brown with cloudy dark blotches. New Guinea.
**257. S. ASPILOS** Bleeker 37 cm. Snout hooked, nostril tubular, head fringed. Uniform brown, faintly spotted when young. East Indies, Melanesia.
**258. S. DICHOLEPIS** Peters 32 cm. Greenish, irregularly spotted with black. Bismarck Archipelago.
**259. S. CORNUTA** Kaup 17 cm. First dorsal ray swollen, Grey-brown with 14–17 dark transverse bands. South and E. Africa to C. Indo-Pacific.

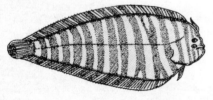

*Synaptura cornuta*

## Family CYNOGLOSSIDAE **Tongue Soles**
Numerous species of small elongated tongue-shaped flatfishes of little economic importance. Mostly inhabitants of sandy bottoms in shallow coastal waters. Extremely compressed, elongated, tapering sharply at the tail. Scales small, ctenoid, but cycloid on blind side in some species. Lateral line may be absent, single, branched, double or triple. Dorsal and anal always confluent with tail. Pectorals absent. Left ventral well developed, but sometimes connected with anal. Preopercular margin embedded in skin. Eyes very small; teeth minute, generally on blind side only. Left-handed.

## 260. PARAPLAGUSIA BILINEATA (Bloch) 1784
Patterned Tongue Sole

25 cm; D 96–116; A 75–93; L 1 90–114. Snout hooked. Lips on ocular side with fringe of branched filaments. Scales ctenoid; two lateral lines, superior and mid-lateral, separated by 16–19 series of scales. Lateral line absent from lower side. Brownish with dark speckles forming a pattern of faint wavy lines, some meeting to enclose pale areas. South and E. Africa to the Central Indo-Pacific and W. Pacific.

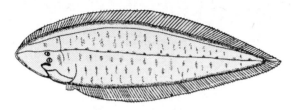

Patterned Tongue Sole

OTHER SPECIES:

**261. CYNOGLOSSUS BILINEATUS** (Lacépède) 30 cm. Two lateral lines on both sides. Brownish with irregular dark patch on operculum. Red Sea and Natal to the Philippines, Japan, Queensland.

**262. C. PUNCTICEPS** (Richardson) 20 cm. Two lateral lines above, one below. Reddish brown with diffuse dark spots sometimes forming cross-bands. India, E. Indies, Melanesia.

**263. C. BRACHYCEPHALUS** Bleeker 13 cm. Two lateral lines above, none below. Brown with irregular dark spots. Red Sea and E. Africa to the W. Pacific.

**264. C. LINGUA** (H.-B.) 40 cm. Two lateral lines above, traces of one below. Very elongated. Brown, operculum blackish, fins dark posteriorly. South and E. Africa to C. Indo-Pacific.

**265. C. LIDA** (Bleeker) 20 cm. Two lateral lines above, none below. Brown with a blackish spot on operculum. East and S. Africa to E. Indies.

**266. SYMPHURUS SEYCHELLENSIS** Chab 8 cm. Type only, Seychelles.

## Order BERYCIFORMES (Berycomorphi, Berycoidei)

Primitive fishes with fin spines, transitional between the Isospondyli (Herrings and Salmon-like fishes) and the perch-like Percomorphi. Several families of deep water fishes (Melamphaidae, Polymixiidae, Berycidae, Trachichthyidae), but one small family which includes one well known aquarium fish (Monocentridae) and a large family of brilliant shallow water coral fishes (Holocentridae).

Family MONOCENTRIDAE **Knight-fishes**

Two species of small rounded fishes with few large scales fused to form a rough armoured box. Both species occur in rather deep water and have luminous organs on the chin which are thought to lure their prey. Also known as Pineapple fishes and Pine-cone fishes because of their peculiar appearance; *Cleidopus gloria-maris* De Vis, 23 cm, is known from Australia, while *Monocentris japonicus* (Houttuyn), 12 cm, is known from scattered localities including Japan and S. Africa. Frequently washed ashore after storms.

*Cleidopus gloria-maris*

## Family HOLOCENTRIDAE **Squirrelfishes, Soldierfishes**

Small brightly coloured shallow water fishes of coral reefs which occur in all warm seas. Very hard, dry fishes with sharp scales and bony, spiny heads. They all sport various shades of red, have large eyes and are nocturnal, usually hiding during the day in crevices in the coral.

 *Myripristis*      *Holocentrus, Kutaflammeo*

Heads of Holocentridae

### 267. KUTAFLAMMEO SAMMARA (Forskål) 1775                    Pl. 1
### =HOLOCENTRUS SAMMARA =FLAMMEO SAMMARA
Bloodspot Squirrelfish, Lion Male (M)
23 cm; D XI/10–11; A IV/7; L 1 40–44; tr 4/6. Elongated. Preopercular spine broad, reaching gill opening; two long opercular spines. One of the commonest squirrelfishes; coral reefs throughout the tropical Indo-Pacific including the Red Sea and Hawaii, but not in Queensland. Dark area at front of dorsal distinguishes 267 from other elongated species (268, 269, 270).

### 268. KUTAFLAMMEO OPERCULARIS (Cuvier & Valenciennes) 1831
### =HOLOCENTRUS OPERCULARIS
Black-finned Squirrelfish
25 cm; D XI/12–13; A IV/9–10; L 1 38–39; tr 3–4/7–8. Elongated. Preopercular spine long and broad; two opercular spines; third anal spine longest. Red above, yellow below. Spinous dorsal black, white at margin and subbasally. Coral reefs from E. Africa to the W. Pacific as far as Tahiti.

### 269. KUTAFLAMMEO ANGUSTIFRONS (Ogilby) 1908
### =HOLOCENTRUS ANGUSTIFRONS
15 cm; D XI/10; A IV/7; L 1 41; tr 4/8. Elongated; preopercular spine short, reaching subopercular edge; two strong opercular spines. Third anal spine

longest. Silvery yellow with 8 faint longitudinal bands. Fins pale, unspotted. Coral reefs in Melanesia.

### 270. KUTAFLAMMEO LAEVIS (Günther) 1859
### =HOLOCENTRUM LAEVE
Smooth Squirrelfish
20 cm; D XI/10; A IV/7; L 1 39–41; tr 3/7. Elongated. Preopercular spine short and flat; two opercular spines. Brilliant rosy silver with faint longitudinal bands on body and spots on cheeks. Fins yellow shading to red. Coral reefs from E. Africa to the E. Indies, Melanesia and the Society islands.

### 271. HOLOCENTRUS SPINIFER (Forskål) 1775     Pl. 1
### =HOLOCENTRUS LEO Jordan & Everman
Spiny Squirrelfish, Scarlet-fin Squirrelfish (Q), Lion (S), Lion baroque (M)
27 cm; D XI–XII/13–15; A IV/9–11; L 1 42–46; tr 4–5/8–10. Preopercular spine reaches gill opening. Three flat opercular spines above numerous small ones. Third anal spine longest. Fins uniformly orange or vermilion; may be separated from 272 by the absence of white tips to the dorsal. Coral reefs throughout the Indo-Pacific, from the Red Sea and S. Africa to Hawaii, the Society islands and Queensland. *H. andamanensis* Day 1878, is probably the young of this species.

### 272. HOLOCENTRUS VIOLACEUS Bleeker 1853     Pl. 1
Violet Squirrelfish
23 cm; D XI/13–14; A IV/9; L 1 34–37; tr 3/6–8. Preopercular spine reaches beyond gill opening; two large opercular spines; third anal spine longest. May be distinguished from 271 by its darker red colour and by the white dorsal tips. Coral reefs from E. Africa to Indonesia, Melanesia and Polynesia as far as Tahiti.

### 273. HOLOCENTRUS MICROSTOMUS Günther 1859
Silver Squirrelfish
17 cm; D XI/11–12; A IV/8–9; L 1 49–52; tr 3/9. Preopercular spine does not reach gill opening. Two opercular spines, upper as long as preopercular. Fourth anal spine longest. Red above, silvery below; 6–11 pale yellowish longitudinal bands. A wide silvery blotch below end of spinous dorsal. Spinous dorsal with dark red submarginal band and white tips, other fins yellow shading to red. Coral reefs from Indonesia and New Guinea to the Tuamotu, Society and Hawaiian islands.

### 274. HOLOCENTRUS DIADEMA Lacépède 1803     Pl. 1
Crowned Squirrelfish, Lion parasol (S)
17 cm; D XI/11–13; A IV/8–9; L 1 46–50; tr 3/7–8. Preopercular spine reaches beyond gill opening; two large opercular spines, upper longer than preopercular. Third anal spine longest. Purple to brown spinous dorsal with irregular pale longitudinal band distinguishes this very common species from all other squirrelfishes. Coral reefs throughout Indo-Pacific from the Red Sea and Natal to China, Hawaii, Tahiti and Queensland.

### 275. HOLOCENTRUS CORNUTUS Bleeker 1853     Pl. 1
Horned Squirrelfish, Red and White Squirrelfish (Q)
20 cm; D XI/12–13; A IV/9; L 1 35–36; tr 3/7. Preopercular spine subequal to eye. Two opercular spines, upper longest. Third anal spine longest. Common

in coral reefs from E. Africa to Indonesia, the Philippines, Queensland and
Melanesia.

### 276. HOLOCENTRUS RUBER (Forskål) 1775                    Pl. 1
### =HOLOCENTRUS PRASLIN Jordan & Seale
Red Squirrelfish, Cardinal, Lion (S), Lolong (Malay)
23 cm; D X/11–12; A IV/8–10; L 1 33–36; tr 3/7. Preopercular spine reaching
gill opening. Two opercular spines, upper longest. Third anal spine longest.
Coral reefs from the Red Sea and E. Africa to the Philippines, Japan, Micronesia,
Queensland and Tahiti.

### 277. HOLOCENTRUS TIERE Cuvier & Valenciennes 1829
25 cm; D XI/14–15; A IV/9–10; L 1 47–49; tr 3/6–7. Preopercular spine long.
Two opercular spines, lower very small. Red with silvery scale centres. Fins red,
dorsal with white spot between each pair of spines. Coral reefs below 6 m from
E. Africa to Seychelles, Indonesia, Marshall islands, Hawaii and Tahiti.

### 278. HOLOCENTRUS TIEREOIDES Bleeker 1853
18 cm; D XI/12–14; A IV/8–9; L 1 38–41; tr 3/7–8. Preopercular spine to
beyond gill opening. Two opercular spines, upper longest. Third anal spine
longest. Red above, orange laterally, yellow below. Each scale with silvery spot,
forming longitudinal bands. Fins pale yellow. Coral reefs from Indonesia and
Melanesia through Micronesia to Tahiti.

### 279. HOLOCENTRUS CAUDIMACULATUS Rüppell 1835–40
Tail-spot Squirrelfish
30 cm; D X/13–14; A IV/9–10; L 1 41–44; tr 3/7–8. Preopercular spine very
strong, reaching far beyond gill opening. Two large, almost equal opercular
spines. Third anal spine longest. Deep red with violet streaks on lower parts.
Pectoral axil deeper red. A prominent dark blotch on upper part of caudal
peduncle. Fins deep red or yellow red. Coral reefs from E. Africa to Seychelles,
E. Indies, Melanesia and Tahiti.

### 280. HOLOCENTRUS SEYCHELLENSIS Smith 1963
20 cm; D XI/13; A IV/9; L 1 40. Golden yellow with 6–7 purplish brown
longitudinal bands. Spinous dorsal yellow, basally red and tipped with red.
Other fins yellow, caudal with narrow upper and lower red margins. Coral
reefs in the Seychelles.

### 281. HOLOCENTRUS XANTHERYTHRUS
Jordan & Everman 1903                                        Pl. 1
18 cm; D XI/11–12; A IV/8–9; L 1 45–48; tr 3/9. Very distinctively marked
with alternating bright red and silver longitudinal bands. Hawaii only, where
it is very common on the outer reefs, between 6 and 15 m.

### 282. HOLOCENTRUS LACTEOGUTTATUS
Cuvier & Valenciennes 1829
### =H. ARGENTEUS Cuvier, =H. GRACILISPINUS Fowler
Lion aux ailes rouges (M), Ala-ihi (H)
23 cm; D XI–XII/12–13; A IV/8–10; L 1 40–44; tr 3/8. Preopercular spine
long, but slender. Lower opercular spine longer than upper. Pink, each scale
with a large silvery centre. Fins light pink, spiny dorsal and tail with a distinct
deeper pink margin. Coral reefs from the Red Sea and E. Africa to the E. Indies,
Melanesia, Micronesia and Polynesia as far as Tahiti and Hawaii.

**283. HOLOCENTRUS SCYTHROPS** Jordan & Everman 1903
25 cm; D XI/13–14; A IV/9; L 1 44–45; tr 4/7½. Third anal spine very long. Soft dorsal rays and outer caudal rays very long. Rather pale silvery with 9–10 narrow longitudinal red bands, darker on back. Fins white, dorsal rays red, soft dorsal and caudal tipped with pink. Found in deeper water than most species, Hawaii.

**284. HOLOCENTRUS ENSIFER** Jordan & Everman 1903     **Pl. 1**
30 cm; D XI/14; A IV/10; L 1 44–45; tr 4/7. A single large opercular spine. The yellow and pink longitudinal bands are characteristic. Hawaii only.

The following Holocentrid species lack preopercular spines; most of them are very similar and difficult to identify.

**285. MYRIPRISTIS MURDJAN** (Forskål) 1775     **Pl. 1**
Crimson Squirrelfish, Blotcheye (Q), Lion gros yeux (S)
30 cm; D XI/12–14; A IV/13–14; L 1 36; tr 3/7. One opercular spine. Outer caudal rays, 1st dorsal and anal rays white, followed proximally by dark red rays and by blackish areas in some individuals. Coral reefs from the Red Sea and E. Africa to Indonesia, Melanesia, Queensland, Micronesia and Polynesia as far as the Tuamotu and Society islands. Common. Very similar to 287.

**286. MYRIPRISTIS LEIOGNATHOS** Valenciennes 1855
Smooth-jawed Squirrelfish
18 cm; D XI/11–12; A IV/13–14; L 1 36; tr 3/7. One large opercular spine. Brick red above, yellowish on sides and below. A series of pale golden bands along scale rows. A narrow brown bar on operculum. A brown spot at base of pectoral. Fins yellow. Coral reefs in the E. Indies and Melanesia.

**287. MYRIPRISTIS PRALINIUS** Cuvier & Valenciennes 1829
=**M. SYMMETRICUS** Jordan & Everman 1905
Port Praslin Squirrelfish, Lion Scie (M)
20 cm; D XI/13–16; A IV/12–15; L 1 36–40; tr 3–4/7. One large opercular spine. Similar to 285, but fins bright red. Coral reefs from E. Africa to the Seychelles, India, Indonesia, Melanesia and Polynesia as far as Tahiti.

**288. MYRIPRISTIS HEXAGONUS** (Lacépède) 1802
20 cm; D XI/14–15; A IV/12–13; L 1 32–33; tr 3/7. Brilliant scarlet with paler longitudinal bands below lateral line. Hind edge of operculum and pectoral axil blackish; fins uniform red, lighter than body. Coral reefs from Mauritius to the E. Indies, Micronesia and Polynesia, including Fiji and the Society islands.

**289. MYRIPRISTIS CHRYSERES** Jordan & Everman 1903
Pa'u'u (H)
25 cm; D XI/14; A IV/12; L 1 33–35. More elongated than other species of the genus. Red with yellow fins. Coral reefs, Hawaii.

**290. MYRIPRISTIS MULTIRADIATUS** Günther 1874
17 cm; D XI/16–17; A IV/15–16; L 1 38–43. More ovate than other Hawaiian species. Red. Dark opercular bar extending further forward than in other species and continuing to inner base of pectoral. Vavau and Hawaii.

### 291. MYRIPRISTIS BERNDTI Jordan & Everman 1903
U'u, Menpachi
35 cm; D XI/14–15; A IV/12–13; L 1 29–30. Almost identical in appearance with 285 which however does not occur in Hawaii. May be separated from other Hawaiian species by the white anterior dorsal and anal rays. Dark spot restricted to upper half of pectoral axil. Hawaii. Similar to 292.

### 292. MYRIPRISTIS ARGYROMUS Jordan & Everman 1903
U'u, Menpachi
35 cm; D XI/15–16; A IV/13–14; L 1 33–36. Very similar to 291, but fins often tipped with black, never with white. Hawaii.

### 293. MYRIPRISTIS AUSTRALIS Castelnau 1875
Blunt-nosed Soldierfish
17 cm; D XII/14; A IV/12; L 1 28; tr 2½/5½. Rose pink above, silvery pink below, each scale edged with darker pink. Lips and snout bright pink. Upper part of opercular edge dark red. A large white mark at posterior edge of pupil. Eye surrounded by scarlet. Spinous dorsal pink edged with scarlet, other fins rose-pink. Coral reefs in N. Queensland, very common.

### 294. MYRIPRISTIS ADUSTUS (Bleeker) 1853     Pl. 1
Blue Squirrelfish
25 cm; D X–XI/13–14; A IV/13–14; L 1 27–29; tr 2–3/6. One opercular spine. Coral reefs from S. and E. Africa to the Seychelles, Ceylon, the E. Indies, Melanesia, Micronesia, and Polynesia as far as Christmas island, Tahiti and the Society islands.

### 295. MYRIPRISTIS PARVIDENS Cuvier & Valenciennes 1829
Small-toothed Squirrelfish
10 cm; D XI/13–14; A IV/13–14; L 1 30; tr 3/6. One opercular spine. Violet red. Opercular margin and pectoral axil blackish. Fins rosy red. Outer caudal rays, anterior dorsal and anal rays dark violet. East Indies and Melanesia.

### 296. MYRIPRISTIS MICROPHTHALMUS (Bleeker) 1852
Small-eyed Squirrelfish
18 cm; D XI/14–15; A IV/13; L 1 27–29; tr 3/7. One opercular spine. Reddish brown, scale margins darker, forming dark network. Opercular edge and pectoral axil dark brown. Fins uniformly pale brownish pink. East Indies and Melanesia to the Tuamotu islands in Polynesia.

### 297. HOLOTRACHYS LIMA (Cuvier & Valenciennes) 1831
Fleshy Squirrelfish
20 cm; D XII/13–14; A IV/11; L 1 36–42; tr 4–5/8–11. Two strong opercular spines. A deeper fish with smaller eyes and scales than most Holocentrids. Uniform brick red. Spinous dorsal blood red, other fins paler red. Coral reefs throughout the Indo-Pacific, from E. Africa to the Pacific as far as Hawaii, the Society islands and Tahiti.

The family also includes the following Indo-Pacific species: *Ostichthys japonicus* (C. & V.), *Holocentrus erythraeus* Günther, *H. ittodai* Jordan & Fowler, *H. furcatus* Günther, *Rhynchichthys brachyrhynchos* Bleeker, *Myripristis undecimalis* Herre, *M. intermedius* Günther, *M. mooreanus* Herre, *M. melanostictus* Bleeker, *M. kuntee* (C. & V.).

## Order **SYNGNATHIFORMES** (Solenichthyes)

An immensely varied group of rather degenerate fishes which feed by sucking water and small organisms into a very small mouth placed at the end of a long tubular snout. Most species live in shallow coastal waters, but a few penetrate fresh water.

### Suborder **Aulostomoidei**

Family CENTRISCIDAE **Razorfish, Shrimpfish**
Small, extremely modified tropical fishes. Almost transparent and very flattened, with a knife-like ventral keel, hence the name: 'razorfish'. Lateral line absent. Protected by a stiff transparent papery carapace consisting of thin fused bony plates which are expansions of the vertebral column. The carapace terminates in a sharp spine which is the 1st dorsal spine and displaces the soft dorsal and tail to a ventral position. Razorfish swim in small schools, each one in a vertical position with snout pointing down. One species is said to seek protection among the spines of sea-urchins. Mouth tubular, toothless.

**298. AEOLISCUS STRIGATUS** (Günther) 1860
Razorfish, Shrimpfish, Ikan Pisan (Malay)
13 cm; D III/9–10; A 11–12. Yellowish with a black band from snout through eye to base of tail. Shallow coastal waters, often among sea-urchins. Seychelles to the E. Indies, Melanesia and Hawaii.

Razorfish

**299. AEOLISCUS PUNCTULATUS** (Bianconi) 1854
15 cm. Differs from 298 in being less elongated, having a shorter snout and shorter dorsal spine and in having many small black spots instead of the black longitudinal band. South and E. Africa to the C. Indo-Pacific.

**300. CENTRISCUS SCUTATUS** Linnaeus 1758
Guttersnipe-fish
15 cm; D III/10–12; A 12. Silvery with dark lateral streak and 7–8 silver crossbars on ventral plates. Indonesia and Melanesia.

**301. CENTRISCUS CRISTATUS** (De Vis) 1885
30 cm; D III/13; A 13–14. Silvery; a red band from snout to eye, followed by a golden spot. A further red or orange band through opercle to pectoral base and thence to base of dorsal spine. Abdomen yellowish with 8–10 oblique red crossbars. Coral reefs in Queensland.

Family AULOSTOMIDAE **Flutemouths, Trumpetfish**
A few shallow water species, less modified than the Centriscidae. Scales small, lateral line present, spinous dorsal consisting of isolated spines which are often erected and used as a defence weapon. Tubular snout very long; a short barbel

under lower jaw. Solitary, often seen moving very slowly at a steep angle to the surface, sometimes lying on the bottom, or head down among corals and algae. Able to change colour from brown to green, yellow and orange, so as to harmonise with the background.

### 302. AULOSTOMA CHINENSIS (Linnaeus) 1766
Flutemouth, Trumpetfish, Nunu (Hawaii)
75 cm; D VIII–XII; 24–27; A 22–25. Central Indo-Pacific to Hawaii, Tahiti and Queensland.

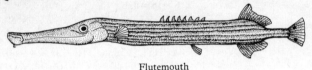

Flutemouth

### 303. AULOSTOMA VALENTINI Bleeker 1853
60 cm. East Africa to the C. Indo-Pacific. Probably a synonym of 302.

### Family FISTULARIIDAE Cornetfish, Hair-tailed Flutemouths
Fairly strong swimmers with long attenuated snout and long whip-like prolongation of the central caudal rays. Large individuals can suck in small fishes and prawns despite the small size of the mouth. Scales replaced by small spines embedded in the skin. Lateral line well developed, spinous dorsal absent.

### 304. FISTULARIA PETIMBA Lacépède 1803
Smooth Flutemouth, Trompette (S)
90 cm; D 14–17; A 14–16. Skin naked and smooth. Brown or green, paler below, sometimes with two incomplete blue longitudinal lines. Throughout the Indo-Pacific, including the Red Sea, Queensland, Tahiti and Hawaii.

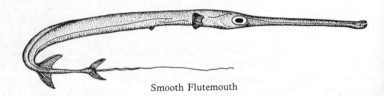

Smooth Flutemouth

### 305. FISTULARIA VILLOSA Klunzinger 1871
Rough Flutemouth
100 cm; D 13–15; A 13–15. Two parallel ridges on snout. Skin armed with scattered small spines. Brown or pinkish, paler below; fins dusky. Generally distributed in the tropical Indo-Pacific, including E. Africa and Hawaii.

Suborder **Syngnathoidei** (Lophobranchii)

A large and very varied group of small fishes with tubular mouth and lacking teeth and lateral line.

Family SOLENICHTHYIDAE (SOLENOSTOMIDAE) **Ghost Pipefish**
Small fishes of deeper water, rather like sea-horses, but with better developed fins. Males have free ventral fins, but in the females these fins are fused to each other and to the sides of the body to form an egg pouch. The eggs are fastened to filaments on the abdominal skin. Short and compressed. Skin with star-shaped bony patches arranged in longitudinal and transverse series. Two separate dorsal fins, ventral and tail large. Snout long and compressed, mouth small and terminal. Few species.

**306. SOLENICHTHYS CYANOPTERUS** (Bleeker) 1854
Blue-finned Ghost Pipefish
15 cm; D V; 18–20; A 16–20. Brown to pink with small black and white spots. Two black ocelli in spinous dorsal. Eye red. Coastal waters from S. and E. Africa to Indonesia, Melanesia and the W. Pacific.

ALLIED SPECIES:
**307. SOLENICHTHYS PAEGNIUS** (Jordan & Thompson) 8 cm. Green, yellow or red. Western Pacific.

*Solenichthys paegnius*

Family SYNGNATHIDAE **Pipefishes, Seahorses**
Small degenerate and highly specialised fishes. Very poor swimmers. Protected by camouflage colours and in some cases by dermal appendages resembling weeds and by bony armour consisting of numerous transverse rings and of several longitudinal ridges. Caudal fin often lacking, tail prehensile in some genera (seahorses). The eggs are attached to the ventral surface of the males or laid into a special ventral pouch of the male. Gill opening reduced to a small orifice at the upper angle of the operculum. No fin spines, a single dorsal fin. Numerous species in all warm seas; coastal waters, some species in fresh water.

**308. STIGMATOPHORA ARGUS** (Richardson) 1840
Peacock Pipefish
25 cm; D 37–50; A 4–6; trunk rings 17–22; tail rings 68–90. Tail thread-like, not prehensile, caudal fin absent. Brood pouch a double skin fold under the tail. Olive green with white streaks and white spots with black centres. Estuaries in Indonesia, Melanesia, Australia and Fiji.

### 309. SYNGNATHOIDES BIACULEATUS (Bloch) 1785
Double-ended Pipefish

30 cm; D 37–50; A 4–6; trunk rings 14–17; tail rings 40–54. Tail prehensile, no caudal fin. Dermal filaments on head, a barbel on chin. Eggs attached to expanded ventral surface of trunk, without protection. Pale green to brownish above, yellowish below. Estuarine. South and E. Africa to Indonesia, Melanesia and the W. Pacific.

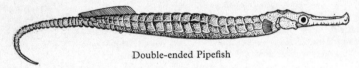

Double-ended Pipefish

### 310. HIPPOCAMPUS KUDA Bleeker 1852
=H. FISHERI Jordan & Everman 1903
Spotted Seahorse, Kuda Laut (Malay)

30 cm; D 15–18; A 4; trunk rings 11; tail rings 33–37. Tail prehensile, without caudal fin. Spines above eyes and blunt knobs where rings and longitudinal ridges meet. Brood pouch present under tail of males. Blackish to brown with darker bands and spots, sometimes white dots. Throughout the Indo-Pacific, from S. and E. Africa to Hawaii.

### 311. HIPPOCAMPUS HISTRIX Kaup 1856
Spiny Seahorse, Kuda Laut (Malay)

15 cm; D 17–19; A 4; trunk rings 11; tail rings 33–34. Long pointed spines above eyes and slender, sharp spines at intersection of rings and ridges. Brownish yellow with dark transverse lines, pale spots and vermiculations. Brood pouch as in 310. Throughout Indo-Pacific, from S. and E. Africa to Hawaii and Tahiti.

ALLIED SPECIES:

**312. HIPPOCAMPUS CAMELOPARDALIS** Bianconi 10 cm. Very prominent coronet on top of head. Olive to dark brown. East Africa.

**313. H. PLANIFRONS** Peters 10 cm. Coronet low. Olive with irregular bright orange spots all over. Queensland and N.-W. Australia.

**314. H. FOLIATUS** Perry 30 cm. Coronet high, but tubercles on body and tail poorly developed. East Africa, E. Indies, Melanesia, Micronesia, Polynesia.

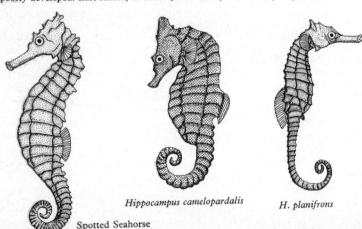

*Hippocampus camelopardalis*      *H. planifrons*

Spotted Seahorse

**315. ICHTHYOCAMPUS MACULATUS** Alleyne & Macleay 1877
Spotted Pipefish
27 cm; D 25; trunk rings 20; tail rings 57. Very slender with elongated snout.
Caudal fin minute. Brown with a yellowish spot on each ring of trunk, below
lateral line. North Queensland, New Guinea.

ALLIED SPECIES:
**316. ICHTHYOCAMPUS ERYTHRAEUS** Gilbert 5 cm. Hawaii, very rare.
**317. I. KAMPENI** Weber 6 cm. Brown with 10 transverse white bands on back
alternating with a dark brown spot. East Indies, Fiji.

**318. CHOEROICHTHYS SCULPTUS** (Günther) 1870
Sculptured Pipefish
6 cm; D 26–35; A 3–4; trunk rings 19; tail rings 21–24. Rather short and
thickset with short upturned snout. Tail fin rounded. Brood pouch abdominal
consisting of lateral bony plates and anterior skin folds. Coral reefs from E.
Africa and the Red Sea to the Philippines, Japan, Melanesia and Polynesia as
far as Christmas Island and the Society islands.

Sculptured Pipefish

ALLIED SPECIES:
**319. CHOEROICHTHYS BRACHYSOMA** (Bleeker) 6 cm. More slender than
318; tail truncate. Indonesia, Melanesia.
**320. C. SUILLUS** Whitley 5 cm. Two horizontal keels on each operculum. Tail very
small, slightly rounded. A dark bar through eye and a series of reddish spots along upper
sides anteriorly. Queensland.

**321. DORYRHAMPHUS MELANOPLEURA** (Bleeker) 1858
Blue-banded Pipefish                                          **Pl. 41**
6 cm; D 21–25; A 4; trunk rings 16–18; tail rings 13–15. Caudal fin large.
Brood pouch consisting of lateral skin flaps on abdomen. Coral reefs throughout
Indo-Pacific, from E. Africa, Mauritius and the Seychelles to Ryukyu islands,
Hawaii, Polynesia and Queensland.

**322. DUNCKEROCAMPUS DACTYLIOPHORUS** (Bleeker) 1853
Banded Pipefish
18 cm; D 21–26; A 4; trunk rings 16–18; tail rings 19–21. Very slender, tail
large. Eggs attached to abdominal surface without protection. Coral reefs in
the E. Indies, Melanesia and W. Pacific.

**323. MICROGNATHUS BREVIROSTRIS** (Rüppell) 1840
Thorn-tail Pipefish
7 cm; D 17–22; A 4; trunk rings 15–17; tail rings 28–32. Snout short, upturned,
with median keel above. Tail fin rounded. Dermal appendages present on head,
nape and ridges. Brood pouch consisting of skin flaps under the tail. Variously
coloured, but usually with darker cross-bands and an ocellus on operculum.
Throughout the Indo-Pacific from the Red Sea and E. Africa to Japan, Fiji
and Queensland.

Thorn-tail Pipefish

ALLIED SPECIES:

**324. MICROGNATHUS SUVENSIS** Herre 8 cm. Snout longer than in 323, dermal appendages lacking. Whitish with minute black dots. Fiji.

**325. M. EDMONSONI** Pietschman 18 cm. Elongated. The largest pipefish in Hawaii. Rocky tidal pools.

## 326. SYNGNATHUS CYANOSPILUS Bleeker 1854
Blue-spotted Pipefish

15 cm; D 21–25; A 2–3; trunk rings 13–14; tail rings 32–36. Brown with dark cross-bars. Dorsal with oblique darker striations, tail rounded and spotted with blue. East Africa to Indonesia, Melanesia and the W. Pacific.

ALLIED SPECIES:

**327. SYNGNATHUS ALTERNANS** Günther 17 cm. Type only, Seychelles.

**328. S. ACUS** L. 38 cm. One of the largest pipefishes. Common among sea-grass (*Zostera*) in all warm seas including the Atlantic.

**329. S. PELAGICUS** L. 15 cm. A dark streak before eye, dorsal with oblique dark bars. All warm seas, including the Atlantic.

**330. S. BALLI** Fowler 10 cm. Tail very small, half length of snout. Tidal pools, Hawaii only.

## 331. BOMBONIA UNCINATA (Weber) 1913
6 cm; D 28; trunk rings 15; tail rings 42. Anal rudimentary, tail rounded. Operculum with longitudinal keel and oblique ridges above and below it. Yellowish, darker on belly. Six pale cross-bands on tail. Coral reefs in Indonesia and Melanesia.

## 332. CORYTHOICHTHYS INTESTINALIS (Ramsay) 1881
Messmate Pipefish

15 cm; D 27–30; trunk rings 15–17; tail rings 35–40. Anal rudimentary. Tail rounded, operculum with serrated keel. Brood pouch a wide skin fold below tail. Often lives in the intestine of Holothurians (Sea Cucumbers). Indonesia and Melanesia.

## 333. CORYTHOICHTHYS FASCIATUS (Gray) 1832
Messmate Pipefish

16 cm; D 25–32; A 3–4; trunk rings 15–18; tail rings 33–37. Often a dark longitudinal band on belly and a network of irregular dark lines on sides, particularly on operculum. Differs from 332 in having a larger anal fin. Often in the intestine of Holothurians (Sea Cucumbers). Throughout the Indo-Pacific, from the Red Sea and E. Africa to Indonesia and Queensland.

Messmate Pipefish

OTHER SPECIES:

**334. HALICAMPUS GRAYI** Kaup 15 cm. Slender with spiny crests on dorsal profile of head. Brown mottled with whitish. Queensland.

**335. YOZIA TIGRIS** (Castelnau) 30 cm. Slender; dark olive above, whitish below; 12–15 dark cross-bands and a white spot on each body scute. Queensland.

**336. Y. BICOARCTATA** (Bleeker) 38 cm. Slender. Brown with dark spots on head and body. South and E. Africa to C. Indo-Pacific.

**337. RUNCINATUS DUNCKERI** (Whitley) 45 cm. Slightly compressed. Tail prehensile, finless. A dorsal and a ventral keel and 2 lateral keels on each side. Queensland, Lord Howe Island.

*Yozia bicoarctata*

## Order **PEGASIFORMES** (Hypostomides)

Family PEGASIDAE **Sea Moths**
Highly specialised fishes of warm seas which superficially resemble the pipe-fishes. They differ in having their mouth, which is toothless, overhung by a bony process (rostrum), in the enlarged, wing-like pectorals and in having the ventrals reduced to a few isolated rays. Broad and depressed. Body enclosed by bony rings fused on the trunk and head, but free on the tail, allowing some movement. One dorsal fin only, supported by unbranched rays. Operculum and preoperculum fused into a bony plate, gill openings narrow. A few small species which live in shallow weed beds and rise to the surface at night.

### 338. **PEGASUS VOLITANS** Linnaeus 1758
Winged Dragonfish, Short-tailed Dragonfish
15 cm; D 5; A 5; P 11; tail rings 8; first and second ventral rays fused to form a finger-like limb. Dark red or brown with darker cross-bands. Dorsal and pectorals with large dark spots. Eyes blue. India to the E. Indies, Melanesia, Japan and Queensland.

ALLIED SPECIES:
**339.** PEGASUS PAPILIO Gilbert 5 cm. Hawaii.

### 340. **PARAPEGASUS NATANS** (Linnaeus) 1766
5 cm; D 5; A 5; V 3; tail rings 12. Yellowish to olive with a dark transverse band on head, one above vent and three on tail. Fins with dusky dots. Throughout Indo-Pacific, from S. and E. Africa to the E. Indies, China and Queensland.

*Parapegasus natans*

### 341. **ZALISES DRACONIS** (Linnaeus) 1766
5 cm; D 5; A 5; P 9–11; V 2; tail rings 8. Tail very short. Three transverse dorsal ridges on thorax. Rostrum flat and spatulate. First ventral rays long and finger-like. Brown with darker reticulations; snout and last rings of tail black. Pectorals edged with white, spotted with brown. South and E. Africa to the E. Indies and Melanesia.

## Order **MUGILIFORMES** (Stromatoidei)

Very large to small coastal fishes of varied habits and appearance. All have two widely separated dorsal fins and ventrals set rather well back.

## Suborder **Sphyraenoidei**

Family SPHYRAENIDAE **Barracudas, Sea-pike**
Large, fast, gregarious predatory fishes. The larger species are known to be
dangerous to man. Good eating, but must be absolutely fresh. All warm seas.
Scales small, cycloid. Lateral line always present, usually straight. Spinous
dorsal well separated from soft dorsal. Five dorsal spines. Tail forked. Mouth
large, horizontal, armed with large, strong fang-like teeth.

### 342. SPHYRAENELLA FLAVICAUDA (Rüppell) 1840
Dingofish, Tazar Rouge, Goemon (S)
38 cm; D V;9; A II/8–9; L 1 80–90; tr 6/9. Green above, silvery below with
one or more brownish longitudinal stripes. Fins yellowish. Red Sea and E.
Africa to E. Indies, Melanesia and the W. Pacific.

### 343. AGRIOPOSPHYRAENA BARRACUDA (Walbaum) 1792
Barracuda, Giant Sea-pike, Kaku (H)
240 cm; D V;9; A II/7–8; L 1 75–90; tr 9–10/9–15. Grey-blue above, silvery
below with about twenty diffuse darker cross-bars on back. Irregular dark
patches on lower body and tail. Fins blackish with pale tips. Sometimes dangerous to man. Near coral reefs in all warm waters, including the tropical
Atlantic.

### 344. CALLOSPHYRAENA TOXEUMA (Fowler) 1904
75 cm; D V;9; A II/8–9; L 1 110–124; tr 12–15/13–18. Dark green above,
silvery below. Base of pectoral blackish, 2nd dorsal and anal blackish with pale
bases and tips. Tail blackish. Coastal waters from E. Africa to Indonesia,
Melanesia and the W. Pacific.

### 345. SPHYRAENA JELLO Cuvier & Valenciennes 1829
Slender Sea-pike, Pick-handle (A), Becune (S)
240 cm; D V;9; A II/8; L 1 123–140; tr 13–18/12–24. Purplish above, silvery
below; 10–14 cross-bars on back, fading below lateral line. Dorsal blackish,
other fins grey. Coastal waters, dangerous. From the Red Sea to S. Africa,
Madagascar and across the Indian Ocean to the E. Indies, Taiwan, Ryukyu
islands, Melanesia, Micronesia, Polynesia and Queensland.

Slender Sea-pike

ALLIED SPECIES:
### 346. SPHYRAENA QENIE Klunzinger 120 cm. Black above, silvery below. 18–23
dark, slightly oblique cross-bars. Fins black, last 2 anal rays white. South and E. Africa
to E. Indies, Melanesia.
### 347. S. FORSTERI C. & V. 55 cm. Olive brown above, sides and belly silvery. Fins
dusky except anal, which is white. India to Taiwan and Fiji.
### 348. S. HELLERI Jenkins (Kawalea). 60 cm. Pectorals short, L 1 scales 135. Hawaii.
### 349. S. JAPONICA Schlegel 180 cm. Grey-green above, sides and belly silvery; 12
short dark cross-bars on upper part of body. Fins dusky, tail yellow. South and E.
Africa to Indonesia and the W. Pacific.
### 350. S. OBTUSATA C. & V. 180 cm. Back grey-green, in sharp contrast to silvery
sides and belly. Fins yellowish. South and E. Africa to Micronesia, Polynesia and
Queensland.

## Suborder **Mugiloidei**

Family MUGILIDAE **Grey Mullet**

Small to medium-sized littoral fishes which usually occur in large schools in shallow weedy areas in all warm seas. They feed on small algae on the bottom. Excellent eating, some species of considerable economic importance. Scales large, lateral line lacking. Dorsal fins well separated, the first with four spines, the second with one spine and branched rays. Anal with three spines. Teeth small or absent. Mostly silvery, but some species show brilliant blues, greens, violets and yellows on fins and tail, but such colours disappear as soon as the fish is taken from the water.

### 351. SQUALOMUGIL NASUTUS (De Vis) 1883
Shark Mullet, Mud Mullet, Sharp-nosed Mullet

30 cm; D IV; I/7; A II/8; Sc 28. Easily recognised by having the eyes on top of the head. Dark slaty grey above, silvery on sides and below; fins yellowish. Usually found in small schools in muddy water, always swimming at the surface with eyes and snout exposed. Queensland.

### 352. LIZA OLIGOLEPIS (Bleeker) 1859
Large-scaled Mullet, Mulet (S)

30 cm; D IV; I/8–9; A III/9; Sc 26–28; tr 10–11. Greenish above, silvery below. Coastal waters, entering rivers. East and S. Africa, Seychelles, India, Indonesia, Philippines and S. China Sea.

Large-scaled Mullet

### 353. LIZA VAIGIENSIS (Quoy & Gaimard) 1824
Diamond-scale Mullet

60 cm; D IV; I/8; A III/8; Sc 25–29; tr 10–12. Olive above, silvery laterally, yellowish below. Fins yellow with darker margins. Pectorals dark with yellow margin; tail square. Red Sea and E. Africa to India, E. Indies, Philippines, China, Melanesia, Queensland, Micronesia and Polynesia.

ALLIED SPECIES:

**354. LIZA MACROLEPIS** (Smith) 35 cm. Sc 31–35; tr 11–12. Back dark green; vertical fins with dark margin. South Africa to Japan, Melanesia and Polynesia.
**355. L. DUSSUMIERI** (C. & V.) 35 cm. Sc 28–32; tr 10–13. Five faint longitudinal lines. Pectorals yellow with blue spot in axil. India to China, Queensland and Polynesia.
**356. L. STRONGYLOCEPHALUS** (Richardson) 25 cm. Sc 33–35; tr 11–12. Back green. Tail with dusky margin. South and E. Africa to E. Indies, Melanesia and Queensland.
**357. L. SPEIGLERI** (Bleeker) 22 cm. Sc 40–42; tr 11–12. Back grey, sides of head gold, dorsal tips black. India, E. Indies, Melanesia.
**358. L. OPHUYSENI** (Bleeker) 20 cm. Sc 35–40; tr 12–13. Back grey, dorsals and tips of tail dusky. Indonesia, Melanesia.

### 359. CRENIMUGIL CRENILABRIS (Forskål) 1775
Warty-nosed Mullet, Mulet ordinaire (S)

38 cm; D IV; I/8; A III/9; Sc 38–42; tr 13–14. Lips thick and warty. Olive

above, silvery below. Purplish spot in pectoral axil. Red Sea and E. Africa to Indonesia, Melanesia and Queensland.

### 360. PLICOMUGIL LABIOSUS (Cuvier & Valenciennes) 1836
Fringe-lipped Mullet
27 cm; D IV; I/8; A III/9; Sc 33–36; tr 11–12. Thick lips. Olive above, silvery below, with purplish pectoral axil. East Africa to the E. Indies and Melanesia.

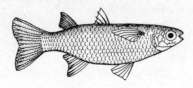

Fringe-lipped Mullet

### 361. MUGIL CEPHALUS Linnaeus 1758
Mangrove Mullet, Bully Mullet, Hardgut Mullet, Sea Mullet, Ama'ama (H)
56 cm; D IV; I/8; A III/8; Sc 38–42; tr 14–15. Olive above, silvery below. A black spot in pectoral axil and a golden spot at upper angle of operculum. Dorsal and pectorals dark blue-grey, anal and tail yellow-green. Appear to spend most of their lives in rivers and creeks. When mature (3–4 years old) they return to the sea to spawn. Of considerable economic importance, especially in Australia. All warm waters, including the Atlantic.

ALLIED SPECIES:
**362. MUGIL ENGELI** Bleeker 14 cm. Sc 32–35; tr 10–12. Back olive, fins hyaline. Indonesia, Melanesia.
**363. M. TADE** Forskål 47 cm. Sc 33–35; tr 11. Back pale olive; 5–7 indistinct dark longitudinal lines. Red Sea to China, Polynesia and Queensland.
**364. M. RAMSAYI** Macleay 25 cm. Sc 36–37; tr 11–12. Back bluish. Upper lip rather thick. Queensland.
**365. M. DIADEMA** Gilchrist & Thompson 75 cm. Sc 30–31; tr 11–12. Back grey; 1st dorsal hyaline with olive spines; 2nd dorsal and pectorals grey; ventrals bright yellow or orange, anal dusky with yellow or orange margin. Tail grey, blackish terminally. South and E. Africa to Australia.
**366. M. ARGENTEUS** Q. & G. 45 cm. Sc 28; tr 10. Back steel blue; a golden blotch and small black spot at pectoral base. Soft dorsal, anal and tail with golden yellow margins. Queensland to Fiji and Samoa.

### 367. VALAMUGIL SEHELI (Forskål) 1775
Blue-tail Mullet, Sand Mullet, Long-finned Mullet (A)
48 cm; D IV; I/8; A III/9; Sc 38–42; tr 12–14. Blue above, silvery on sides and below. Dorsals and tail blue, anal and ventrals yellow, pectorals yellow with blue spot in axil. Throughout Indo-Pacific, including the Red Sea and Queensland.

OTHER SPECIES:
**368. VALAMUGIL BUCHANANI** (Bleeker) 38 cm. Sc 34–36; tr 11–13. Back green, eye and operculum yellow; a dark spot in pectoral axil. East Africa to C. Indo-Pacific.

**369. NEOMYXUS CHAPTALII** (Eydoux & Souleyet) (Uouoa) 45 cm. Differs from 361, the other Hawaiian species, in having large protruding teeth in lower jaw. Hawaii.

**370. MYXUS ELONGATUS** Günther 40 cm. Sc 43–46; tr 15–16. Back dark green to dark brown. A black spot at upper pectoral base; a diffuse golden spot on upper posterior part of operculum. Fins and tail greenish brown. Australia, Lord Howe and Norfolk islands.

## Family ATHERINIDAE (including PSEUDOMUGILIDAE)
### Silversides, Hardyheads
Small silvery fishes which congregate in large schools in shallow coastal waters. Used as bait, but otherwise of no economic importance. Atherinids feed on small plankton organisms. The eggs are large and covered with sticky threads which anchor them to sea weeds. Elongated, subcylindrical. Scales fairly large; lateral line absent, but some scales with a pore or pit. Dorsal fins widely separated, spines of 1st dorsal flexible, leading spines of 2nd dorsal and anal minute.

**371. PRANESUS PINGUIS** (Lacépède) 1803
Broad-banded Hardyhead, Petre longue (S)
12 cm; D IV–VII; I/7–10; A I/11–15; Sc 41–46; tr 6–7. Greenish above, whitish below, with a broad silvery lateral band. Harbours, often schooling around wharf piles. South and E. Africa and Red Sea to Indonesia, Melanesia and Polynesia.

Broad-banded Hardyhead

ALLIED SPECIES:

**372. PRANESUS EENDRACHTENSIS** (Q. & G.) 11 cm. Back green. Several dark horizontal streaks on sides. Indonesia, Melanesia, Queensland.
**373. P. DUODECIMALIS** C. & V. 9 cm. Back greenish. P 12–14. Melanesia.
**374. P. OGILBYI** Whitley 17 cm. Back pale green, scales with dark margins and spots. Numerous black dots on sides and head. Fins tipped with black. East Indies, Micronesia, Polynesia, Australia.
**375. P. INSULARUM** J. & E. ('Iao) 10 cm. Abdomen rounded in section; head length greater than body depth. Hawaii.

**376. ATHERINA FORSKALI** (Rüppell) 1835–40
12 cm; D V–VII; I/8–9; A I/11–13; Sc 41–43; tr 6. Blue-green above, white below, with silvery mid-lateral band. Tip of snout dark, black patch on outer half of pectoral. Red Sea and E. Africa to Indonesia, Melanesia, Polynesia, and China.

ALLIED SPECIES:

**377. ATHERINA OVALAUA** Herre 6 cm. A black spot on top of head extending along back to dorsal origin. A large blackish spot on operculum. Fiji.
**378. A. AFRA** (Peters) 7½ cm. Back dark blue, silvery mid-lateral stripe conspicuous; posterior and ventral parts of body transparent in life. South Africa to C. Indo-Pacific.

OTHER SPECIES:

**379. ISO HAWAIIENSIS** Gosline 5 cm. Abdomen keeled, head length less than body depth. Hawaii.

**380. STENATHERINA TEMMINCKI** (Bleeker) 8 cm. A black mark on upper operculum and a black crescent before eye. Indonesia, Melanesia, Micronesia and Polynesia.

**381. ALLANETTA VALENCIENNEI** (Bleeker) 10 cm. Back blue-green; tip of snout dark. East Indies and Melanesia.

**382. HYPOATHERINA BARNESI** Schultz 6 cm. Back deep blue; snout and mandible black. Melanesia.

**383. H. LACUNOSA** (B. & S.) 10 cm. Back green. East Indies, Melanesia, Queensland.

**384. H. UISILA** Jordan & Seale 9 cm. Back blue-green. A small dark ocellus in centre of upper scales. Melanesia.

## Order POLYNEMIFORMES

Family POLYNEMIDAE **Threadfins, Tasselfish, Bastard Mullet (S.A.)**
Fishes of sandy shores and muddy estuaries, well adapted to poor visibility by their projecting snout, prolonged free pectoral rays and adipose eyelids. Predatory, but sluggish; excellent eating. Rather compressed fishes with fairly large ctenoid scales. Lateral line continued on to tail. Dorsal fins well separated, 1st with 7–8 weak spines. Anal fin with 2–3 spines followed by branched rays, opposite 2nd dorsal. Tail forked. Pectorals set low down, lower three or more rays prolonged into free filaments. Snout projecting well beyond large mouth. Teeth weak, but numerous.

### 385. POLYNEMUS INTERMEDIUS Nichols 1954
Streamered Tasselfish
10 cm; D VI–VII; I/13–14; A III/11; 7 free pectoral filaments; L 1 53–58. Tail deeply forked. Yellowish brown with darker speckles on back. Tips of 1st dorsal, distal part of pectoral and tail blackish. Estuaries in New Guinea.

### 386. ELEUTHERONEMA TETRADACTYLUM (Shaw) 1804
Giant Threadfin, Cooktown Salmon
180 cm; D VIII; I–II/13–15; A II/15–17; P 16–17/4 free filaments; L 1 78–80; tr 9–10/13–14. Upper lip lacking, lower reduced to small fold at corner of mouth. Preoperculum serrated, operculum rounded. Silvery green above, yellowish below; fins yellowish, pectorals occasionally dark. Coastal waters. India, E. Indies, Philippines, China, Melanesia, Queensland and N.W. Australia.

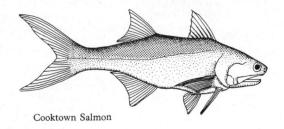

Cooktown Salmon

**387. POLYDACTYLUS SEXFILIS** (Cuvier & Valenciennes) 1831
Six-fingered Threadfin, Kuru, Moi, Moi-li'i (H) Mulet Barbe (S)
40 cm; D VIII; I/13; A II–III/11–12; P 15–17/6 free filaments; L 1 61–68; tr
6–7/10–11. Lower lip present, but upper lacking. Preoperculum serrated,
operculum angular. Silvery yellow, darker above; pectorals black, anal with dark
margin, centre of ventrals blackish. Juveniles with three dark vertical bands,
black dorsal and tail. India and the Seychelles to the E. Indies, Melanesia and
Polynesia including Hawaii.

ALLIED SPECIES:
**388. POLYDACTYLUS PLEBEIUS** (Broussonet) 35 cm. Golden with dark
lines along scale rows. Pectorals blackish, other fins grey. South and E. Africa to E.
Indies, Taiwan, Japan, Polynesia, Melanesia and Queensland.
**389. P. MICROSTOMUS** (Bleeker) 25 cm. Golden; a black oval spot at beginning
of lateral line. Fins yellowish. East Indies and Melanesia.
**390. P. SEXTARIUS** (B. & S.) 30 cm. Back golden olive, silvery on sides and belly.
A black oval spot at beginning of lateral line. Fins dusky. South and E. Africa to E.
Indies and Melanesia.
**391. P. NIGRIPINNIS** Munro 15 cm. Golden. Head, back and vertical fins speckled
with black. Pectorals black. New Guinea.
**392. P. HEPTADACTYLUS** (C. & V.) 30 cm. Golden; pectorals black, other fins
yellowish, blackish distally. East Indies and Melanesia.
**393. P. SEALEI** (Jordan & Richardson) 20 cm. Blue above, silvery on sides and
belly. A dark blotch on operculum. Fins yellowish, blackish distally. East Indies,
Philippines, Melanesia.
**394. P. INDICUS** (Shaw) 112 cm. Golden, much darker above, faint dark lines along
scale rows. Fins yellowish. South and E. Africa to India and W. Pacific.
**395. P. KURU** Bleeker 45 cm. Possibly a synonym of 387. Seychelles to India, E.
Indies and W. Pacific.

## Order **PERCIFORMES** (Percomorphi)

This order includes the great majority of the modern bony fishes. A very varied
assemblage with few, if any common characters, comprising generalised perch-
like fishes as well as highly modified forms.

## Suborder **Scombroidei**

Mostly large, fast surface predators, many oceanic, a few littoral species. Most
of the best known game fishes belong to this group and some are of great economic importance. Slightly compressed, beautifully streamlined fishes with
slender caudal peduncle. Two well separated dorsal fins, the first spinous. A
series of isolated finlets from second dorsal to base of tail and a similar series
behind anal. Caudal peduncle armed with one or two lateral keels. Lateral line
generally present. Teeth small and sharply pointed.

## Family SCOMBRIDAE **Mackerel, Large-scaled Tuna**

Small to moderate pelagic fishes, usually found in large shoals. Several species
are of great economic importance. Somewhat compressed, with short caudal
peduncle. Scales medium-sized. Lateral line simple, or with one branch. 5–7

dorsal finlets and an equal number of ventral finlets. *Scomber japonicus* Houttuyn and *Rastrelliger kanagurta* (Cuvier) are well known species of wide distribution.

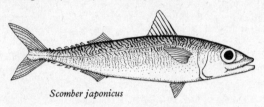

*Scomber japonicus*

Family ACANTHOCYBIIDAE
**Wahoo, Ono (H), Poisson becune (S)**
A single solitary species (*Acanthocybium solandri* (C. & V.)) found near coral reefs throughout the Indo-Pacific and tropical Atlantic. Excellent eating and a splendid sporting fish. Elongated and compressed. Scales small, anterior ones larger, forming a corselet which includes pectoral base. Lateral line with numerous short branches terminating at caudal keel.

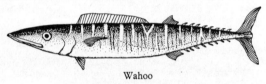

Wahoo

Family SCOMBEROMORIDAE **Spanish Mackerel**
Moderate to large schooling fishes of open coastal waters. Excellent eating and sporting fishes. Elongated and somewhat compressed. Naked except for a few large scales behind head. Lateral line simple, terminating on caudal peduncle. *Scomberomorus commersoni* (Lacépède) and *S. guttatus* (Bloch & Schneider) are well known wide ranging Indo-Pacific species.

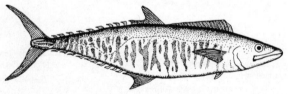

*Scomberomorus commersoni*

Family THUNNIDAE
**Tuna, Tunnies, Thon, Albacore, Bonito**
Heavy, compact pelagic schooling fishes of all warm waters. Excellent eating and game fishes of great economic importance. Thick-set fishes with very narrow caudal peduncle. Scales small, but larger behind head, forming a conspicuous corselet. Lateral line simple. The Yellow-fin Tuna (*Neothunnus*

*macropterus* (Temminck & Schlegel)) and the Albacore (*Thunnus alalunga* Bonnaterre) are among the better known species.

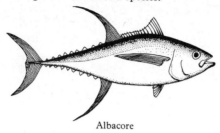

Albacore

## Family KATSUWONIDAE
**Skipjacks, Frigate-mackerel**

Pelagic fishes which occur in large migratory schools in most warm waters. They may be distinguished from the true Tunny fishes by the absence of scales. The Skipjack (*Katsuwonus pelamis* (L.)) is a well known species.

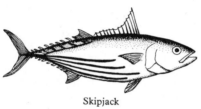

Skipjack

## Family ISTIOPHORIDAE
**Marlin, Bayonetfish, Sailfish, Billfish**

Large, powerful, graceful pelagic fishes which have the upper jaw produced into a long sword or bill which is used as a weapon of defence and also for stunning or impaling smaller fishes. The family includes a number of famous sporting fishes; some species are fished commercially by Japanese long-liners. Elongated, deepest behind head, with slender caudal peduncle. Skin thick, scales long, embedded in the skin. Lateral line simple, terminating in a double lateral keel on caudal peduncle. First dorsal fin elevated in front, or along its entire length; second dorsal small, placed near tail. Anal fin divided in two parts. Pectorals and ventrals long. Such well known fishes as the Pacific Sailfish (*Istiophorus orientalis* (T. & S.)), the Striped Marlin (*Makaira audax* (Philippi)), the Blue Marlin (*Makaira nigricans* (Lacépède)) and the Black Marlin (*Istiompax marlina* (Jordan & Hill)) belong to this family.

Sailfish                    Blue Marlin

## Family XIPHIIDAE **Broadbill Swordfish**

A single very widely distributed species (*Xiphias gladius* Linnaeus) which differs from the Marlin and Sailfish in having no scales in the adult, in the absence of the lateral line and in the presence of a single lateral keel on the caudal peduncle.

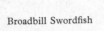

## Suborder **Trichiuroidei**

## Family GEMPYLIDAE **Snake-Mackerel**

A group of deep water oceanic Mackerel-like fishes. Elongated and compressed. Scales small or absent. Lateral line single or double. Lateral keel generally lacking. A single dorsal fin, the front portion supported by spines. Pectorals very short. Teeth sharp and compressed, longer and stronger than in the Scombroidei. The Snake-Mackerel (*Gempylus serpens* Cuvier) is an oceanic predator of deep waters, often taken on long lines.

## Family TRICHIURIDAE

Voracious medium-sized predatory fishes which congregate in large schools in shallow coastal waters, sometimes penetrating fresh water. Very elongated and compressed, tapering posteriorly to a long thin point. Caudal fin absent. Scaleless, with a single lateral line. A single dorsal fin from nape to tip of body. Anal fin long, pectorals small, ventrals absent, or reduced to small spines. Mouth large, teeth large and strong.

*Trichiurus savala*

## Suborder **Stromateoidei**

Mostly small surface dwelling pelagic fishes, often sheltering under floating objects or among the tentacles of jellyfish. There are two families: Centrolophidae and Nomeidae. Fig., p. 21.

## Suborder **Tetragonuroidaei**

## Family TETRAGONURIDAE **Ravenfish, Square-tails**

A small group of widely distributed small deep water fishes. Elongated and posteriorly compressed, covered by hard rhomboidal keeled scales. A single lateral line terminating in a lateral keel on caudal peduncle.

## Suborder **Percoidei**

## Family CORYPHAENIDAE
## **Dolphinfish, Dorade (S), Mahi-mahi (H)**

Two very similar species (one only according to some authors) of circumtropical distribution. Spectacular sporting fishes of great speed and beauty. Very compressed and elongated, with a sharp, almost vertical profile. A single very long dorsal fin which starts on top of the head and a sharply forked tail with elongated lobes. The common species is *Coryphaena hippurus* Linnaeus.

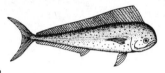

Dolphinfish

## Family BRAMIDAE **Pomfrets**
Small to moderate deep water oceanic fishes. Oval and compressed. Scales small to medium-sized with median keels which form longitudinal ridges along body. A single long-based dorsal fin, elevated in front. Anal similar, but shorter. Tail deeply forked, pectorals long and sickle-shaped.

## Family PARASTROMATEIDAE **Black Pomfret**
The family consists of a single wide-spread Indo-Pacific species (*Parastromateus niger* (Bloch)). Occurs in schools in deepish coastal waters. Excellent eating. Strongly compressed, diamond-shaped. A single long-based dorsal fin, elevated in front; anterior spines are lost with age. Anal fin similar to dorsal. Pectorals long and falcate, ventrals lost with age. Tail deeply forked, peduncle slender. Lateral line slightly arched in front, scales small, but conspicuous.

Black Pomfret

## Family CARANGIDAE
**Trevally, Jacks, Scad, Horse-mackerel, Darts, Pilotfish, Runners, Cavallys, Kingfish, Carangues (S), Kole-kole (Swahili), Opelu, Ula (H)**
A large group of fast swimming surface predators of moderate to large size. They usually run in fairly large schools in the vicinity of coral reefs. Excellent eating and good sporting fishes; some species are of considerable economic importance. Compressed fishes of various shape, with slender caudal peduncle and forked tail. Scales very small and inconspicuous. Lateral line simple, arched anteriorly and armed posteriorly with large keeled scutes. Two dorsal fins, the second dorsal and anal elevated and falcate in front. Two detached spines in front of anal. Pectorals long and falcate, teeth small.

## 396. MEGALASPIS CORDYLA (Linnaeus) 1758
Finny Scad
45 cm; D VIII/9–11; 7–9; A II/8–10; 6–8; P 21; 53–58 keeled scutes on lateral line. Dorsal and anal followed by isolated finlets. Torpedo-shaped. Dark blue-green above, silvery below; a prominent black spot on upper corner of operculum.

Fins yellowish. Shallow coastal waters from S. and E. Africa to the W. Pacific; rare in Hawaii, where it is reputed to attain 150 cm.

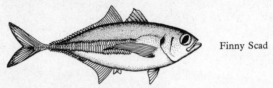

Finny Scad

### 397. DECAPTERUS PINNULATUS (Eydoux & Souleyet) 1841
Mackerel Scad, Opelu, Opelu-mama (H)
50 cm; D I/VIII/32–35; A II/27–30; P 22–23; 20–28 scutes on lateral line. Cigar-shaped; dorsal and anal followed by a single finlet. Upper jaw toothless, lower jaw with a few anterior teeth in some individuals. Green to blue-green above, silvery below with a black spot at upper angle of operculum. The young move offshore after birth, but return to inshore waters in large schools when about 12 cm in length. Central Indo-Pacific and W. Pacific, including Hawaii.

ALLIED SPECIES:
### 398. DECAPTERUS RUSSELLI (Rüppell) 45 cm. 40–45 scutes. Silvery blue-green with dark opercular spot. Fins yellowish. Red Sea, S. and E. Africa to the W. Pacific.
### 399. D. LAJANG Bleeker 30 cm. 28–30 scutes. Silvery, light blue above. Fins light yellow, anal white. South and E. Africa to E. Indies.

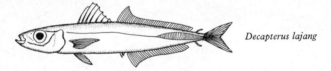

*Decapterus lajang*

### 400. D. MUROADSI (Schlegel) 30 cm. 27–33 scutes. Back slaty green, dark opercular spot present. Indian Ocean to E. Indies and Hawaii.

### 401. ALECTIS CILIARIS (Bloch) 1787
Pennantfish, Thread-finned Trevally, Ulua kihikihi, Kagami ulua (H)
37 cm; D VI; I/19–22; A II; I/15–17; P 19. Diamond shaped, very compressed. 6–7 anterior rays of dorsal and anal prolonged into long free trailing filaments which become shorter with advancing age. Dorsal spines lost in adults. 8–15 scutes on lateral line. Glittering silvery, bluish dorsally, yellowish ventrally; young individuals with 6–7 dark cross-bars. Prolonged rays black. All warm waters, including the Atlantic.

### 402. ALECTIS INDICUS (Rüppell) 1828
Plumed Trevally, Indian Thread-finned Trevally, Mirrorfish, Carangue à plumes (S); Kagami ulua (H), Chermin (Malay)
150 cm, 15 kg; D I; VIII; 1/23–24; A II; I/19–22; P 19–23. 5–12 scutes on lateral line. 7–8 anterior dorsal rays and 3–4 anterior anal rays prolonged into free filaments. Diamond shaped, very compressed. Glittering silvery, greenish dorsally. Juveniles with faint dark cross-bands. A large irregular blackish spot

on operculum. Fins light green, free filaments dark blue. Coastal waters throughout the Indo-Pacific, including the Red Sea and Hawaii.

Plumed Trevally                    Cale Cale Trevally

### 403. ULUA MANDIBULARIS (Macleay) 1883

Cale Cale Trevally, Kole-kole (E. Africa)

90 cm; D V–VIII; I/20–21; A II; I/17–18; P 19–21; 29–33 scutes on lateral line. Oval and compressed. Second dorsal and anal with anterior falcate lobes. Olive green dorsally, silvery on sides and below. A blackish spot on pectoral axil. First dorsal smoky, other fins greenish with darker anterior margins. Coastal waters from E. Africa to the C. Indo-Pacific and W. Pacific.

### 404. GNATHANODON SPECIOSUS (Forskål) 1775

Golden Trevally, Carangue chasseur (S), Gerong (Malay), Pa'opa'a (H), Golden Ulua (H)

120 cm; D I; VII–VIII; I/18–21; A II; I/16–17; P 19–22. 15–25 scutes on lateral line. Small juvenile teeth lost with age. Bright silvery gold, especially when young. Five broad black bands alternating with 5–6 narrow black cross-bands, the first through eye. A dark patch on operculum; fins yellow. A most beautiful fish, often found in the vicinity of coral reefs. Throughout the Indo-Pacific, including the Red Sea, Hawaii and Queensland.

OTHER SPECIES:

**405. SELAROIDES LEPTOLEPIS** (C. & V.) 20 cm. 22–30 small scutes. Back dark blue-green. A golden mid-lateral band and a round black spot at upper corner of operculum. Melanesia and Indonesia.

**406. SELAR CRUMENOPHTHALMUS** (Bloch) 30 cm. 31–43 scutes. Blue back, golden mid-lateral band, black opercular spot. Fins pale green, tips of tail black. South and E. Africa, C. Indo-Pacific, Polynesia, Hawaii.

**407. S. BOOPS** (C. & V.) 25 cm. 43–46 scutes. Back dark blue, sides and belly silvery. Opercular spot present. India, East Indies, Melanesia.

**408. ALEPES MATE** (C. & V.) 25 cm. 40–50 scutes. Back blue-green. Some yellow on sides, silvery below. 9–10 narrow dark cross-bars. South and E. Africa to W. Pacific and Hawaii.

**409. A. DJEDABA** (Forskål) 37 cm. 26–31 scutes. Back blue-black. 6–10 faint dark cross-bars. Large black opercular spot. Red Sea and E. Africa to the W. Pacific.

...den Trevally                    *Alepes djedaba*

**410. A. KALLA** (C. & V.) 25 cm. 40–46 scutes. Back blue-green. 7 faint dark cross-bars. Black opercular spot. Tail bright yellow, upper lobe greenish. India to C. Indo-Pacific and Hawaii.

## 411. CARANX MELAMPYGUS Cuvier & Valenciennes 1833

Bluefin Trevally, Carangue verte (S), Blue Crevally (H), Omilumilu (H)

90 cm; D I; VIII; I/20–25; A II; I/17–20; P 19–20. 30–40 scutes on lateral line. Anterior lobes of second dorsal and anal sickle-shaped. Brilliant blue above and on sides, silvery below; irregularly scattered black spots on older individuals; fins bright blue. Coral reefs throughout Indo-Pacific, from S. and E. Africa to Polynesia and Hawaii.

## 412. CARANX SEXFASCIATUS Quoy & Gaimard 1824

Great Trevally, Six-banded Trevally, Ulua (H), Pake Ulua, Papio (H), Carangue platte (S)

150 cm; 40 kg; D I; VII–VIII; I/19–21; A II; I/16–18; P 21–22. 28–37 scutes on lateral line. Second dorsal and anal with anterior falcate lobes. Dark blue-green above, yellowish green to gold laterally and below. Young with 5–7 broad dark vertical bands. A dark spot at upper angle of operculum. Tail yellow with black upper tip. Near coral reefs from S. and E. Africa to the E. Indies and W. Pacific, including Hawaii. See also 414.

## 413. CARANX IGNOBILIS (Forskål) 1775

Lowly Trevally, Pa'u'u, Ulua (H), Yellow-fin Trevally

150 cm, 25 kg; D I; VIII; I/18–21; A II; I/15–17; P 18–20. 28–30 large scutes on lateral line. Anterior lobes of second dorsal and anal falcate. Grey-green above, silvery below. Fins yellowish to dusky, anal with white edge. Opercular spot lacking. Near coral reefs throughout the Indo-Pacific, including the Red Sea and Hawaii.

Lowly Trevally

ALLIED SPECIES:

**414. CARANX LUGUBRIS** Poey 120 cm. Similar to 412, but darker, head almos black. Hawaii and E. Pacific.

**415. C. CHEILIO** Snyder (Butaguchi) 90 cm. Snout pointed, a slight depression ir profile above eyes. A broad golden yellow band from eye to base of tail. Hawaii.

**416. C. SANSUN** (Forskål) 90 cm. 30–39 scutes. Back yellowish bronze, greenish yellow below. First dorsal and anterior part of 2nd dorsal blackish, other fins yellowish Red Sea and E. Africa to the W. Pacific.

**417. C. BUCCULENTUS** Alleyne & Macleay 65 cm. 35–38 scutes. Pale oliv above, dotted with blue, silvery below. Large black opercular spot and one in pectora axil. Melanesia and Queensland.

**418. C. EMBURYI** (Whitley) 35 kg. 40–42 scutes. Blue with yellow spots above silvery below. A series of dark brown spots along base of anal. A small black opercula blotch, pectoral axil black. Fins dusky olive. Queensland.

**419. C. RADIATUS** Macleay 32 cm. 38–45 scutes. Dorsal and anal rays more or less prolonged into free filaments. Pale greenish blue with 6 or more dark cross-bars and a dark opercular blotch. Tail yellowish, upper lobe tipped with black. Queensland.

**420. C. COMPRESSUS** Day 45 cm. 12–15 scutes. Back bluish. South and E. Africa, India, E. Indies.

**421. C. OBLONGUS** C. & V. 50 cm. 35–40 scutes. Back silvery blue. No opercular spot. Dorsals and upper lobe of tail blue, other fins yellow. South and E. Africa, Seychelles, E. Indies. Melanesia.

**422. C. ADSCENSIONIS** (Osbeck) 90 cm. 23–29 small scutes. Back blue, opercular blotch present. Tail yellow. All Indo-Pacific and tropical Atlantic.

**423. C. STELLATUS** Eydoux & Souleyet 68 cm. 30–35 scutes. Light olive above with scattered black dots, light gold below. A large silvery area below lateral line and behind pectoral. Fins pale. South and E. Africa to E. Indies.

**424. C. EQUULA** Schlegel 25 cm. 21–22 scutes. Green above, 5–6 wide dark cross-bars in young. All Indo-Pacific including Hawaii.

**425. C. HIPPOS** L. 75 cm. 33–38 scutes. Silvery blue, barred when young. All Indo-Pacific and Tropical Atlantic.

**426. C. HELVOLUS** Forster (Black Ulua) 75 cm. 36–37 scutes. Generally dusky. Inner mouth blue-black, tongue and palate white. Western Pacific and Hawaii.

**427. CARANGOIDES MALABARICUS** (Bloch & Schneider) 1801
Malabar Trevally, Monique (S)
37 cm; D I; VIII; I/22–23; A II; I/17–19; P 19–20. 10–28 scutes on lateral line. Anterior lobes of second dorsal and anal falcate, reaching base of tail in juveniles. Blue-green above, golden below; juveniles with six dark transverse bands, and an oblique line through eye; a dark patch on operculum. Shallow coastal waters from S. and E. Africa to the Seychelles, Ceylon, India, E. Indies and Melanesia.

Malabar Trevally

**428. CARANGOIDES FERDAU** (Forskål) 1775
Ferdau's Trevally
75 cm; D I; VII; I/26–30; A II; I/22–26. 18–28 scutes on lateral line, some lost with age. Greenish-blue above, golden below, fins yellow. Young with 6–7 dark vertical bands. Shallow coastal waters from S. and E. Africa and the Red Sea to the Seychelles, India, Ceylon, the E. Indies, Melanesia and Polynesia, including Hawaii.

ALLIED SPECIES:

**429. CARANGOIDES FULVOGUTTATUS** (Forskål) 120 cm. 10–22 scutes. Blue-green with many small golden spots above, silvery below. Several dark blotches along lateral line. Fins yellowish green. Red Sea to C. Indo-Pacific.

**430. C. LATICAUDIS** (Alleyne & Macleay) 75 cm. 22–28 scutes. Grey-blue above, silvery below. Some scattered grey spots. Fins olive. Melanesia.

**431. C. GYMNOSTETHOIDES** Bleeker 90 cm. 15–25 scutes. Greenish above, silvery below. A diffuse opercular spot. Fins greenish with black spots. South and E. Africa to E. Indies and W. Pacific, including Hawaii.

**432. C. CHRYSOPHRYS** (C. & V.) 50 cm. 17–28 scutes. Anterior dorsal and anal lobes strongly falcate. Blue-green above, silvery below. A large dusky opercular blotch. Fins dusky. South and E. Africa, E. Indies, Melanesia.

**433. C. DINEMA** Bleeker 75 cm. 25 scutes. Back greenish; a faint opercular blotch. Ceylon, E. Indies, Melanesia.

**434. C. ARMATUS** (Forskål) 60 cm. 18–23 scutes. Blue-green above, silvery below. Ventrals dusky. Anterior dorsal and anal rays black. Red Sea to S. Africa and C. Indo-Pacific.

**435. C. DIVERSA** (Whitley) 15 cm. 18–25 scutes. Silvery, darker above. Large dark opercular blotch. Anterior dorsal and anal rays black. Melanesia, Australia.

**436. C. AJAX** Snyder (White Ulua) 105 cm. Silvery above, white below. Fewer anal rays than most species (16). Hawaii only.

### 437. CHORINEMUS TOLOOPARAH (Rüppell) 1828
### =C. SANCTI-PETRI C. & V. 1831

Black-tipped Leatherskin, Queenfish, Saint Peter's Leatherskin, Sabre (S) 120 cm; D I; VI–VII; I/19–21; A II; I/16–19. Skin leathery with conspicuous rhomboid, pointed embedded scutes. Rather oblong. Lower jaw with two rows of conical teeth. Blue-green above, silvery below. Two rows of round blackish spots, 6–10 above lateral line, 3–5 below. Fins yellowish, anterior part of soft dorsal blackish. Coastal waters throughout Indo-Pacific, including the Red Sea and Hawaii.

ALLIED SPECIES:

**438. CHORINEMUS TOL** C. & V. 90 cm. Blue above, white below. A series of 5–8 dark spots along lateral line. Soft dorsal and caudal tips black. East Africa to E. Indies, Melanesia and W. Pacific.

**439. C. TALA** C. & V. 45 cm. Very similar to 438, but deeper. India, E. Indies and Melanesia.

**440. C. LYSAN** (Forskål) 120 cm, 15 kg. Like 439, but median series of dark spots above median line. Arabia, India, E. Indies, Melanesia.

*Chorinemus lysan*

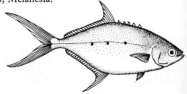

Baillon's Dart

### 441. TRACHINOTUS BAILLONI (Lacépède) 1802

Baillon's Dart, Black-spotted Swallowtail, Lune (S), Muscadin (S) 60 cm; D I; V–VI; I/22–24; A II; I/21–24; P 16–17. Dorsal spines short and without membrane. Falcate lobes of second dorsal and anal, very long. Lateral line almost straight. Cheeks scaly. Greyish green above, silvery below; 2–5 round black spots along lateral line. Anterior margins of fin lobes blackish blue. Coastal waters from S. and E. Africa to India, Ceylon, the E. Indies, Melanesia and Queensland.

ALLIED SPECIES:

**442. TRACHINOTUS RUSSELLI** C. & V. 60 cm. Similar to 441. but spots above lateral line and more diffuse. Ceylon and India, E. Indies, Melanesia, Queensland.

**443.** **T. BOTLA** Shaw 60 cm. Dark spots not diffuse, larger than in 441, above lateral line. Polynesia and Australia.

**444.** **T. BLOCHI** (Lacépède) 90 cm. Lateral spots lacking. South and E. Africa to India, E. Indies, Melanesia, Queensland.

## 445. **ELEGATIS BIPINNULATUS** (Quoy & Gaimard) 1824
Rainbow Runner, Galati (S), Kamanu (H), Hawaiian Salmon (H)

120 cm; D VI; 24–27; 2; A II; 15; 2. L 1 100. A single dorsal and a single ventral finlet before tail; anterior lobes of fins only slightly elevated. A slender, very graceful fish. Blue above, light pink to white below; a broad mid-lateral longitudinal golden band passing through eye and placed between two narrower bright blue longitudinal bands. Fins generally yellow. An excellent sporting fish and very good eating. Usually solitary, off coral reefs throughout the Indo-Pacific, including the Red Sea, Natal, Hawaii and Queensland.

 Rainbow Runner

## 446. **NAUCRATES DUCTOR** (Linnaeus) 1758
Pilotfish, Pilote (S).

60 cm; D IV–VI; 26–28; A II; 16–17; P 19. Dorsal spines short, weak and connected by fin membrane in young only; anal spines lost with age. Lateral line very slightly arched, almost straight, terminating in a lateral keel on caudal peduncle. Blue above, silvery below; 5–7 broad vertical dark bands extending on to fins. Pectorals and ventrals yellow, tail dusky with white tips. Young often shelter under floating objects or among tentacles of jellyfish. Adults generally associated with large sharks and tuna, presumably feeding on scraps from the large fish's prey. Throughout the entire Indo-Pacific and tropical Atlantic.

 Pilotfish

OTHER SPECIES:

**447.** **ZONICHTHYS NIGROFASCIATA** (Rüppell) 90 cm. Lateral line ends in a ridge on caudal peduncle. Bluish above, whitish yellow below. First dorsal very small, black, other fins grey marbled with black and yellow. Juveniles with 5–7 oblique cross-bands. Red Sea, India, E. Indies, Melanesia.

The genus *Seriola* (Amberjacks, or Kingfish) comprises several large widely ranging species of deeper offshore waters. Good sport, but very poor eating.

Family RACHYCENTRIDAE **Cobia**
Comprises a single species which occurs in all warm waters.

## 448. **RACHYCENTRON CANADUS** (Linnaeus) 1766
Black Kingfish, Sargeantfish, Cobia

180 cm; 75 kg; D VII–IX/30–33; A II–III/23–25. Cigar-shaped with broad

head. Scales small, embedded in thick leathery skin, extending to operculum and head. Lateral line not ending in lateral keel. Dorsal spines without membrane, usually carried depressed into a dorsal groove. Dark brown above, yellowish below. A good sporting fish and excellent eating. Solitary, usually in the vicinity of coral reefs.

Cobia

### Family LACTARIIDAE **Milk Trevally, Susu**
A single widely distributed Indo-Pacific species (*Lactarius lactarius* (Bloch & Schneider) 1801). Elongate-oval and compressed, similar to the Carangidae, from which it may be distinguished by its covering of large deciduous, cycloid scales and by the long anal fin. Usually in slow-moving schools near sandy bottoms.

Milk Trevally

### Family MENIDAE **Moonfish**
The family consists of a single widespread Indo-Pacific species which frequents deeper waters in the vicinity of coral reefs.

### 449. **MENE MACULATA** (Bloch & Schneider) 1801
Moonfish, Razor Trevally, Golok Kassut (E. Indies)
20 cm; D 40–43; A 30–33; P 15. Extremely compressed and thin; triangular in profile. Scales minute. Lateral line ends below end of dorsal. A single dorsal fin preceded by 3–4 spines which are lost with age; tail forked, pectorals small, ventrals with first ray prolonged in adults. Mouth protractile, directed upwards. Blue above, silvery below, 2–3 rows of black spots on upper part of flanks. Dried without salting and eaten in India. Usually in shoals, from S. and E. Africa to the Seychelles, India, Ceylon, the E. Indies, Philippines, Melanesia and Queensland.

Moonfish

Family LEIOGNATHIDAE
## Ponyfish, Slipmouths, Slimys, Soapys, Sap-sap (S)
Small to moderate predatory fishes of the tropical Indo-Pacific. Usually in schools in shallow sheltered waters, often in tidal pools. Scales small, invisible under a covering of slimy mucus. Elevated and greatly compressed. Lateral line well developed. Top of head with bony ridges forming a backward directed spine. A single dorsal fin, supported by spines in front. Anal with three spines; both fins can be folded into a basal sheath; caudal peduncle very slender, tail deeply forked. Mouth small, at the end of a long protrusible tube. Dried without salting and eaten in some areas.

### 450. GAZZA MINUTA (Bloch) 1797
15 cm; D VIII/16; A III/13–14; L 1 60. Scales absent on head and breast. Mouth points downwards when protruded. A pair of prominent canines in upper jaw. Lateral line extending to base of tail. Silvery, darker above, with irregular orange bands and spots on upper sides. A dark spot on anterior part of dorsal. Entire Indo-Pacific, but not in Hawaii.

*Gazza minuta*

ALLIED SPECIES:
**451. GAZZA ACHLAMYS** Jordan & Starks 13 cm. Similar to 450, but without orange bands; scale-less area extending further back. East Indies and Melanesia.
**452. SECUTOR INSIDIATOR** (Bloch) 10 cm. No canines. Mouth very oblique, pointing upwards. Dark irregular spots on upper sides. South and E. Africa to C. Indo-Pacific and Polynesia as far as Tahiti.
**453. S. RUCONIUS** (H.-B.) 8 cm. South and E. Africa, E. Indies, Melanesia, Queensland.

### 454. EQUULA EQUULA (Forskål) 1775
Common Ponyfish, Sap-sap (S)
25 cm; D VIII/16; A III/14; L 1 60. Lower margin of preoperculum serrated. Mouth horizontal, pointing downwards when protruded. Lateral line extends to base of tail. Greyish with faint dark cross-bars above, silvery on sides and ventrally. Red Sea and S. Africa to Indonesia and Melanesia.

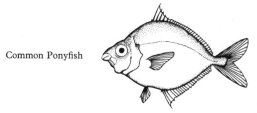

Common Ponyfish

ALLIED SPECIES:
455. EQUULA FASCIATA (Lacépède) 20 cm. Dark cross-bars more distinct than in 454. Second dorsal spine prolonged into a free filament. Dark spot on nape and in pectoral axil. Seychelles, E. Indies, Melanesia, Tahiti.
456. EQUULITES BINDUS (C. & V.) 8 cm. Black line along dorsal base. First dorsal broadly edged with orange. East Indies, Melanesia.
457. E. NOVAEHOLLANDIAE (Steindachner) 11 cm. Second dorsal and anal spines prolonged into long free filaments. Tip of snout black. Melanesia.
458. E. BERBIS (C. & V.) Similar to 457, but dorsal and anal filaments not prolonged. Melanesia.
459. LEIOGNATHUS SPLENDENS (Cuvier) 13 cm. Mouth horizontal, preoperculum naked, breast scaly. Silvery with 12 irregular dark cross-bands when young. Outer half of 1st dorsal black. Ceylon, E. Indies, Melanesia and Polynesia as far as Tahiti.
460. L. RAPSONI Munro 8 cm. Similar to 459, but preoperculum scaly, cross bars more numerous and persistent. New Guinea.
461. L. DUSSUMIERI (C. & V.) 18 cm. Similar to 459 and 460, but no black mark on 1st dorsal. India, E. Indies, Polynesia as far as Fiji and Tahiti.

## Family APOGONIDAE (AMIIDAE) Cardinalfishes, Siphonfishes

A large family of small colourful carnivorous fishes which occur in all warm seas, but are especially numerous in the Indo-Pacific. Generally associated with coral reefs, some species in shallow tidal pools, a few in deep waters and one group in fresh water. In most species the eggs and newly hatched young are carried in the mouth of the male. No economic importance, but a few are favourite aquarium fishes. Oblong, sometimes rather elevated. Scales small to large, cycloid on head, cycloid or ctenoid on body. Lateral line simple, sometimes interrupted. Two dorsal fins, first with 6–9 strong spines, second with a leading spine and 8–10 rays. Anal fin with 2–3 spines and 7–17 rays. Head large, mouth large, lower jaw generally protruding. Anterior teeth sometimes large and caniniform. The genus *Siphamia* has a long silvery gland of unknown function along entire ventral profile. Apogonids tend to be nocturnal and to shun bright sunlight. Over 100 Indo-Pacific species.

### 462. PARAMIA QUINQUELINEATA (Cuvier & Valenciennes) 1828
Five-lined Cardinalfish                                              **Pl. 2**
10 cm; D VI; I/9; A II/8; L 1 23–26; tr 2–3/6–7. Small canines in both jaws. Usually in small schools around coral heads from E. Africa and the Seychelles to India, Indonesia, Queensland and Polynesia as far as Tahiti.

### 463. CHEILODIPTERUS LINEATUS (Lacépède) 1802
17 cm; D VI; I/9; A II/8; L 1 22–26; tr 2/6. Canines in both jaws. Pinkish above, silvery below. 10 narrow longitudinal lines, middle one from snout through eye, all of them ending before caudal peduncle which is pale yellow with a prominent round black spot. Fins pinkish, spinous dorsal with black leading edge; tail slightly emarginate, pink with narrow dark brown margin. Around coral heads from S. and E. Africa to the Seychelles, E. Indies and Polynesia as far as the Line islands.

ALLIED SPECIES:
464. CHEILODIPTERUS ISOSTIGMA Schultz 10 cm. Markings and colour as in 462; prominent canines in both jaws. Melanesia.
465. C. MACRODON (Lacépède) 20 cm. 8 dusky longitudinal lines; canines large. East Indies, Melanesia, Queensland and Polynesia to Moorea and Borabora.

**466. C. ARTUS** Smith 12 cm. Similar to 465, but canines larger. Western Indian Ocean.

## 467. SIPHAMIA TUBULATA (Weber) 1913
Siphonfish
4 cm; D VII; I/9; A II/8; L 1 24; tr 1/5. Teeth small and equal. A silvery tubular gland under the skin along ventral profile. Yellowish with faint dark markings above, silvery below. Tail sharply forked. Indonesia, Melanesia.

ALLIED SPECIES:
**468. SIPHAMIA CUNEICEPS** Whitley 5 cm. Brassy with small black dots. Eye brilliant blue surrounded by gold. Ventral gland present. Queensland.
**469. S. PERMUTATA** Klausewitz. Ventral gland present. Red Sea.

## 470. ARCHAMIA LINEOLATA (Cuvier & Valenciennes) 1828
Bronze-streaked Cardinalfish
8cm; D VI; I/9; A II/13–15; L 1 24–27; tr 2–3/6–8. Preopercular margin serrated. Pinkish brown speckled with numerous small blackish dots, pale lilac below. A large diffuse blackish spot at base of tail. Numerous narrow transverse orange brown lines. Fins brownish pink. Coral reefs from India and Ceylon to the E. Indies, Melanesia and Queensland.

ALLIED SPECIES:
**471. ARCHAMIA BUROENSIS** (Bleeker) 10 cm. Yellowish brown with 3 dark longitudinal lines and a dark spot on caudal peduncle. Indonesia and Melanesia.
**472. A. ZOSTEROPHORA** (Bleeker) 7 cm. Pale brown, silvery on head and belly. An oblique transverse dark band from dorsal to anal, a dark bar from snout to eye and a dark spot at base of tail. Indonesia and Melanesia.
**473. A. FUCATA** (Cantor) 8 cm. Pinkish with numerous narrow vertical red lines and a black spot at base of tail. South and E. Africa to Seychelles and E. Indies.
**474. A. MOZAMBIQUENSIS** Smith 8 cm. Green above, silvery below. A red band along lateral line and orange spots below it. A black spot at base of tail. Fins bright pink. East Africa and Seychelles, among weeds.

## 475. RHABDAMIA CYPSELURUS (Weber) 1909
5 cm; D VI; I/9; A II/9; L 1 24; tr 2/5. More elongated, less elevated than most other species. Pale silvery pink, darker above. A dark band from snout through eye to upper angle of operculum; snout yellowish. Area surrounding pectoral base light silvery violet. Fins light pink. Tail forked, with a dark submarginal line along upper and lower margins. East Africa and Seychelles to E. Indies and W. Pacific. Similar to 476.

## 476. RHABDAMIA GRACILIS (Bleeker) 1856
6 cm. Similar to 475, but differs in having 12–13 anal rays. East Africa and Seychelles to Indonesia.

## 477. SPHAERAMIA ORBICULARIS (Cuvier & Valenciennes) 1828
♀=**APOGON NEMATOPTERUS** Bleeker                    **Pl. 2**
Polka-dot Cardinalfish, Pajama Cardinalfish
10 cm; D VI; I/9; A II/8–9; L 1 25–26; tr 2/6–7. More boldly marked specimens with prolonged second dorsal (*nematopterus*) are females. A well-known aquarium fish. Usually in small schools around coral heads; also near mangroves. East Africa, Seychelles, Aldabra to E. Indies, Melanesia and Fiji.

### 478. APOGON LEPTACANTHUS Bleeker 1856
Threadfin Cardinalfish

5 cm; D VI; I/9–10; A II/9–10; L 1 23–25; tr 1–2/6–7. Second dorsal spine prolonged into a free filament, especially in ♀. Pearly pinkish brown above, sometimes yellowish; silvery purple below, sometimes red on breast. Narrow light violet-blue vertical streaks on operculum and shoulder. Dorsal fin orange brown, prolonged filament blackish; other fins pinkish. ♀ with dark blotch at base of tail. In small schools around coral heads, from E. Africa to the Seychelles, E. Indies and Melanesia.

### 479. APOGON SANGIENSIS Bleeker 1857
Bar-cheeked Cardinalfish

8 cm; D VI; I/9; A II/8; L 1 23–25; tr 2/6–7. Third and 4th dorsal spines often prolonged into free filaments. Golden red, paler below. A dark band from snout, through eye to upper angle of operculum. A black spot at base of tail. Usually three smaller black spots along base of dorsal fins. Fins red, but anterior margin and free filaments of 1st dorsal black. Coral heads, from S. and E. Africa to Indonesia, the Philippines, Melanesia, Micronesia and Fiji.

### 480. APOGON QUADRIFASCIATUS Cuvier & Valenciennes 1828
Four-banded Cardinalfish

10 cm; D VI; I/9; A II/8; L 1 25–27; tr 2/7. Pale yellowish brown, silvery below. A dark silvery-edged longitudinal band from head above eye to caudal peduncle and a similar band from snout, through eye, to distal margin of tail. Fins brown, often with a dark subbasal line. Coral formations from E. Africa, the Persian Gulf, Reunion and the Maldives to Indonesia, the Philippines, Taiwan, Ryukyu, Queensland and Fiji.

### 481. APOGON LATERALIS Valenciennes 1832
9 cm; D VI; II/9; A II/8; L 1 22–23; tr 2/6. Head dark dusky blue. Back olive, sides silvery pink, pale silvery yellow below. A narrow blackish line from eye to upper angle of operculum and thence to caudal peduncle. A small black spot at base of tail. A diffuse orange yellow spot on cheek. First dorsal yellow tipped with black, 2nd dorsal and anal yellow tipped with pink and with a diffuse blackish submarginal band. Pectorals and ventrals pink. Tail olive, edged distally with pinkish. Weedy areas near river mouths from Madagascar and the Seychelles to the Nicobars, E. Indies, Philippines, Ryukyu islands, Micronesia and Polynesia.

### 482. APOGON SNYDERI Jordan & Everman 1903
Upapalu (Hawaii)

22 cm; D VI; I/9–10; A II/9; L 1 25–26; tr 2/7–8. Bright red. A black band from snout through eye to caudal base. Fins red; leading edge of 1st dorsal and of pectorals, base of 2nd dorsal and anal, upper and lower margins of tail black. Coral heads throughout the Indo-Pacific, from E. Africa and the Seychelles to Hawaii.

### 483. APOGON TAENIATUS Cuvier & Valenciennes 1828          Pl. 2
12 cm; D VII; I/8–9; A II/8; L 1 25–28; tr 2/7. Weedy tidal pools from S. and E. Africa to the E. Indies.

ALLIED SPECIES:

### 484. APOGON COMPRESSUS (Smith & Radcliffe) 10 cm. Yellowish brown above, silvery below. Three broad longitudinal dark bands which bifurcate below 1st dorsal and break into spots on caudal peduncle. East Indies, Melanesia.

**485. A. TRIMACULATUS** C. & V. 15 cm. Variable; generally olive above, paler below. 6–7 faint dark longitudinal bands. Sometimes a dark blotch on operculum and two broad diffuse dark cross-bands. Young ♂ and ♀ with dark spot on caudal peduncle. East Indies, Melanesia, Queensland.

**486. A. HYALOSOMA** Bleeker 18 cm. Pinkish brown above, brassy on sides. A diffuse black spot at base of tail. First dorsal tipped with black; other fins pink, but a black basal spot on 2nd dorsal and anal. East Africa, E. Indies, Melanesia, Queensland.

**487. A. CERAMENSIS** Bleeker 10 cm. Pale yellowish brown speckled with darker brown. A narrow dark line from operculum to base of tail. A dark spot on caudal peduncle. One or more dark lines radiating from eye. Indonesia, Melanesia.

**488. A. AMBOINENSIS** Bleeker 10 cm. Pale brown above, silvery below. A dark line from snout through eye ending in a dark spot on caudal peduncle; a second line from eye, along lateral line, meeting first line on caudal peduncle. Brackish water. Indonesia, Melanesia.

**489. A. FUSCUS** Q. & G. 10 cm. Pinkish with 2 bronzy longitudinal stripes and a small black spot at base of tail. Fins yellow. Red Sea, S. and E. Africa, E. Indies, Philippines and W. Pacific.

**490. A. MACULIFERUS** Garrett 12 cm. Scales with central dark spot forming 8 darkish longitudinal bands. Hawaii and Fiji.

**491. A. WAIKIKI** J. & E. 10 cm. Brownish with tail and all fins very rounded. Hawaii.

**492. A. ERYTHRINUS** Snyder 7 cm. Bright red, 6 dorsal spines. Hawaii.

**493. A. MENESEMUS** Jenkins. Base, centre, upper and lower margins of tail black. Hawaii.

**494. A. CRASSICEPS** Garman 10 cm. Reddish brown, darker above. Caudal peduncle darker, tail margin blackish. Fiji.

**495. A. ATRIPES** (Ogilby) 10 cm. Dark brown; a prominent white ringed dark ocellus behind operculum, above pectoral base. Tail and pectorals yellow. Other fins blackish, soft dorsal with orange margin. Queensland.

**496. A. COCCINEUS** Rüppell 5 cm. Uniform brilliant red. Red Sea, E. Africa, Seychelles.

**497. A. FRAGILIS** Smith 4 cm. Transparent with pinkish reflections. A small black spot on caudal peduncle and a brown bar from snout to hind edge of eye. Western Indian Ocean.

**498. A. NIGRIPES** Playfair 5 cm. Brown above, pinkish below. A series of bluish vertical bars from belly to lateral line. Eye red. Fins pink, anterior half of ventrals blackish. East Africa, among weeds.

**499. A. SEMIORNATUS** Peters 5 cm. Bright red. A black dorsal band to end of soft dorsal. A black line from eye to middle of rear margin of tail and a 3rd line from eye through pectoral base to base of anal. Eye dark blue. Western Indian Ocean.

**500. PRISTIAPOGON FRAENATUS** (Valenciennes) 1832    **Pl. 2**
Spiny-eyed Cardinalfish

8 cm; D VII; I/8–9; A II/8; L 1 23–24; tr 2/6–7. Coral reefs and tidal pools, occasionally entering fresh water. Red Sea, E. Africa and the Seychelles to India, the E. Indies, Philippines, Taiwan, Micronesia, Melanesia, Queensland and Polynesia as far as the Marquesas and Tuamotus.

ALLIED SPECIES:

**501. PRISTIAPOGON TAENIOPTERUS** (Bennett) Olive brown. First dorsal with black spots; 2nd dorsal and anal with basal black bands, 2 black streaks on tail, ventrals with black margins. East Indies and New Guinea.

**502. P. EXOSTIGMA** (Jordan & Starks) 8 cm. Light brown, silvery below. A black band from snout through eye to base of tail. A large black spot on peduncle, above end of band. First dorsal black anteriorly; 2nd dorsal and anal with black basal bands. Melanesia.

**503. P. KALLOPTERUS** (Bleeker) Solomon Islands and New Guinea. Possibly a senior synonym of *Apogon snyderi* (J. & E.). See 482.

**504. GRONOVICHTHYS CYANOSOMA** (Bleeker) 1853          Pl. 2
Pale-lined Cardinalfish
7 cm; D VII; I/9; A II/8; L 1 21–23; tr 2/6–7. Coral reefs from E. Africa and
the Seychelles to the E. Indies, Melanesia and Fiji.

**505. GRONOVICHTHYS BANDANENSIS** (Bleeker) 1854          Pl. 2
10 cm; D VII; I/9; A II/8; L 1 23–27; tr 2/6–7. Coral reefs and tidal pools
throughout the Indo-Pacific, including the Red Sea and Queensland, but not
in Hawaii.

ALLIED SPECIES:
**506. GRONOVICHTHYS HARTZFELDI** (Bleeker) 11 cm. Yellowish brown,
paler below, head dusky. A pearly dorsal line; a pearly line from snout to upper part of
eye and caudal peduncle and a third such line from mouth to lower eye and operculum.
A round black spot at base of tail. Tail with transverse rows of black dots. Indonesia
and Melanesia.

**507. LOVAMIA NOVEMFASCIATA** (Cuvier & Valenciennes) 1828
Nine-banded Cardinalfish          Pl. 2
7 cm; D VII; I/9; A II/8; L 1 24–28; tr 2/6. Tidal pools from Ceylon and
India to the E. Indies, Melanesia, Queensland and Fiji. Treated by some
authors as a form or subspecies of 508.

ALLIED SPECIES:
**508. LOVAMIA FASCIATA** (Shaw) 1790 10 cm. Yellowish brown above, silvery
below. 5 dark brown longitudinal bands. Fins reddish brown, 2nd dorsal and anal with
dark basal bands. See 528. East Indies, Melanesia, Queensland.
**509. L. AROUBIENSIS** (Hombron & Jacquinot) 7 cm. Brown above, pinkish on
sides and below. 3 very wide dark bands ending abruptly at base of tail; no secondary
intermediate bands. East Indies, Philippines and Queensland. Treated by some authors
as a form or subspecies of 508.
**510. L. COOKI** (Macleay) 8 cm. Similar to 507, but mid-lateral band thickened on
caudal peduncle; a dark mark on operculum near pectoral base. Melanesia.

**511. APOGONICHTHYS MARMORATUS** Alleyne & Macleay 1877
Eared Cardinalfish
6 cm; D VII; I/9; A II/8; L 1 20; tr 2/5. Tail rounded. Lateral line ends below
2nd dorsal. Reddish yellow with 8–9 dark cross-bars which almost encircle body.
A large black ocellus enclosed by a golden ring on operculum. Fins bright red
with darker lines or spots. Coral reefs in Melanesia. Very similar to 512 but
more brightly coloured.

**512. APOGONICHTHYS AURITUS** (Cuvier & Valenciennes) 1828
6 cm; D VII; I/8–9; A II/8; L 1 19–22; tr 2/6. Very similar to 511, but much
duller and paler in colour. Coral reefs from the Red Sea and E. Africa to the
Seychelles, Ceylon, India, Mauritius, E. Indies, Philippines, Queensland,
Melanesia, Micronesia and Polynesia.

**513. APOGONICHTHYS NIGRIPINNIS** (Cuvier & Valenciennes) 1828
          Pl. 2
10 cm; D VII; I/8–9; A II/8; L 1 24–25; tr 2/6. Weedy tidal pools on coral
reefs. Feigns death when pursued. East Africa and the Seychelles to the E.
Indies. *A. uninotatus* (Smith & Radcliffe) is probably a synonym.

### 514. APOGONICHTHYS OCELLATUS Weber 1913
4 cm. Tail rounded. Olive brown. Operculum with coppery patches and a dark line from eye which is red, to lower angle of preoperculum. Spinous dorsal blackish with a black ocellus encircled by a yellowish ring. Other fins yellowish, basally blackish. Tidal pools from E. Africa and the Seychelles to the Malay Archipelago.

### 515. APOGONICHTHYS BRACHYGRAMMA (Jenkins) 1902
7 cm; D VI; I/9; A II/8; L 1 22–24; tr 2/5. Lateral line interrupted below 2nd dorsal. Tail rounded. Olive green, somewhat mottled with darker olive, especially on back. Fins pinkish spotted with brown. Throughout the Indo-Pacific, from S. and E. Africa to Hawaii. Usually in weedy tidal pools and among dead coral rubble.

ALLIED SPECIES:
**516. APOGONICHTHYS ELLIOTI** Day 12 cm. Tail slightly rounded with white margin and white inner area. Pale gold above, silvery on sides and belly. Snout and top of head with small black dots. Tail and fins mainly black. India, Indonesia, Melanesia.
**517. A. POECILOPTERUS** (C. & V.) 10 cm. Operculum with two pointed flaps. Tail truncate. Pale brown, silvery in some lights, usually with narrow dark vertical bars. Fins dusky, often with whitish spots. Indonesia and Melanesia.
**518. A. PERDIX** Bleeker 5 cm. Tail and fins very rounded. Body irregularly reticulated with dark lines. East Africa to E. Indies, Taiwan and Polynesia.
**519. A. FRAXINEUS** Smith 8 cm. Tail truncate. Coppery on back, brassy on sides. A black mark from eye to preopercular corner. First dorsal pinkish, with broad black margin; ventrals black, other fins pink. Western Indian Ocean.

OTHER SPECIES:
**520. ZORAMIA GRAEFFI** (Günther) 4 cm. Uniform olive brown, dorsal fins elevated. Fiji, Samoa, Marshall islands. Rare.
**521. PSEUDAMIOPS GRACILICAUDA** Lachner 5 cm. Slender and elongated; fins and tail rounded. Transparent. Hawaii and Marshall islands.
**522. ASPERAPOGON RUBELLUS** Smith 7 cm. Dark red; all fins bright red; tail very rounded, almost circular. Coral rubble, E. Africa. See also 524.
**523. GYMNAPOGON AFRICANUS** Smith 5 cm. Elongated, tail forked, but other fins very rounded. Small black dots on snout and round eye. Western Indian Ocean.
**524. LEPIDAMIA MULTITAENIATA** (C. & V.) 10 cm. Similar to 522, but scales much smaller, tail forked; 1st dorsal tipped with black. Indian Ocean.
**525. PSEUDAMIA GELATINOSA** Smith 45 mm. Slender; fins rounded, tail large, obtusely pointed, edged with white. Dark blackish green with numerous narrow black lines. Fins hyaline, tail with closely spaced dark dots and vermiculations. Western Indian Ocean.

### 526. NEAMIA OCTOSPINA Smith & Radcliffe 1912
45 mm; D VIII; I/9; A II/8; L 1 24; tr 2/7–8. Uniform pinkish, yellowish on belly. Three black bars radiating from behind eye, one to top of head, one to upper angle of operculum and one to lower margin of preoperculum. Tail long, rounded. Fins pink. Coral reefs from E. Africa to Seychelles, E. Indies and W. Pacific.

### 527. OSTORHINCHUS AUREUS (Lacépède) 1802     Pl. 2
=**O. FLEURIEU** (Lacépède) 1802
Ring-tailed Cardinalfish
12 cm; D VII; I/9; A II/8; L 1 24–27; tr 2/7. In small schools around coral

heads in shallow water; a most beautiful fish. Throughout the tropical Indo-Pacific, from E. Africa and the Seychelles to the E. Indies, Melanesia and Queensland.

### 528. OSTORHINCHUS ENDEKATAENIA (Bleeker) 1852　　Pl. 2
Bengali (Seychelles)

10 cm; D VII; I/9; A II/8; L 1 25–27; tr 1½/7. Very common in tidal pools from E. Africa and the Seychelles to the E. Indies. Very probably a race or a synonym of 508.

ALLIED SPECIES:

**529. OSTORHINCHUS ANGUSTATUS** S. & R. 8 cm. Silvery, darker above. A narrow black dorsal line and a narrow black ventral line. Three broad black bands from snout to base of tail, the middle one expanded into a round spot on base of tail fin. Fins bright pink, anterior part of 1st dorsal bright red. Last rays of 2nd dorsal and anal produced. East Africa to E. Indies and W. Pacific as far as the Marquesas.

**530. O. APOGONIDES** (Bleeker) 7 cm. Pinkish; snout black; two blue lines from snout through eye to opercular margin. Fins orange pink, 1st dorsal with a subterminal black spot. East Africa to E. Indies and Polynesia as far as Tahiti.

**531. O. SAVAYENSIS** (Günther) 7 cm. Similar to 527, but lacking blue lines, 1st dorsal tipped with black. East Africa to E. Indies and W. Pacific.

**532. O. NITIDUS** Smith 7 cm. Pinkish orange with darker longitudinal lines. Blue spots and streaks before pectoral axil, on breast and belly. East Africa.

## Family KUHLIIDAE (DULEIDAE) **Flagtails**

Small to moderate perch-like fishes of shallow Indo-Pacific waters. Most species are found in brackish water, often in the vicinity of mangroves; some species are permanent residents of fresh water. Others appear to prefer waters shaded by overhanging rocks or by mangroves. The salt water species are bright silvery, the others have distinctive patterns. Oval and somewhat compressed, typically perch-like in shape. Scales fairly large, ctenoid. Lateral line well developed and complete. Cheeks and operculum scaly, but preopercular flange naked. Operculum with two spines. A single dorsal fin consisting of 10 anterior spines and 9–13 posterior rays. Anal fin preceded by three spines. Dorsal and anal fins can be folded into a scaly sheath. Tail emarginate or forked. Mouth protractile.

### 533. KUHLIA TAENIURUS (Cuvier & Valenciennes) 1829
### =DULES TAENIURUS
Barred Flagtail

20 cm; D X/10–12; A III/11–13; L 1 55–56; tr 5–6/12–14. Silvery, brownish above. Fins dusky yellow, dorsal with black margin in young. Tail forked; yellowish with five black longitudinal bands. Coral reefs and brackish waters near mangroves and under rocky overhangs. Throughout the Indo-Pacific, from the Red Sea and S. Africa to the E. Indies and Polynesia as far as the Marquesas and Tahiti.

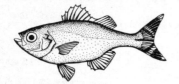

Barred Flagtail

### 534. KUHLIA RUPESTRIS (Lacépède) 1802
### =DULES RUPESTRIS
Rock Flagtail

40 cm. D X/11; A III/9–10; L 1 41–44; tr 4–5/9–11. Tail slightly emarginate, with rounded lobes. Bluish to dusky above, silvery on sides and below. Scales of sides and operculum with a dark brown basal dot. Similar dots at base of dorsal and anal. A blackish bar on soft dorsal and a large black blotch on each caudal lobe becoming fused into a wide vertical band in older individuals. Mangroves and estuaries throughout the Indo-Pacific, from S. and E. Africa to the E. Indies, Melanesia and Polynesia as far as Tahiti.

ALLIED SPECIES:

**535. KUHLIA MARGINATA** (C. & V.) 22 cm. Silvery, darker above. Upper sides, tail peduncle and tail with large irregular blackish spots. Soft dorsal and anal with submarginal black band. Throughout Indo-Pacific excluding Hawaii and Queensland.
**536. K. MUNDA** (De Vis) 24 cm. Fins elevated; a very deep notch between spinous and soft dorsal. Plain silvery. Tail deeply forked, edged or tipped with black. East Indies, Melanesia, Queensland and Fiji.
**537. K. SANDVICHENSIS** (Steindachner) (Aholehole, H) 30 cm. Plain silvery, darker on back. Good eating. Polynesia, Fiji, Hawaii.

Family LATIDAE (=CENTROPOMIDAE), including AMBASSIDAE (=CHAN-DIDAE) **Barramundi, Glass Perch**
Small to large carnivorous silvery fishes with elevated back and depressed or pointed head. Lateral line continuous. Coastal waters, most species being partial to brackish waters. Some ascend rivers and others are permanent residents of fresh water.

### 538. LATES CALCARIFER (Bloch) 1790
Giant Perch, Barramundi (A.)

180 cm; D VII–VIII; I/10–11; A III/7–8; L 1 52–61; tr 6/13. Mouth large, teeth villiform, preoperculum serrated below, ending in a spine. Tail rounded. Silvery, green or brown dorsally. Eye bright pink. Good eating, especially if taken in salt water; often found in river mouths. Ceylon, E. Indies, Melanesia and Queensland.

### 539. PSAMMOPERCA WAIGIENSIS (Cuvier & Valenciennes) 1828
Sand-bass, Glass-eye Perch

38 cm; D VII; I/12; A III/8; L 1 45–50; tr 6/11. Teeth small and granular. A spine at angle of preoperculum. Reddish brown above, silvery on sides and belly. Vertical fins reddish brown, paired fins yellowish white. Eyes glassy. Tail rounded. Coastal waters. Often taken by handline in rocky areas. Ceylon, E. Indies, Melanesia and Queensland.

Sand-bass

## 540. AMBASSIS COMMERSONI Cuvier & Valenciennes 1828
Chanda Perch, Glass Perch, Perchlet
10 cm; D I, VII, I/9–10; III/9–10; L 1 24–27; tr 2–3/7–8. Mouth moderate, oblique. Tail deeply forked. Lateral line interrupted below end of spinous dorsal. Yellowish with bright silvery midlateral band. A black blotch on spinous dorsal and a black streak on each lobe of tail. Estuaries and brackish waters, usually in shoals. South and E. Africa to C. Indo-Pacific.

ALLIED SPECIES:
Numerous Indo-Pacific species; all are small, closely related to each other, very similar and difficult for the non-specialist to identify. The following are some of the better known species:

**541. AMBASSIS MARIANUS** Günther 11cm. Queensland.
**542. A. NALUA** H.-B. 12 cm. India, E. Indies, Melanesia.
**543. A. MACKLEAYI** (Castelnau) 8 cm. East Indies, Melanesia, Queensland.
**544. A. SAFGHA** (Forskål) 10 cm. East Africa, E. Indies, Polynesia, Fiji.
**545. A. UROTAENIA** Bleeker 10 cm. South and E. Africa to E. Indies, Polynesia and Fiji.
**546. A. GYMNOCEPHALUS** (Lacépède) 10 cm. South and E. Africa to C. Indo-Pacific.
**547. A. MIOPS** Günther 10 cm. Melanesia.
**548. A. INTERRUPTUS** Bleeker. Central Indo-Pacific.
**549. A. BURUENSIS** Bleeker 75 mm. Central Indo-Pacific.
**550. A. MACRANTHUS** Bleeker 15 cm. India to C. Indo-Pacific.

*Ambassis urotaenia*

Family SERRANIDAE
Subfamily *Epinephelinae* Rock-cod, Coral-cod, Coral-trout, Groupers, Gropers, Garrupa (S. Africa, Mozambique), Chewa (Swahili), Vieilles (Seychelles, Mauritius)
Moderate to large predatory fishes, especially abundant in the vicinity of coral reefs and rocks. Highly territorial and sedentary, solitary bottom-dwellers. Usually seen resting on their pectorals with head emerging from their habitual hole, waiting to snap at any passing fish of suitable size. Large-mouthed and voracious. Excellent eating, except when very large, when they are rather coarse. About 100 Indo-Pacific species. Oblong, somewhat compressed, robust perch-like fishes. Scales generally small, often invisible under thick mucus. Lateral line complete, slightly arched. 2–3 opercular spines; a single dorsal fin; anal fin with 3 spines. Pectorals broadly rounded, almost fleshy. Teeth mostly villi-form or conical, small; some outer teeth may sometimes be enlarged canines. The large genus *Epinephelus* is particularly confusing, even to experts, as many of the species are similar, yet variable and may prove to be no more than synonyms.

### 551. CENTROGENYS VAIGIENSIS Quoy & Gaimard 1824
False Scorpion Fish
15 cm; D XIII–XIV/9–11; A III/5; L 1 40–42; tr 4–5/14–16. 3–4 spines on lower margin of preoperculum, a single opercular spine. Anterior nostril with a fleshy tentacle. Tail rather rounded. Brown with irregular dark spots and blotches. Dorsal with dark spots, other fins with irregular alternating light and dark bands. Indonesia, Melanesia, Queensland.

### 552. CROMILEPTES ALTIVELIS (Cuvier & Valenciennes) 1828 Pl. 5
Humped Rock-cod, Barramundi Cod (Aus.) Kerapu Sonoh (Malay)
65 cm; D X/17–19; A III/10; L 1 74–100; tr 21–24/34–37. Juveniles with fewer, relatively larger spots. Small individuals are popular aquarium fishes. India, E. Indies, Philippines, Taiwan, Melanesia, Queensland.

### 553. ANYPERODON LEUCOGRAMMICUS
(Cuvier & Valenciennes) 1828
White-lined Rock-cod, Chevalier de Bois (S)
50 cm; D XI/14–15; A III/9; L 1 57–85; tr 12–15/55–65. Lower margin of pre-operculum spineless. Operculum extended into an angular flap with 3 spines. Teeth villiform. Head entirely scaly. Tail rounded. Brown to dark olive; 3–5 narrow white longitudinal stripes, the lower ones reaching tail. Head, body and fins dotted with orange red. Markings disappear with age. Coral reefs from E. Africa and the Seychelles to the E. Indies, Melanesia and Queensland.

### 554. PLECTROPOMA MACULATUM (Bloch) 1790 Pl. 5
Coral-cod, Leopard Cod, Vieille, Babonne (S), Kerapu Bara (Malay)
95 cm, 25 kg; D VII–VIII/11–12; A III/8; L 1 80–106; tr 12–20/60–80. 3–4 antrorse spines on lower margin of preoperculum. Three opercular spines. Snout, front of head and below eyes naked. Tail emarginate. Colour very variable, but some blue spots and lines usually present, especially in young specimens. Common on coral reefs throughout the tropical Indo-Pacific, but not in Hawaii. See 560.

ALLIED SPECIES:
### 555. PLECTROPOMA OLIGACANTHUS Bleeker 58 cm. Soft dorsal and anal elevated anteriorly, tail emarginate. Red with wavy blue lines on head and body and blue spots on caudal peduncle and tail. East Indies and Melanesia.

### 556. VARIOLA LOUTI (Forskål) 1775 Pl. 3
Fairy Cod, Lunar-tailed Rock-cod, Vroissant (S)
75 cm; D IX/13–14; A III/8; L 1 76–100; tr 10–14/54–60. Canines present. A very beautiful and common reef fish. Throughout the Indo-Pacific including the Red Sea and Queensland, but not in Hawaii.

### 557. AETHALOPERCA ROGAA (Forskål) 1775
Red-flushed Rock-cod, Matongo (S)
60 cm; D IX/17–18; A III/9; L 1 50–55; tr 11–13/29–48. Dorsal profile humped, particularly in old individuals. Canines present. Fins angular, tail emarginate. Uniformly dark brown; inside of mouth and gill chamber bright orange. Juveniles with white tipped dorsal and white edged tail. Throughout the tropical Indo-Pacific including the Red Sea and Queensland, but not in Hawaii.

ALLIED SPECIES:
**558. AETHALOPERCA ALBOMARGINATA** Fowler 45 cm. Dark with blue lines. Rare. Deep water. East Africa to E. Indies.

## 559. AULACOCEPHALUS TEMMINCKI Bleeker 1857
35 cm; D IX/12; A III/9. Scales very small. Fins angular, tail truncate. Brown with a yellowish stripe from snout through eye along upper part of body to base of tail. South and E. Africa to the C. Indo-Pacific, China and Japan.

## 560. CEPHALOPHOLIS MINIATUS (Forskål) 1775          Pl. 3
Coral Trout, Vieille Anana (S), Garrupa (S. Africa)
45 cm; D IX/15–16; A III/9; L 1 48–60; tr 8–10/27–45. Similar to 556 and to the red form of 554, but may be recognised by the rounded tail. Common among coral throughout the Indo-Pacific from the Red Sea to Queensland and Tahiti, but not in Hawaii. See also 561.

## 561. CEPHALOPHOLIS COATESI Whitley 1937
Freckled Rock-cod
75 cm; D IX/15; A III/9; L 1 55; tr 9–10/38–40. Fins and tail broadly rounded. Similar to 560, but usually with 6 or more broad dark saddles on back. Eye black ringed with yellow. Melanesia and Queensland.

## 562. CEPHALOPHOLIS CYANOSTIGMA
(Cuvier & Valenciennes) 1828
Blue-spotted Rock-cod
35 cm; D IX/16; A III/8; L 1 45–56; tr 9–11/38–40. Reddish brown with 6 indistinct darker cross-bands and paler mottlings. Body and fins with small black-ringed blue spots. Spinous dorsal tipped with red. East Indies, Melanesia and Queensland.

## 563. CEPHALOPHOLIS BOENACK (Bloch) 1790
Blue-lined Rock-cod
30 cm; D IX/15–17; A III/8; L 1 44–63; tr 8–11/32–40. Dark brown with numerous undulating longitudinal blue lines. Spinous dorsal tipped with black; inside of mouth and gill cavity orange. Ceylon, E. Indies and Melanesia.

## 564. CEPHALOPHOLIS PACHYCENTRON
(Cuvier & Valenciennes) 1828
Brown-banded Rock-cod, Spotted-faced Rock-cod
25 cm; D IX/15–17; A III/8; L 1 43–53; tr 8–10/30–37. Chocolate brown, often with 8 indistinct darker cross-bands. Head and anterior part of body with small blue spots. Tips of spinous dorsal black; soft dorsal, tail and anal with narrow white margin. Coral reefs from S. and E. Africa to the E. Indies, Melanesia and Queensland.

## 565. CEPHALOPHOLIS ARGUS Bloch & Schneider 1801          Pl. 3
Peacock Rock-cod, Vieille Cecille (S)
42 cm; D IX/15–17; A III/8–9; L 1 40–55; tr 9–10/32–40. Coral reefs from S. and E. Africa to the E. Indies, Philippines, Melanesia, Micronesia and Polynesia as far as the Marquesas and Tuamotu islands.

## 566. CEPHALOPHOLIS LEOPARDUS (Lacépède) 1802
40 cm; D IX/14–15; A III/9; L 1 43–53; tr 6-7/28–34. White or yellowish,

covered with small red spots. Breast and cheeks with network of reddish brown
lines. A dark brown bar from eye to edge of operculum. 1–2 blackish saddles
on caudal peduncle and 1–2 oblique dark bands on tail, sometimes united in a
crescent. Coral reefs from E. Africa to the Seychelles, Ceylon, E. Indies,
Melanesia and Polynesia as far as Tahiti and the Marquesas.

### 567. CEPHALOPHOLIS URODELUS (Cuvier & Valenciennes) 1828
Flag-tailed Rock-cod
25 cm; D IX/14–16; A III/9; L 1 54–70; tr 8–10/35–40. Dark red-brown,
breast paler. Generally marbled with darker brown and covered with light
spots. Peduncle and middle of tail blackish; tail with two oblique white bands
converging towards distal margin and forming an edge to the dark area. Coral
reefs from E. Africa to the E. Indies, Melanesia, Queensland and Polynesia as
far as the Tuamotu islands.

### 568. CEPHALOPHOLIS AURANTIUS
(Cuvier & Valenciennes) 1828
Orange Rock-cod, Maconde (S)                           Pl. 3
35 cm; D IX/14–15; A III/8–9; L 1 40–55; tr 8–10/29–40. Coral reefs from
S. and E. Africa to the E. Indies, Melanesia and Polynesia as far as Tahiti.

### 569. CEPHALOPHOLIS SONNERATI
(Cuvier & Valenciennes) 1828
Tomato Rock-cod, Vieille Anana (S)
60 cm; D IX/14–15; A III/9; L 1 53–60; tr 12–15/40–50. Brilliant tomato red
with a network of fine blue lines on head. All fins with black margins. Coral
reefs (deeper water) from S. and E. Africa to the Seychelles, Ceylon, the E.
Indies, Melanesia, Queensland and Polynesia as far as Fanning island.

### 570. CEPHALOPHOLIS NIGRIPINNIS
(Cuvier & Valenciennes) 1828
Brown-finned Rock-cod
42 cm; D IX/14–16; A III/9; L 1 53–60; tr 12–15/40–50. Dark reddish brown;
head sometimes spotted with yellow or blue. Dorsal, anal and ventrals dark
brown; pectorals and tail with wide white margin. Ceylon to E. Indies and
Melanesia.

ALLIED SPECIES:

### 571. CEPHALOPHOLIS HEMISTICTUS (Rüppell) 20 cm. Dark brown with
blue spots. possibly a form of 560. East Africa from Natal to the Red Sea.

### 572. PROMICROPS LANCEOLATUS (Bloch) 1790             Pl. 5
Queensland Grouper, Brindled Sea-bass (Natal)
360 cm; D XI/14–15; A III/8; L 1 58–67; tr 14–15/42–50. Variable, changing
with age. Adults usually uniform blackish. Large specimens can be aggressive
and dangerous and in some places are feared more than sharks. South and E.
Africa to the E. Indies, Melanesia and Queensland.

### 573. EPINEPHELUS FLAVOCAERULEUS (Lacépède) 1802       Pl. 4
Purple Rock-cod, Vieille Platte (S)
90 cm, D XI/15–17; A III/8; L 1 65–75; tr 20–25/55–65. The amount of
yellow decreases as the fish grows older. Coral reefs from S. and E. Africa to the
E. Indies, Melanesia and Queensland.

## 574. EPINEPHELUS MORRHUA                                    Pl. 4
(Cuvier & Valenciennes) 1833
60 cm; D XI/14–15; A III/7–8; L 1 60; tr 14–38–40. South and E. Africa to
the C. Indo-Pacific. See 575.

ALLIED SPECIES:
**575. EPINEPHELUS UNDULOSUS** Q. & G. 38 cm. Similar to 574, but longitudinal lines narrower and more numerous. Indonesia and Melanesia.

## 576. EPINEPHELUS AREOLATUS (Forskål) 1775                   Pl. 5
Vieille Maconde (S), Chewa (Swahili)
40 cm; D XI/15–16; A III/8; L 1 50–57; tr 12–15/41–50. The truncated tail
readily distinguishes this species from most other *Epinephelus*. Red Sea and
S. and E. Africa to the E. Indies, Melanesia and Queensland. Very common in
the Seychelles. See 598.

## 577. EPINEPHELUS DIACANTHUS (Cuvier & Valenciennes) 1828
Double-thorned Rock-cod
50 cm; D XI/15–17; A III/8; L 1 52–54; tr 11–15/36–38. Two prominent spines
at angle of preoperculum. Tail truncated in adults. Brown with faint irregular
dark blotches. Six broad darker vertical bars. Coral reefs from India to the E.
Indies, Melanesia and Polynesia. See 578.

## 578. EPINEPHELUS DAMELII (Günther) 1876
Saddled Rock-cod.
42 cm; D X–XI/14; A III/7–8; L 1 72–75; tr 15–17/50. Similar to 577, but
lacks preopercular spines. Tail rounded. Vertical fins with narrow white margins.
Indonesia and Melanesia.

## 579. EPINEPHELUS TAUVINA (Forskål) 1775                     Pl. 4
Greasy Cod, Estuary Rock-cod
210 cm; D XI/15–16; A III/8; L 1 57–70; tr 12–15/34–45. Large individuals
are reputed to be aggressive and dangerous. Very variable, most markings lost
with age. Moderately common throughout the Indo-Pacific including the Red
Sea, Queensland and Hawaii.

## 580. EPINEPHELUS FARIO (Thunberg) 1793                      Pl. 4
Trout Cod
45 cm; D XI/15–16; A III/8; L 1 50–51; tr 11–12/38–40. Sometimes with 2–3
dark saddles below soft dorsal and on caudal peduncle and pale margins to
fins. South and E. Africa to India, E. Indies, Philippines, Melanesia, Micronesia, Polynesia and Queensland.

## 581. EPINEPHELUS CORALLICOLA (Cuvier & Valenciennes) 1828
Coral Rock-cod
45 cm; D XI/15–16; A III/8; L 1 53–70; tr 11–15/35–45. Brown with widely
spaced dark round spots smaller than pupil. 2–3 dark saddles below dorsal and
on caudal peduncle. All fins with narrow white margins. Coral reefs in the E.
Indies, Melanesia, Queensland and Polynesia as far as Tahiti and Fanning
island.

## 582. EPINEPHELUS SEXFASCIATUS (Cuvier & Valenciennes) 1828
Six-banded Rock-cod
28 cm; D XI/14–15; A III/8; L 1 52–56; tr 9–10/30–35. Brown with 6 darke

vertical bands as broad as interspaces. Vertical fins with large round dark spots.
Pectorals pale yellow. East Indies and Melanesia.

**583. EPINEPHELUS SLACKSMITHI** Whitley 1959
Lace-finned Coral-cod
33 cm; D XI/15; A III/8; L 1 55–70; tr 9/36. Dark brown with light spots on
back and caudal peduncle. Spots on fins larger than darker interspaces which
form a network. Vertical fins with a dark submarginal band and narrow pale
margin. Maxillary groove black. Melanesia and Queensland.

**584. EPINEPHELUS FUSCOGUTTATUS** (Forskål) 1775    **Pl. 4**
Black Rock-cod, Carpet Cod, Vieille Machatta (S)
90 cm; D XI/14–15; A III/8; L 1 55–70; tr 15/45–60. Throughout the Indo-
Pacific including the Red Sea and Queensland, but not in Hawaii.

**585. EPINEPHELUS SUMMANA** (Forskål) 1775
Speckled-finned Rock-cod
50 cm; D XI/14–15; A III/8; L 1 52–62; tr 11–14/40–46. Blackish brown to
very dark olive, densely speckled with small yellow spots which sometimes
coalesce into blotches and irregular lines. Coral reefs, occasionally entering
fresh water. Throughout Indo-Pacific including the Red Sea and Queensland,
but not in Hawaii.

**586. EPINEPHELUS CHLOROSTIGMA** (Cuvier & Valenciennes) 1828
Brown-spotted Reef-cod, Vieille Maconde (S)
62 cm; D XI/16–17; A III/8; L 1 56; tr 20/33. Brown with numerous round
dark spots larger than interspaces. Tail truncate, with a pale margin. East
Africa, Seychelles, India, E. Indies, Philippines, Indo-China and Taiwan.

**587. EPINEPHELUS BLEEKERI** (Vaillant & Bocourt) 1877
=**E. COROMANDELICUS** Day 1878
65 cm; D XI/16–17; A III/8; L 1 60–67; tr 17–22/30–31. Tail truncate. Reddish
brown, paler below; covered with light dark-ringed spots smaller than eye.
Lower $\frac{2}{3}$ of tail much darker than upper third. India, Ceylon, Maldives and
Laccadives.

**588. EPINEPHELUS MALABARICUS** (Bloch & Schneider) 1801
45 cm; D XI/14–15; A III/8; L 1 60–64; tr 16–18/30–33. Brown, paler below,
with obscure, diffuse dark blotches. Fins heavily spotted. Possibly a form of
579. India and Ceylon, E. Indies, Philippines and Polynesia.

**589. EPINEPHELUS CAERULEOPUNCTATUS** (Bloch) 1790   **Pl. 4**
Ocellated Rock-cod
75 cm; D XI/15–16; A III/8; L 1 51–65; tr 12–14/38–45. Coral reefs throughout
the Indo-Pacific, including the Red Sea and Queensland, but not in Hawaii.
Young often in shallow tidal pools.

ALLIED SPECIES:
**590. EPINEPHELUS AUSTRALIS** (Castelnau) 18 cm. Similar to 589, but pale
spots much smaller. East Indies, Melanesia, Queensland and Polynesia.

**591. EPINEPHELUS MERRA** Bloch 1793    **Pl. 4**
=**E. HEXAGONATUS** Günther 1873
45 cm; D XI/15–17; A III/8; L 1 55–70; tr 10–13/32–44. Coral reefs throughout
the Indo-Pacific including the Red Sea and Queensland, but not in Hawaii.
See 592.

ALLIED SPECIES:

**592. EPINEPHELUS MEGACHIR** (Richardson) 45 cm. Similar to 591, but pectoral fins much longer. East Africa to E. Indies, Melanesia and Queensland.

**593. E. MACROSPILOS** (Bleeker) 37 cm. Similar to 591 and 592, but dark spots larger, pectorals average length. South and E. Africa to C. Indo-Pacific.

## 594. EPINEPHELUS FASCIATUS (Forskål) 1775                    Pl. 3
Black-tipped Rock-cod, Vieille rouge (S), Keretang (Malay)

37 cm; D XI/16; A III/8; L 1 50–62; tr 9–12/36–42. Colour variable, some specimens being uniform dark red, but dorsal fins always tipped with black. Common among coral reefs throughout the Indo-Pacific including the Red Sea and Queensland, but not in Hawaii.

ALLIED SPECIES:

**595. EPINEPHELUS RHYNCHOLEPIS** Bleeker. Reddish brown; all scales white-centred, paired fins orange. Central Indo-Pacific.

**596. E. GRAMMATOPHORUS** Boulenger 37 cm. Reddish brown; 6–7 faint dark cross-bands. Numerous close-set very small dark spots all over, a dark red mark at pectoral base. South and E. Africa to C. Indo-Pacific.

**597. E. SPINIGER** (Günther) 25 cm. Uniform brown. Second dorsal spine elevated. Very rare. Known from Natal and from the Marquesas.

**598. E. DISPAR** (Playfair) 75 cm. Numerous small dark spots as in 576, but tail broadly rounded with wide dark margin. Western Indian Ocean.

**599. E. LEPROSUS** Smith 60 cm. Blackish with irregular whitish spots and freckles. Rare, Western Indian Ocean.

**600. E. SALONOTUS** Smith 60 cm. Spotted as in 591, but always with 4 dark saddles on back. Western Indian Ocean.

**601. E. TUKULA** Morgans 120 cm. Reddish brown with large darker spots on body and caudal peduncle. Spots on head and fins much smaller. Western Indian Ocean.

**602. E. MOARA** (T. & S.) 60 cm. Similar to 579, but lacks small reddish spots. Taiwan and S. Japan.

**603. E. SEPTEMFASCIATUS** (Thunberg) 60 cm. Dark brown with 7 light cross-bands, 1st at rear margin of operculum, last at end of dorsal and anal. Stripes extend onto fins. Tail and pectorals yellowish. South Japan and Taiwan.

**604. E. GILBERTI** Richardson 40 cm. Similar to 591, but last dorsal spine much shorter than third. East Indies, Queensland and Polynesia.

**605. E. QUERNUS** Seale 90 cm. Nearly black with lighter spots, fins with pale margins. Hawaii.

OTHER SPECIES:

**606. POGONOPERCA OCELLATA** Günther 23 cm. Deep, dorsal profile somewhat humped. Very dark brown with black blotches and numerous close-set small white spots. East Africa, Seychelles, Mauritius.

**607. DERMATOLEPIS STRIOLATUS** Playfair 60 cm. Profile elevated, fins very rounded. Brown with very irregular lighter and darker streaks, blotches and spots. Rare. East Africa, Persian Gulf.

**608. D. ALDABRENSIS** Smith 60 cm. Similar to 607, but fins smaller. Covered all over except breast, belly and fins, with small dark round spots. Type only, Aldabra.

**609. YPSIGRAMMA SUSUMI** (Jordan & Seale) 12 cm. Two dorsal fins. Pinkish with 8 narrow lines from head to tail base. Fins orange. Superficially like an Apogonid. East Africa to C. Indo-Pacific.

**610. Y. AFRICANUM** Smith 12 cm. Like 609, but stripes fewer, wider. Rare Western Indian Ocean.

Subfamily *Grammistinae*
A small group of tropical perch-like fishes which includes the American Soap-fishes and one well known Indo-Pacific species. They differ from the *Epine-phelinae* in having a low dorsal fin count and a dermal barbel on the chin.

### 611. GRAMMISTES SEXLINEATUS (Thunberg) 1792     Pl. 3
Six-lined Perch
30 cm; D VI–VII, I/13–15; A I–II/9–10; L 1 59–72; tr 9–11/40–43. Chin barbel rudimentary. 3–4 preopercular spines, 3 opercular spines. Skin slimy, flesh bitter. Juveniles with only three light longitudinal bands. Coral reefs and tidal pools; solitary and shy, darting for cover at the least provocation. Red Sea and E. Africa to E. Indies, Philippines, Melanesia, Micronesia and Polynesia as far as Tahiti and Nukuhiva.

Subfamily *Anthiinae* Butterfly Perch, Sea Perch, Barbers
Structurally very closely allied to the *Epinephelinae*, but quite different in appearance and behaviour. Scales large, ctenoid; operculum with 2–3 spines. Head entirely scaly, or naked in front of eyes. Tail truncate to deeply forked, often with prolonged lobes. Pectoral and ventral fins often elongated, anterior dorsal spines produced into filaments in the ♂ of some species. Beautifully coloured, small to moderate predatory fishes of coral reefs and of deeper waters. Most shallow water species occur in small shoals which appear to station themselves by a particular coral outcrop. The males seem to be polygamous and most small schools consist of one dominant mature male and a number of females and possibly young males. In some species adult males differ consider-ably from the females and are very active and pugnacious, often displaying to their harem and to rival males by erecting their gorgeously coloured dorsal fins. A little known group which has yielded a number of recent discoveries.

### 612. ANTHIAS HUCHTI Bleeker 1857     Pl. 6
10 cm; D X/17; A III/7; L 1 34–40; tr 3–4/15. Variable in colour; ♂ may be grey violet with orange red fins. Coral reefs from S. and E. Africa to Indonesia and Melanesia.

### 613. ANTHIAS SQUAMIPINNIS (Peters) 1855     Pl. 6
12 cm; D X/17–18; A III/7–9; L 1 40–44; tr 2–3/14–17. A very variable and beautiful small fish and one of the commonest and most widespread of the group. Coral reefs from S. and E. Africa to the C. Indo-Pacific.

ALLIED SPECIES:
**614. ANTHIAS BIMACULATUS** Smith 12 cm. Dorsal spines and caudal lobes not produced. Violet red, with red head and dorsal fin and red bar from eye to pectoral base (probably ♂), or orange red above, golden yellow belly, dorsal and tail with dark irregular longitudinal streaks, especially on tail. East Africa.
**615. A. EVANSI** Smith 10 cm. Red, belly lilac. Some dark scaling on back. Dorsal and deeply lunate tail golden yellow. Pectorals red, ventrals lilac, anal yellow with red margin and lilac base. East Africa, rare.

### 616. PSEUDANTHIAS MANADENSIS (Bleeker) 1856
Crimson-banded Sea Perch
10 cm; D X/17–18; A III/7–8; L 1 40–45; tr 2–3/15–16. Tail crescent-shaped with lobes prolonged into free filaments. Rosy, darker above with 5 longitudinal

rosy-red bands on lower sides. Fins orange with blue margins. Coral reefs from
S. and E. Africa to the E. Indies and New Guinea.

ALLIED SPECIES:

**617. PSEUDANTHIAS KELLOGGI** J. & E. 20 cm. Red and white; rather deep
water; Hawaii.

**618. P. TAIRA** Schmidt 6 cm. Uniform salmon pink, eyes lilac, tail light orange.
South Japan.

### 619. HOLANTHIAS NATALENSIS (Fowler) 1925

62 cm; D X/17–18; A III/8–9; L I 50; a rather deep fish with convex profile,
elongated anterior dorsal rays and caudal lobes. Red mottled with golden yellow,
fins yellow. Rather deep water. So far known from Natal and Madagascar.

**620. HOLANTHIAS BORBONIUS** C. & V. 30 cm. Similar to 619, but 3rd dorsal
spine elevated, anterior dorsal rays less prolonged, profile of head not so convex. Bright
golden yellow with a bold network of red markings. Middle caudal rays red. Western
Indian Ocean.

OTHER SPECIES:

**621. NEMANTHIAS CARBERRYI** Smith 10 cm. First dorsal spines, ventrals and
tail lobes elongated. Red above, lilac below. A darker bar from snout to eye and to
pectoral base. Dorsal red, yellow posteriorly. Tail deeply crescentic, red with yellow
distal margin. In shoals. W. Indian Ocean.

**622. PTERANTHIAS LONGIMANUS** Weber 5 cm. General appearance of a
Cirrhitid (Hawkfish). Distinguished by 2 large round black spots at base of tail, one at
base of dorsal and one at base of anal. Malay Archipelago and Hawaii.

**623. PIKEA AURORA** J. & E. 20 cm. Red with longitudinal yellow lines on head,
dorsal, anal and tail. The only Hawaiian Serranid with 8 dorsal spines. Hawaii.

**624. CAESIOPERCA THOMPSONI** J. & E. 17 cm. Generally pinkish. Posterior
dorsal rays and outer caudal rays elongated. Deep water, Hawaii.

**625. ODONTANTHIAS FUSCIPINNIS** Jenkins 23 cm. Tail deeply forked,
3rd dorsal spine longest. Bright yellow. Hawaii.

**626. O. ELIZABETHAE** Fowler 17 cm. Similar to 625, but has a conspicuous white
bar on caudal peduncle and the 3rd and 4th dorsal rays prolonged. Hawaii.

**627. SAKURA MARGARITACEA** (Hilgendorf) 13 cm. Anterior dorsal rays and
outer caudal rays prolonged. Rosy red with pearly spots and a pearly line from corner of
mouth to pectoral base. A black blotch on dorsal when young. Taiwan and S. Japan.

**628. FRANZIA FASCIATA** Kamohara 8 cm. Bright orange with a broad mid-
lateral red stripe from edge of operculum to base of tail. A faint lilac line from corner of
mouth to pectoral base. Taiwan and S. Japan.

**629. LUZONICHTHYS ADDISI** Smith 75 mm. Slender, elongated. Spinous
dorsal and soft dorsal separate, tail forked. Red above, lilac below, outer caudal rays
blackish. Aldabra and Astove (Indian Ocean). See 630.

**630. L. MICROLEPIS** Smith 7 cm. Very similar to 629, but more slender, scales
smaller. Aldabra.

Subfamily *Diploprioninae*

Moderate sized marine fishes which differ from the *Epinephelinae* in having a
divided dorsal fin and a reduced number of fin spines. Scales small, ctenoid.
A single Indo-Pacific species.

### 631. DIPLOPRION BIFASCIATUM Cuvier & Valenciennes 1828     Pl. 6

Yellow Emperor, Double-banded Perch, Sebekah (Malay)

25 cm; D VIII; 12–15; A II/12–13; L I 68–70; tr 17–18/43–46. Coral reefs
from India and Ceylon to the E. Indies, China, Japan, Philippines, Melanesia
and Queensland.

Subfamily *Pseudochrominae* Dottybacks

Small, active, sometimes brightly coloured carnivorous fishes. Fin spines generally reduced, lateral line interrupted. A single dorsal fin. Anterior teeth caniniform. They usually shelter among coral branches when alarmed. Often in tidal pools.

### 632. PSEUDOGRAMMA POLYACANTHUS (Bleeker) 1856
One Spot Dottyback

7 cm; D VII/19–21; A III/16–17; L 1 22–28; tr 4–5/19–20. One flat preopercular spine. Spinous dorsal membranes deeply indented. Soft dorsal, anal and tail rounded. Lateral line interrupted below middle of soft dorsal and continued 6 scale rows lower down. Dark brown with darker reticulations and a round black spot on operculum. Coral heads from E. Africa to the Seychelles, E. Indies, Philippines, Micronesia, Melanesia, Polynesia and Hawaii.

One Spot Dottyback

OTHER SPECIES:

**633. APOROPS BILINEARIS** Schultz 15 cm. Superficially similar to 632. Lacks black ear-like marking on operculum. Phoenix, Marshall and Hawaiian islands.

**634. A. ALLFREEI** Smith 12 cm. Opercular spot lacking. Head with coarse dark vermiculations, body with broken dark vertical bars. Tail with dark margin. East Africa, Aldabra.

### 635. PSEUDOCHROMIS FUSCUS Müller & Troschel 1849

10 cm; D III/25–28; A III/14–15; L 1 24–34/8–10; tr 3/12–14. Soft dorsal and anal angular posteriorly. Tail rounded. Lateral line interrupted below dorsal, continued 4 scale rows further down. Brown to yellowish with dark scale centres forming horizontal rows of spots. Dorsal and anal with 6–7 pale irregular, sometimes broken lines. Ventrals blackish. Coral heads in the E. Indies, Philippines, Melanesia and N. Queensland.

### 636. PSEUDOCHROMIS NOVAE-HOLLANDIAE
(Steindachner) 1879

18 cm; D III/37; A III/20; L 1 42–43/12; tr 20. Variable: dark brown tinged with red, or head and thorax brilliant pink, remainder grey-green. A blue line below and behind eye, two blue marks on cheek. Dorsal and anal green with blue and yellow margin, a dark spot on spinous portion and small spots along base. Tail grey-green with an oblique red and blue band at margin of each lobe. A most beautiful small fish found on coral heads in N. Queensland.

*Pseudochromis novae-hollandiae*

ALLIED SPECIES:
**637. PSEUDOCHROMIS DUTOITI** Smith 10 cm. Head and body green, shading
to red on peduncle and tail. A blue line from snout to pectoral base; pectoral base blue,
opercular and preopercular margins blue; eye red. Paired fins orange, dorsal and anal
black with narrow blue margins. Tail red with oblique blue submarginal bars, one on
each lobe, edged distally with white, converging, but not meeting. East Africa, Aldabra,
India and Maldives.
**638. P. OLIVACEUS** Klunzinger 8 cm. Olive green with a red dot on each scale.
East Africa and Red Sea.
**639. P. TAPEINOSOMA** Bleeker 7 cm. Uniform brown. Dorsal and anal with darker
border and dark longitudinal bands. Tail with dark transverse bands. Central Indo-
Pacific.

### 640. DAMPIERIA LINEATA Castelnau 1875
25 cm; D II/25; A III/14; L 1 60/21; tr 4/17. Anal and dorsal prolonged
posteriorly, tail somewhat pointed. Orange brown. An incomplete blue ring
around eye, open in front. A series of oblique blue lines from eye and from
upper opercular edge to upper lip. Each scale with a black basal spot with blue
centre, forming about 16 lines from behind operculum to base of tail. 8–9
wavy longitudinal dark lines on dorsal and anal which are continued on tail.
Western Australia and Queensland.

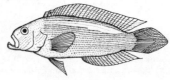

*Dampieria lineata*

ALLIED SPECIES:
**641. DAMPIERIA SPILOPTERA** (Bleeker) Dark red; each scale with a blue
spot; blue lines on cheeks and dorsal. Vertical fins with blue margin. New Guinea
E. Indies, Philippines, Taiwan and Ryukyu.
**642. LABRACINUS CYCLOPHTHALMUS** (Müller & Troschel) 10 cm.
Bright reddish purple with numerous narrow wavy blue lines on head and cheeks.
Fins mauve with narrow blue margins, dorsal with a pattern of dark red spots and lines.
Philippines.

Family PSEUDOPLESIOPIDAE **False Roundheads**
The family consists of two aberrant species which are intermediate in some
characters between the *Serranidae* and the *Plesiopidae*. Posterior portion of
lateral line absent, fin spines modified into soft, flexible, unbranched rays.

### 643. PSEUDOPLESIOPS TYPUS Bleeker 1858
50 cm; D 16/9–10; A 7/9; L 1 36; tr 16. Vertical fins and tail broadly rounded.
Body and fins pink. Dorsal and anal with a bright red submarginal line and pale
blue margin. Tail with a broad red border. Pupil ringed with red. Coral reefs
in the E. Indies, New Guinea and Queensland.

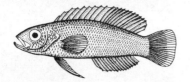

*Pseudoplesiops typus*

**644. CHLIDICHTYS JOHNVOELCKERI** Smith 1953
5 cm; D 23; A 14; Sc 54; tr 38. Lateral line absent. Dark violet. Eyes dark green, tail blackish purple, dorsal and anal with red margins. Known from 2 specimens taken from the mouth of *Aethaloperca rogaa* (Forskål) in Mozambique.

Family PLESIOPIDAE **Roundheads, Longfins**
A small family of carnivorous perch-like fishes confined to the coral reefs of the Indo-Pacific. Oblong and compressed, with large rounded heads. Scales rather large, lateral line interrupted: anterior portion follows dorsal profile, posterior portion mid-lateral, beginning opposite the 1st dorsal rays. Operculum and preoperculum scaly. Anal with 3 spines. Teeth villiform, but a few enlarged canines.

**645. PLESIOPS COERULEOLINEATUS** Rüppell 1840
=**P. MELAS** Bleeker 1849
Red-tipped Longfin
50 cm; D XI/6–7; A III/8; L 1 18–21/6–13; tr 2–3/8–10. Soft dorsal and anal pointed, tail rounded. Lower pectoral rays free, except at base. Black; dorsal edged with red, obliquely lined with blue at base. Anal lined with blue; tail with submarginal orange crescent. Pupil ringed with red. Tidal pools on coral reefs from the Red Sea and S. Africa to India, the E. Indies, Philippines, Melanesia, Queensland, Micronesia and Polynesia.

**646. PLESIOPS CORALLICOLA** Bleeker 1853
Ocellated Longfin
15 cm; D XII–XIII/6–7; A III/6–8; L 1 17–21/11–16; tr 3–4/8–10. Soft dorsal and anal pointed, tail round, lower pectoral rays free distally. Dark brown to black. A blue spot on most scales and a white-ringed dark ocellus on lower part of operculum. Tail black with white margin; dorsal black with a basal blue band on spinous portion; pectorals tipped with orange. Tidal pools in the E. Indies and Melanesia.

ALLIED SPECIES:
**647. PLESIOPS NIGRICANS** (Rüppell) 25 cm. Similar to 646, but ocellus absent. Throughout the Indo-Pacific including the Red Sea, but not in Hawaii.
**648. PARAPLESIOPS POWERI** Ogilby 20 cm. Purplish black with faint greyish cross-bands. A blue line from nostril to preopercular angle and a few blue spots on cheeks. Pectorals yellowish, other fins purple edged with blue. Queensland.
**649. CALLOPLESIOPS ALTIVELIS** (Steindachner) Blackish with numerous small white spots and a prominent white-ringed black ocellus at base of dorsal. Philippines.

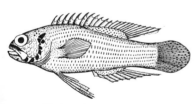

*Plesiops nigricans*

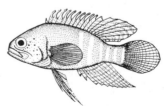

*Paraplesiops poweri*

**650. BARROSIA BARROSI** Smith 20 cm. Fins very broad, tail very large, pointed. Completely covered by small bluish spots. A round dark ocellus at extreme end of dorsal, near base. Western Indian Ocean.

**651. BELONEPTERYGION FASCIOLATUS** (Ogilby) 5 cm. Three lateral lines. D XVIII/6, A X/5. Under rocks in tidal pools. Queensland. Should probably be placed in the family *Acanthoclinidae*.

Family PRIACANTHIDAE
**Bullseyes, Catalufas (S. Africa), Miroir (Seychelles)**
A small family of small to moderate fishes usually found in rather deep water, although the young of some species come inshore at night at certain seasons. Bright red with large eyes, somewhat reminiscent of the *Holocentridae*, but they have much smaller scales and broader fins. The species are similar and difficult to identify.

**652. PRIACANTHUS HAMRUR** (Forskål) 1775                          **Pl. 6**
Lunar-tailed Bullseye, Miroir (S)
40 cm; D X/14–16; A III/14–16; L l 75–90; tr 9/38–45. Tail rounded when young, becoming emarginate with produced tips in old individuals. The young have a short preopercular spine. Deeper waters from the Red Sea and E. Africa to the E. Indies and Melanesia.

ALLIED SPECIES:
**653. PRIACANTHUS MACRACANTHUS** C. & V. 30 cm. Fins faintly spotted. East Indies, Philippines, Japan, Melanesia, Queensland.
**654. P. TAYENUS** Richardson 27 cm. Ventrals heavily spotted. East Indies, Melanesia, Queensland.
**655. P. CRUENTATUS** Lacépède 30 cm. Faint dark cross-bars on back. All fins and tail spotted. East Africa to the E. Indies, Melanesia and Polynesia as far as Hawaii. Also in the tropical Atlantic.

Family LOBOTIDAE **Triple Tail**
Moderate to large carnivorous fishes. Mostly inhabitants of brackish or fresh waters. Fins and tail broadly rounded. Juveniles look like dead leaves and float on their sides. Compressed and deep-bodied. A single lateral line. One species occurs in shallow coastal waters in all warm seas including the Atlantic.

**656. LOBOTES SURINAMENSIS** (Bloch) 1790
Jumping Cod, Triple Tail, Flasher
100 cm; D XI–XII/15–16; A III/11; L l 42–44; tr 9–10/16–18. Olive to brown, darker dorsally. Dusky spots along dorsal and anal base. Pectorals yellowish, other fins darker than body, edged with white. Very good sport and excellent eating.

Jumping Cod

Family LUTJANIDAE

Subfamily *Lutjaninae* Snappers, Sea-perch, Hussars, Bass, Opakapaka (Hawaii). A large group of active carnivorous fishes occurring in all warm seas. Mostly bottom dwellers which move in small schools and feed on small fishes and crustacea. Although a few species are poisonous in some areas, snappers are generally excellent eating and provide good sport; economically, they are among the most important fishes of the tropics. The majority are found on outer coral reefs, but a few species occur in tidal pools and lagoons, in brackish water near mangroves and in deeper offshore waters. More or less compressed and elongated, although a few species are deep-bodied. Scales small to moderate, ctenoid. Lateral line complete and continuous. Cheeks and operculum scaly. A single dorsal fin with well developed spines. Anal with 3 strong spines. Tail forked or truncate. Ventrals with a scaly axillary process. Outer teeth enlarged, conical; anterior teeth often large, caniniform. About 75 species recorded from the Indo-Pacific.

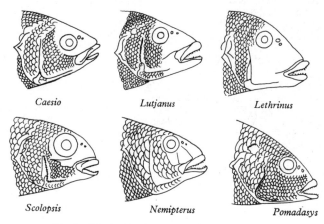

*Caesio*      *Lutjanus*      *Lethrinus*

*Scolopsis*      *Nemipterus*      *Pomadasys*

Heads of Lutjanidae (Adapted from Munro 1967)

**657. SYMPHORUS NEMATOPHORUS** (Bleeker) 1860

Chinamanfish, Threadfin Sea-perch                    **Pl. 7** (Juv.)

90 cm, 15 kg; D X/15–16; A III/9; L 1 49–55; tr 6/16. A deep groove in front of eye. Young, up to about 50 cm, as illustrated. Adults lose long dorsal filaments and are bright rosy red with irregular pale grey cross-bands on body. Poisonous if eaten at certain seasons. Coastal waters in the E. Indies, Philippines, Melanesia and Queensland.

**658. LUTJANUS EHRENBERGI** (Peters) 1869

23 cm; D X/12–13; A III/8; L 1 45–48; tr 6/16. Scale rows above lateral line parallel to it, those below, horizontal. Silvery with olive head and back. A large oval blackish spot above lateral line, below last spines and 1st rays of dorsal. Fins hyaline, tail yellow, dorsal with dusky tip. Sheltered beaches. East Indies and Melanesia. See 659.

### 659. LUTJANUS JOHNI (Bloch) 1792
John's Sea-perch, Gibelot (S)

37 cm; scale and fin counts as in 658; black blotch as in 658. Olive above, silvery, yellow or salmon on sides and cheeks, with brownish streaks on scale rows. Pectorals and ventrals pinkish, other fins yellow. Coastal waters throughout the Indo-Pacific, including the Red Sea and Queensland, but not in Hawaii. Difficult to distinguish from the following three species, especially in the water.

### 660. LUTJANUS FULVIFLAMMA (Forskål) 1775                    Pl. 7
Black-spot Sea-perch, Gibelot (Mauritius), Chemise (S)

35 cm. Fin counts as above, scale counts sometimes slightly higher. Scale rows above lateral line obliquely ascending. Similar to 659, but lacks brownish horizontal streaks. Black blotch mostly below lateral line, tail and dorsal sometimes with reddish margin. Coral reefs and mangrove creeks. Entire Indo-Pacific, excluding Hawaii.

### 661. LUTJANUS RUSSELLI (Bleeker) 1849
Moses Perch, Hublot (S)

42 cm; D X/14–15; A III/8; L 1 50; tr 7/16–17. Upper scale rows obliquely ascending. Reddish to greenish, sometimes with 6–7 oblique longitudinal stripes (3 in juveniles). Blackish blotch mostly above lateral line. Coral reefs and tidal pools from S. and E. Africa to the Seychelles, Ceylon, the E. Indies, Philippines, Melanesia and Queensland. See three preceding species.

### 662. LUTJANUS MONOSTIGMA (Cuvier & Valenciennes) 1828
One-spot Sea-perch, Chemise (Mauritius)

58 cm; D X/12–13; A III/8; L 1 46–54; tr 6–7/16–19; upper scale rows obliquely ascending. Yellowish with faint darker lines along scale rows. Black blotch small, rather diffuse, bisected by lateral line. Fins yellow. Coral reefs in the E. Indies, Philippines, China, Japan, Melanesia and Polynesia. See also 661, 660, 659 and 658.

### 663. LUTJANUS KASMIRA (Forskål) 1775                    Pl. 7
Yellow and Blue Sea-perch; Blue-banded Hussar, Madras (Seychelles, Mauritius)

38 cm; D X–XI/13–16; A III/8; L 1 48–51; tr 6–10/18–24. Upper scale rows obliquely ascending. Black lateral spot often absent, head pink or yellow; a most beautiful fish. Coral reefs throughout the Indo-Pacific. Although not recorded from Hawaii in the recent literature, it was seen by the author in the Honolulu fish market in March 1972. See 664.

ALLIED SPECIES:

### 664. LUTJANUS DUODECIMLINEATUS (C. & V.) 30 cm. Similar to 633, but numerous narrow blue lines on lower sides. Natal and Madagascar.

### 665. L. CARPONOTATUS Richardson 35 cm. Yellowish with brown longitudinal stripes. N.-W. Australia, Queensland and Fiji.

### 666. L. SEMICINCTUS Q. & G. 27 cm. Golden olive above, pinkish below. 7–8 reddish vertical bands on upper sides; a large black blotch at base of tail. Fins yellow. East Indies, Melanesia and Polynesia.

### 667. L. DECUSSATUS (C. & V.) 30 cm. Whitish with six longitudinal black bands on upper sides. A large blackish blotch at base of tail. Fins yellow. Ceylon, India, Maldives and Laccadives.

### 668. L. BOHAR (Forskål) 75 cm. Deep red to dark golden olive above, paler below. Two large pearly blotches below dorsal fins. Fins dusky, pink at base. Red Sea and E Africa to E. Indies and Melanesia.

**669. L. RIVULATUS** (C. & V.) 60 cm. Deeper, dorsal profile more convex than in most species. Brown above, pinkish on sides and below. Numerous narrow wavy blue lines on head. A whitish, black-ringed blotch on side in young. South and E. Africa to E. Indies, Melanesia, Polynesia and Queensland.

**670. L. RUFOLINEATUS** (C. & V.) 23 cm. Reddish brown with golden lines along scale rows. Sometimes a black lateral blotch. Fins yellow. India and Ceylon to E. Indies and Melanesia.

**671. L. WAIGIENSIS** (Q. & G.) 60 cm. Rosy to olive. Six or more golden lines along scale rows. Golden spots and irregular lines on head. Spinous dorsal with reddish margin. Soft dorsal and tail edged with white, other fins yellow. South and E. Africa to E. Indies, Melanesia, Queensland and Polynesia. Introduced to Hawaii.

**672. L. JANTHINUROPTERUS** (Bleeker) 75 cm. Olive with numerous yellow lines along scale rows. Head, dorsal and tail reddish. Dorsal and tail edged with black, other fins yellow. Juveniles with broad dark stripe from eye to base of tail. South and E. Africa to E. Indies, Melanesia and Queensland. *L. lemniscatus* (C. & V.) is probably the juvenile.

**673. L. LUNULATUS** (Mungo-Park) 25 cm. Reddish brown above, silvery below. Faint golden lines along scale rows. Pectorals and ventrals yellow, other fins reddish. Tail with broad blackish submarginal crescent. India, Ceylon, E. Indies and Melanesia.

**674. L. LINEOLATUS** (Rüppell) 37 cm. Purplish red above, golden below. Oblique golden lines above lateral line and horizontal pink lines below it. Mid-lateral line broader than others. Fins yellow. Red Sea and E. Africa to E. Indies and Melanesia.

**675. L. VITTA** (Q. & G.) 35 cm. Red to yellow with a wide blackish mid-lateral line from snout to tail base. Thin olive lines above mid-lateral line, yellow horizontal lines below it. Fins orange. Seychelles and India to E. Indies, Melanesia and Queensland.

**676. L. CHRYSOTAENIA** (Bleeker) 35 cm. Olive above, rosy below. Numerous yellowish horizontal stripes alternating with broader, darker bands. Fins hyaline, tail dark at base. East Indies, Melanesia, Queensland.

**677. L. LUTJANUS** Bloch 25 cm. Olive above, pink on sides, silvery yellow below. Dusky lines along scale rows. Fins pale yellow. Seychelles and India to E. Indies and Melanesia.

**678. L. BIGUTTATUS** (C. & V.) 28 cm. Yellowish grey above, paler below. A black stripe from eye to middle of tail and another from chin to end of anal base. Some pearly spots below dorsal. India, Ceylon, E. Indies.

**679. L. MALABARICUS** (B. & S.) 50 cm. Red with narrow yellow lines along scale rows and a broad brighter red stripe from snout through eye to dorsal origin. A purplish saddle on tail peduncle. Fins red. India and Ceylon to the E. Indies, Melanesia and Queensland.

**680. L. RANGUS** (C. & V.) 30 cm. Head green, back, upper sides and fins golden. Lower sides pale rose with golden lines along scale rows. Lips and eye orange red. South and E. Africa to C. Indo-Pacific.

**681. LUTJANUS SEBAE** (Cuvier & Valenciennes) 1828          **Pl. 7**
Red Emperor, Bourgeois (Mauritius, Seychelles)
105 cm, 22 kg; D XI/15–16; A III/10–11; L 1 48–57; tr 8/21–26. Adults have more rounded fins, lose the dark markings and develop whitish margins to the tail and fins. Entire Indo-Pacific, excluding Hawaii.

**682. LUTJANUS ARGENTIMACULATUS** (Forskål) 1775
Mangrove Jack, River Roman, Carpe (S)
90 cm; D X/13–14; A III/8–9; L 1 44–56; tr 6–7/17–19. Dark brown above, brick red on sides and below. Fins dark purplish brown. Coastal waters, often in mangrove creeks. Entire Indo-Pacific excluding Hawaii.

**683. LUTJANUS COATESI** Whitley 1934
Red Bass, Kelp Sea-perch
77 cm; D X/14; A III/9; L 1 50; tr 10/19. Dark red, darker above, paler below

with faint pink lines along scale rows. Dorsal scarlet, other fins reddish brown with blackish margins. Coral reefs in Melanesia and Queensland. Flesh poisonous at certain seasons.

ALLIED SPECIES:
**684. LUTJANUS GIBBUS** (Forskål) 60 cm. Uniform bright red with some yellow on upper lip, above eye and on pectoral base. Profile of snout concave in old individuals. Poisonous at certain seasons. Coral reefs throughout the entire Indo-Pacific excluding Hawaii.

### 685. LUTJANUS SANGUINEUS (Cuvier & Valenciennes) 1828
Blood Snapper, Tembola (E. Indies)
90 cm; D XI/13–15; A III/9–10; L 1 55–65; tr 12–20. Uniform blood red. Young with broad blackish band from eye to dorsal origin. Adults lose dark band and develop a conspicuous bump on top of head. A black saddle on caudal peduncle. A valued food fish. South and E. Africa to India and the E. Indies.

Blood Snapper

OTHER SPECIES:
**686. APRION VIRESCENS** C. & V. 100 cm. Tail forked with pointed lobes. Greenish or bluish, paler below, fins brownish. Good eating. South and E. Africa to the C. Indo-Pacific.
**687. SYMPHISANODON TYPUS** (Bleeker) 90 cm. Pectorals long, pointed. Tail forked, upper lobe produced. Rosy, paler below, with 6 longitudinal yellow bands. Entire Indo-Pacific including Hawaii.
**688. MACOLOR NIGER** (Forskål) 60 cm. Deep-bodied. Soft dorsal and anal pointed, pectorals long and falcate. Blackish above, white below. Several large white spots on upper sides. A black longitudinal stripe from operculum to lower lobe of tail. Head white, blackish on top with a broad black vertical band behind eye. White markings become indistinct in old specimens. Red Sea to the E. Indies, Philippines, Melanesia and Polynesia.

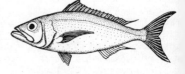

*Aphareus furcatus*

*Macolor niger*

**689. APHAREUS FURCATUS** (Lacépède) 60 cm. Tail deeply forked, last dorsal and anal rays prolonged. Steel blue above, silvery on sides and below. Deeper water throughout the Indo-Pacific including Hawaii.
**690. A. RUTILANS** C. & V. 90 cm. Similar to 689, but brick red. Deeper water throughout the Indo-Pacific including Hawaii.

**691. ETELIS CARBUNCULUS** C. & V. 90 cm. First dorsal spines and rays elevated, caudal lobes produced. Reddish above, silvery on sides and below. Inside of mouth red. Deeper water throughout the Indo-Pacific including Hawaii. See 692.

**692. E. MARSHI** (Jenkins) 60 cm. Similar to 691, but tail lobes not produced, inside of mouth pinkish. Sometimes a mid-lateral golden stripe. Deeper waters throughout the Indo-Pacific including Hawaii.

**693. PRISTIPOMOIDES ARGYROGRAMMICUS** (C. & V.) 120 cm. Rosy red above, silvery on sides and belly. Fins light red, dorsal yellow basally, tail with yellow margin. Throughout Indo-Pacific, not yet recorded in Hawaii.

**694. P. AMOENUS** (Snyder) 60 cm. Pinkish head, back and fins, sides yellow with irregular blue lines and specks. Scattered localities from the Kenya coast to Japan.

**695. TROPIDINIUS ZONATUS** (C. & V.) (= *Rooseveltia brighami* Seale) 50 cm. Rosy red with broad oblique yellow bands. Head red, tail and dorsal yellow. Throughout the Indo-Pacific including Hawaii, but nowhere abundant.

**PRISTIPOMOIDES SIEBOLDII** (Bleeker) (Kalikali, H) and **P. MICROLEPIS** (Bleeker) (Opakapaka, H) are both wide ranging red and silver species of considerable economic importance, especially in Hawaii.

Subfamily *Caesiodinae* Fusiliers, Bananafish, Pisang
Small marine fishes allied to the *Lutjaninae,* from which they differ in the presence of a bony projection on the intermaxilla, usually visible inside the mouth. Elegant, brightly coloured fishes which congregate in immense shoals, usually near rocky shores and coral reefs. Oval to elongated, rather strongly compressed. A single dorsal fin; fin spines rather weak. Lateral line complete, scales small; mouth rather small, tail deeply forked.

**696. CAESIO CUNING** (Bloch) 1791 **Pl. 7**
Red-bellied Fusilier
35 cm; D X/15; A III/11; L l 45–48; tr 6–8/13–16. Usually in large schools on outer reefs. Arabia, India, E. Indies, Philippines, Taiwan, Melanesia, Queensland and Polynesia. See 697.

ALLIED SPECIES:

**697. CAESIO ERYTHROGASTER** C. & V. 35 cm. Similar to 696, but scale count slightly higher, dorsal and pectorals pink. East Indies and Queensland.

**698. CAESIO LUNARIS** Cuvier & Velenciennes 1830 **Pl. 7**
32 cm. D X/13–14; A III/11; L l 48–57; tr 6–8/14–18. In large schools near coral reefs. East Africa to the E. Indies and Melanesia.

**699. CAESIO COERULAUREUS** Lacépède 1802 **Pl. 7**
Gold-banded Fusilier, Maquereau canal (S)
27 cm. D X/14–15; A III/11; L l 48–70; tr 7–8/11–16. The commonest and most widespread of all the fusiliers. Often in immense shoals, rather like sardines. Coral reefs from E. Africa to the E. Indies, Philippines, Melanesia and Queensland. Seen by the author in Fiji and Hawaii, though not recorded from those localities in the recent literature.

ALLIED SPECIES:

**700. CAESIO CHRYSOZONUS** C. & V. 25 cm. Dark blue above, white washed with red below. Two narrow red lateral bands, upper near dorsal profile, lower along lateral line. Fins yellow to orange, tail with black tips. East Africa to Ceylon, E. Indies, Melanesia and Queensland.

**701. C. PISANG** Bleeker 18 cm. Purplish above, white washed with red on sides and belly. A narrow pearly stripe from above eye to base of tail and another below dorsal base. Dorsal purplish with red submarginal line. Other fins red, tail tipped with black. East Africa to E. Indies and Melanesia.

**702. C. XANTHONOTUS** Bleeker 20 cm. Back and dorsal yellow, lower sides and belly pink. A broad mid-lateral blue band from eye to base of tail, tapering towards rear. Eye red. Tail yellow with pink margin, paired fins pink, anal pink with red margin. East Africa to Seychelles, E. Indies and Melanesia. See 703.

**703. C. PULCHERRIMUS** Smith 26 cm. Similar to 702, but top of head blue, dorsal blue with yellow margin. Rare; Aldabra, Seychelles.

## 704. PARACAESIO XANTHURUS Bleeker 1869

50 cm; D X/9; A III/8; L 1 72; tr 9/18. Greenish blue, posterior part of upper sides and caudal peduncle golden. Pectorals reddish. South and E. Africa to the Seychelles and E. Indies.

ALLIED SPECIES:

**705. PARACAESIO PEDLEYI** McCulloch & Waite 37 cm. Blue and yellow. Queensland and Lord Howe island.

**706. PTEROCAESIO CAPRICORNIS** Smith 18 cm. Back blue, sides and belly pink. Fins red, dorsal with some blue at base. Tail tipped with black. East Africa and Seychelles.

**707. P. DIAGRAMMA** (Bleeker) 25 cm. Similar to 706, but a narrow yellow stripe from above eye to base of tail and another along dorsal profile. East Indies, Queensland and recently found in the Seychelles.

**708. P. TILE** C. & V. 30 cm. Head to below eye, back to pectoral base and upper ⅔ of caudal peduncle blue; remainder pink. A golden line from above eye to base of upper tail lobe. Fins red; tail blue with red margins. East Africa to C. Indo-Pacific and Polynesia as far as the Society islands.

**709. GYMNOCAESIO GYMNOPTERUS** (Bleeker) 15 cm. Very elongated. Blue above, very pale pink below. A narrow golden mid-lateral line from eye to base of tail. A 2nd much narrower golden line immediately above and parallel to mid-lateral line. All fins and tail pink. East Africa, Seychelles, E. Indies.

Subfamily *Nemipterinae* Monocle-bream and Threadfin Bream
A large group of small and moderate-sized reef fishes which differ from other subfamilies of the Lutjanidae in having no teeth on the palate. The genera *Scolopsis, Parascolopsis* and *Ctenoscolopsis* have a strong backward directed spine below the eye. Solitary shallow water fishes, often among coral heads.

## 710. CTENOSCOLOPSIS CILIATUS (Lacépède) 1802
Saw-jawed Monocle-bream
20 cm; D X/9; A III/7; L 1 43–45; tr 3½/12–13. Brown above, silvery below. A yellowish-white stripe along back from eye to base of last dorsal spines; young with a second stripe below it. Fins yellow to reddish. Coastal waters in the E. Indies and Melanesia.

## 711. SCOLOPSIS VOSMERI (Bloch) 1792                    Pl.
White-cheeked Monocle-bream
25 cm; D X/9–10; A III/7–8; L 1 38–41; tr 4/11–14. Shallow coastal water from Mozambique to E. Africa, India and the E. Indies.

ALLIED SPECIES:

**712. SCOLOPSIS MARGARITIFER** (C. & V.) 25 cm. Olive above, yellowish below. Scale centres pearly; two pearly lines from snout to eye. Dorsal and pectoral olive, tail and other fins yellow. East Indies, Melanesia, Queensland and Polynesia.

**713. S. LEUCOTAENIA** (Bleeker) 15 cm. Olive brown above, yellowish below. A paler mid-lateral stripe edged above and below with blackish purple, from eye to upper part of peduncle. Fins yellow or orange, dorsal with a prominent anterior black blotch. India to E. Indies and Melanesia.

## 714. SCOLOPSIS BILINEATUS (Bloch) 1793 **Pl. 7**
Two-lined Monocle-bream

20 cm; D X/9; A III/7; L 1 44–46; tr 3½/14–15. Andaman islands, E. Indies, Philippines, Ryukyu, Melanesia, Queensland and Polynesia.

ALLIED SPECIES:

**715. SCOLOPSIS TRILINEATUS** Kner 20 cm. More slender than most species. Grey; two blue lines across forehead. Three oblique pearly lines on upper sides. Fins pink, dorsal edged with orange, anal with blue. East Indies, Philippines, Melanesia, Polynesia.

## 716. SCOLOPSIS FRENATUS (Cuvier & Valenciennes) 1830 **Pl. 7**
Zaneau (Seychelles)

30 cm; D X/9; A III/7; L 1 46–48; tr 5/46–47. Seychelles to the E. Indies and Philippines.

ALLIED SPECIES:

**717. SCOLOPSIS PHAEOPS** (Bennett) 26 cm. Olive above, yellowish below. A white line below dorsal base; a blue spot at pectoral axil and a bluish line from there to the eye and thence to upper jaw as a wide bright blue band. India, E. Indies, Melanesia.

**718. S. PERSONATUS** (C. & V.) 27 cm. Greyish green with a wide yellow or white stripe from eye to base of tail. Snout dark; a bright blue bar between eyes. East Indies, Melanesia, Queensland.

**719. S. XENOCHROUS** Günther 22 cm. Olive brown; a narrow bluish line below dorsal base. Five rows of olive spots and a large yellowish white blotch on flanks. A short oblique white bar with black edges above pectoral. Fins pinkish, tail yellow at centre, lobes tipped with red. Melanesia.

**720. S. GHANAM** Forskål 18 cm. Dark olive above, yellowish below. A yellow line from eye to end of spinous dorsal and one from eye to opercular edge, followed by an arched dark line edged with white which continues to tail base. Tail and fins light orange. East Africa to E. Indies and Melanesia.

**721. S. BIMACULATUS** Rüppell 30 cm. Greenish, paler below. A black blotch on side from below 7th dorsal spine, tapering towards tail base. Dorsal pale orange, tail yellowish with red margin, other fins hyaline. Red Sea and W. Indian Ocean.

**722. S. CANCELLATUS** (C. & V.) 22 cm. Olive brown, paler below, with a pattern of whitish lines which cross each other at right angles on the upper sides. Fins light brown to yellowish, dorsal with blackish anterior spot. East Indies, Melanesia and Queensland.

**723. S. TEMPORALIS** (C. & V.) 42 cm. Greenish with longitudinal yellow lines above lateral line and a broad bronzy mid-lateral stripe. Oblique yellow and lilac stripes on flanks; 3 blue lines on head. Fins yellowish. East Indies, Melanesia, Queensland and Fiji. See 724.

**724. S. DUBIOSUS** Weber 30 cm. Similar to 723, but upper lines brown, lower lines yellow on whitish background. A purplish bar across snout from eye to eye. A brown streak across pectoral base. Melanesia, E. Indies, Philippines, Taiwan, Polynesia.

**725. S. MONOGRAMMA** (C. & V.) 30 cm. Blue-grey above, whitish below. Faint brownish yellow longitudinal lines on upper side and a dozen similar oblique lines below lateral line. A wide yellow bar across snout, from eye to eye. Dorsal purplish with yellow margin, other fins yellowish. India, E. Indies, Philippines, Taiwan, Melanesia, Polynesia.

**726. S. INERMIS** (T. & S.) 30 cm. Red above, silvery on sides and below. Three broad vertical red bands. Dorsal pale reddish, tail light orange, other fins white. South Japan and Taiwan.

**727. S. TOSENSIS** Kamohara 27 cm. Back light red, sides and belly silvery. Two bright yellow mid-lateral lines. Dorsal white edged with light red and with an oblique yellow band across spinous portion. Tail white with narrow pink margin, other fins white. Japan and Taiwan.

**728. PARASCOLOPSIS ERIOMMA** (Jordan & Richardson) 1909
Rosy Monocle-bream                                                              **Pl. 7**
30 cm; D X/9; A III/7; L I 35; tr 3/11. Shallow coastal waters. Mozambique, Kenya, Ceylon, India and Japan. Rare.

**729. MONOTAXIS GRANDOCULIS** (Forskål) 1775
Large-eyed Sea-bream, Levovangan (E. Indies)
75 cm; D X/10–11; A III/9; L I 45–47; tr 4–5/13–15. A thick-set fish with massive head. Tail forked, fins rounded. Blue-grey, scales with silvery centres. Vertical fins orange, paired fins and area surrounding eye yellowish. An important food fish in some areas. Coral reefs throughout the Indo-Pacific, including the Red Sea, Queensland and Hawaii.

**730. SYMPHORICHTHYS SPILURUS** (Günther) 1874
Blue-lined Sea-bream
32 cm; D X/14–16; A III/8–10; L I 50–51; tr 10–12/18–23. A very deep-bodied fish; profile of head convex; anterior dorsal and anal rays elevated and usually prolonged into long free filaments. Brownish or olive yellow with undulating longitudinal blue lines. A dark saddle surrounded by a pale line on caudal peduncle and an orange band across top of head. Fins orange brown. Coral reefs in the E. Indies, Philippines and Melanesia.

Large-eyed Sea-bream                                    Blue-lined Sea-bream

Naked-headed Sea-Bream

**731. GNATHODENTEX AUROLINEATUS** (Lacépède) 1803
Gold-lined Sea-bream, Carandine (S)
45 cm; D X/10; A III/9; L I 70–78; tr 6/16–19. Four anterior canines in upper jaw, 6 in lower. An external serrated ridge on maxilla. Silvery with 8 golden longitudinal stripes. A yellow spot below end of dorsal. Vertical fins reddish, paired fins yellow or rosy. South and E. Africa to the E. Indies, Melanesia and Polynesia as far as Tahiti and the Marquesas.

**732. GYMNOCRANIUS GRISEUS** (Temminck & Schlegel) 1843
Naked-headed Sea-bream
50 cm; D X/10; A III/10–11; L I 46–50; tr 6/15–18. A deep-bodied fish with a

somewhat humped dorsal profile. Tail forked, dorsal and anal rounded, paired fins sharply pointed. Anterior teeth of outer series fang-like. Silvery brown with indistinct darker vertical bands when young. South and E. Africa to the E. Indies, Melanesia and Japan.

ALLIED SPECIES:

**733. GYMNOCRANIUS AUDLEYI** Ogilby 35 cm. Similar to 732, but irregularly spotted. Dorsal and tail with narrow red margins. Queensland.

**734. ODONTOGLYPHIS TOLU** (Cuvier & Valenciennes) 1830
Notched Butterfly-bream
25 cm; D X/9; A III/7; L 1 48–50; tr 4/11–12. More slender than previous species. Canines in upper jaws only. Tail forked. Rosy with 4–5 longitudinal yellow bands. Fins rosy, dorsal spines tipped with orange. East Indies and Melanesia.

**735. NEMIPTERUS PERONII** (Cuvier & Valenciennes) 1830
26 cm; D X/9–10; A III/7; L 1 48–50; tr 3½/12–13. 6 anterior canines in each jaw. Slender, tail forked. Rosy above, silvery on sides and belly. 2–3 broad yellow stripes from opercular edge to tail base. Fins rosy. Seychelles to the E. Indies and Melanesia.

*Nemipterus peronii*

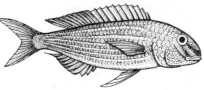

ALLIED SPECIES:

**736. NEMIPTERUS HEXODON** (Q. & G.) 26 cm. Rosy with longitudinal yellow bands. A red spot ringed with yellow at origin of lateral line. Fins orange, dorsal and anal with blue-edged yellow bands. East Indies, Melanesia and Queensland.

**737. N. CELEBICUS** (Bleeker) 20 cm. Rosy with one yellow stripe from snout to base of tail. Fins rosy, dorsal and anal with yellow median bands. East Indies and Melanesia.

**738. N. DELAGOAE** Smith 25 cm. Rosy with narrow golden lines along scale rows. Rear of dorsal tipped with dark red, tail edged with dark red, anal white with 3 irregular yellow bands. Mozambique coast.

**739. N. JAPONICUS** (Bloch) 25 cm. Red with 8 yellowish lines along scale rows. Dorsal and anal pink with median yellow band. India, Ceylon, E. Indies, Taiwan, Japan.

**740. N. FURCOSUS** (C. & V.) 28 cm. Rosy with bright red and yellow spot below origin of lateral line. 5–6 longitudinal yellow bands and 3 silvery ones on lower sides. Dorsal and anal pink with yellow basal band. India and Ceylon.

**741. N. BLEEKERI** (Day) 20 cm. Ventral long, nearly reaching anal. Red with yellow longitudinal bands. A blue spot on operculum. India and Ceylon.

**742. PENTAPODUS SETOSUS** (Cuvier & Valenciennes) 1830
Paradisefish, China Fish, Blue-banded Whip-tail
20 cm; D X/9; A III/7; L 1 50–52; tr 2½/17–18. Tail deeply forked with upper lobe prolonged into a long filament. Brownish lavender above, pale blue below. 3 dark blue bars across snout from eye to eye. A dark blue mid-dorsal line and a dark blue line broadly edged with yellow from eye to base of tail where it

doubles back to reach rear of anal base. Tail pale pink; dorsal light yellow with a pale blue submarginal line. East Indies, Melanesia and Queensland. See 747.

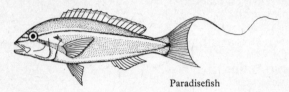

Paradisefish

ALLIED SPECIES:

**743. PENTAPODUS CANINUS** (C. & V.) 28 cm. Tail deeply forked. Dark brown above, white below. Three yellow longitudinal lines from eye; upper two to dorsal base, 3rd wider, to base of tail. A dark bar across pectoral base. East Indies and Melanesia.

**744. P. MICRODON** (Bleeker) 20 cm. Both caudal lobes sometimes produced. Bright yellow; a red spot at pectoral base; oblique blue lines on head and 2 curved longitudinal blue bands reaching base of tail. Fins yellow, dorsal with a row of blue spots. Lower lobe of tail red. East Indies and Melanesia.

**745. P. NEMURUS** (Bleeker) 75 cm. Both caudal lobes produced into filaments. Brown with 2 longitudinal lateral yellow bands. Fins yellow, tail purplish. East Indies and Melanesia. See 746.

**746. P. HELLMUTHI** (Bleeker) 15 cm. Tail forked, but lobes not prolonged. Rosy above, silvery below. A broad brownish mid-lateral band edged with yellow or orange. Probably the juvenile of 745.

**747. P. VITTA** Q. & G. Probably a synonym of 742.

**748. P. CURTUS** (Guichard) 23 cm. Seychelles.

**749. P. DUX** (C. & V.) Madagascar and Mozambique.

Subfamily *Pomadasyinae* Grunters, Javelin-fish

A small group of moderate sized shallow water fishes of all warm seas. Some species penetrate fresh water. Body oblong, compressed; scales moderate, ctenoid; lateral line complete, mid-lateral; a single dorsal fin. Mouth rather small, teeth villiform, palate toothless, canines absent. Two pores on anterior part of chin and a longitudinal groove under the chin. No opercular spines. Some species emit grunting noises when caught, hence the popular name. Javelin-fish refers to the large anal spine. Good eating.

**750. POMADASYS HASTA** (Bloch) 1790
Common Javelin-fish, Trumpeter, Silver Grunter (S. Africa)
45 cm; D XII–XIII/13–15; A III/6–8; L 1 45–52; tr 4–5/12–14. Silvery grey; 4–5 rows of dark spots along scale rows. Dorsal with 2–3 rows of dark spots, old specimens with basal spots only. South and E. Africa to the E. Indies, Melanesia and Queensland.

Common Javelin-fish

ALLIED SPECIES:

**751. POMADASYS MACULATUS** (Bloch) 45 cm. Silvery; nape and back with incomplete vertical blackish bands, often breaking into spots. A large black spot on spinous dorsal. Other fins yellowish with blackish margins. South and E. Africa to Ceylon, E. Indies, Melanesia and Queensland.

**752. P. ARGYREUS** (C. & V.) 20 cm. Silvery with a dark blotch on operculum when young. Fins brownish yellow. East Indies, Melanesia, Queensland.

**753. P. OLIVACEUS** (Day) 30 cm. Olive-grey, head purplish, sides silvery. A large blackish area on operculum, bordered anteriorly with yellow. South and E. Africa to Ceylon and the E. Indies.

**754. P. OPERCULARIS** (Playfair) 100 cm. Silvery with numerous small black spots. A large black spot on operculum and a row of large black spots on dorsal. Good eating and good sport. Coastal waters from S. and E. Africa to the E. Indies and Queensland.

**755. P. GUORAKA** Russell 45 cm. Brown above, silvery on sides, often with a faint dark mid-lateral stripe. South and E. Africa to the E. Indies.

## 756. RHONCISCUS STRIDENS (Forskål) 1775

45 cm; D XII/13–16; A III/7–8; L 1 51–57; tr 7–8/13–14. Silvery, brown above. A curved dark line from eye to end of dorsal base. A broader dark band from operculum, above pectoral base, to middle of tail. A third rather faint line from eye, meeting mid-lateral line below end of dorsal. A prominent black blotch on upper angle of operculum. South Africa to Red Sea and India.

ALLIED SPECIES:

**757. RHONCISCUS ANAS** (C. & V.) 50 cm. 7–8 rather diffuse dark longitudinal lines. East Africa and Madagascar. See 758.

**758. R. FURCATUS** (B. & S.) 38 cm. Similar to 757. Six longitudinal bands. Ceylon and India to the E. Indies.

Subfamily *Plectorhynchinae* (= *Gaterininae*) Sweetlips, Thick-lipped Grunters. Moderate-sized omnivorous fishes confined to the coral reefs of the Indo-Pacific. Often included in the *Pomadasyinae* from which they differ in lacking the median groove under the chin, in having 6 pores behind the lower lip and in developing very thick fleshy lips when adult. Subject to extreme changes in coloration as they mature. Juveniles with brilliant colours and bold markings, swim with a peculiar hesitant motion and are favourite aquarium subjects. Adults excellent eating and economically important. The large genus *Plectorhynchus* is referred to as *Gaterin* by some authors. A difficult group in which the young and adult stages of some species have probably been wrongly associated.

## 759. SPILOTICHTHYS PICTUS (Thunberg) 1787          Pl. 8 (Juv.)
## =DIAGRAMMA PICTUM

Painted Sweetlips, Capitaine-du-Port (S), Morwong (Queensland)

75 cm; D IX–X/21–26; A III/6–8; L 1 57–70; tr 17–19/30–32. Juvenile up to 18 cm as illustrated; as the fish grows, the dark stripes split, becoming more numerous and closely spaced and the ground colour becomes progressively more drab. Adult with truncate tail and very thick lips; grey with numerous faint small blackish spots. Coral reefs from E. Africa to the E. Indies, Philippines, Melanesia and Queensland.

132 SWEETLIPS

**760. PSEUDOPRISTIPOMA NIGRA** (Cuvier & Valenciennes) 1830
=. **LECTORHYNCHUS CRASSISPINA** Bleeker 1877
Brown Sweetlips, Marmite (S)
62 cm; A XIII–XIV/13–18; A III/7–8; L 1 45–50; tr 10–11/18–21. A deep
notch at jui ction of spinous and soft dorsal. Tail rounded at all ages; dark
brown, fins almost black. South and E. Africa to the E. Indies, Melanesia and
Queensland.

**761. PLECTORHYNCHUS CHAETODONTOIDES** Lacépède 1800
Harlequin Sweetlips **Pl. 8**
45 cm; D XI–XII/18–19; A III/8; L 1 52–59; tr 11–14/18–24. Juvenile and
adult. East Indies, Philippines, Melanesia. *P. punctatissimus* Playfair 1867,
known from Zanzibar, Queensland and Tahiti, is probably the adult of
*P. chaetodontoides.*

**762. PLECTORHYNCHUS SCHOTAF** (Forskål) 1775
Grey Sweetlips, Marmite (S)
90 cm; D XII–XIII/18–23; A III/7–8; L 1 55–60; tr 12/20. Grey, with orange
spots when young. Edge of lips and preopercular margin scarlet. Red Sea and
E. Africa to the E. Indies, Philippines, Melanesia and Queensland. See 763.

ALLIED SPECIES:
**763. PLECTORHYNCHUS SORDIDUS** Klunzinger 30 cm. Like 762, but dorsa
spines longer. Western Indian Ocean.

**764. PLECTORHYNCHUS CINCTUS** (Schlegel) 1843
60 cm; D XII/15; A III/7; L 1 90–95; tr 17/23. Deep-bodied; tail rounded
Silvery grey with two oblique dark bands, one from behind nape to behind an
below pectoral base; one from spinous dorsal base to below end of dorsa
Numerous blackish spots on sides, dorsal and tail. Ceylon, India, E. Indies
Taiwan and Japan.

**765. PLECTORHYNCHUS ORIENTALIS** (Bloch) 1792 **Pl. 8** (Juv
40 cm; D XII–XIV/17–21; A III/7–8; L 1 80–85; tr 13/23–25. Young, up t
20 cm as figured. Adult yellow above, white on sides, with 3–4 black longitudin
stripes. Median stripe continued on tail which is rounded. Dorsal yellow wit
wide black basal band, pectorals black with pale margins. East Africa, Se
chelles, E. Indies and Melanesia.

**766. PLECTORHYNCHUS LINEATUS** (Linnaeus) 1758 **Pl.**
Yellow-banded Sweetlips
35 cm; D XII–XIII/18–22; A III/6–8; L 1 49–59; tr 13–14/24–25. Ceylo
India, E. Indies and Melanesia. *P. diagrammus* (Linnaeus) is probably a synonyr

**767. PLECTORHYNCHUS GOLDMANNI** (Bleeker) 1853 **Pl.**
Diagonal-banded Sweetlips
50 cm; D XII–XIII/19–20; A III/7; L 1 55–58; tr 13/26. The number
bands tends to increase with age. East Indies and Melanesia.

**768. PLECTORHYNCHUS CUVIERI** (Bennett) 1830 **Pl.**
Straight-banded Sweetlips
50 cm; D XII–XIII/17; A III/7–8; L 1 52–62; tr 11/25. Dark lines increase
number with age, being only three in juveniles. Ceylon and India to the
Indies and Melanesia.

**769. PLECTORHYNCHUS POLYTAENIA** (Bleeker) 1852
Ribboned Sweetlips
40 cm; D XII–XIII/21–22; A III/7; L 1 50–60; tr 13/24. Tail rounded in
young, truncate in adults. Brownish yellow with 5–9 narrow greyish longitudinal stripes edged with blackish. Number of stripes increases with age. Fins
yellow, with darker stripes in juveniles. Body stripes continued on tail in
juveniles only. East Indies, Philippines, Taiwan and Melanesia.

**770. PLECTORHYNCHUS CELEBICUS** Bleeker 1873
50 cm; D XIII/18–20; A III/6–7; L 1 53–58; tr 12–13/20. Grey above, silvery
on sides. 7–8 longitudinal yellow bands, sometimes breaking into spots. Fins
orange yellow, tail emarginate in adults. East Indies and Melanesia.

**771. PLECTORHYNCHUS ALBOVITTATUS** (Rüppell) 1835    **Pl. 8**
20 cm. Scale and fin counts as above. Red Sea and E. Africa to the E. Indies and
Philippines.

**772. PLECTORHYNCHUS GATERINUS** (Forskål) 1775    **Pl. 8**
40 cm; D XII–XIII/19–20; A III/7–8; L 1 70; tr 14/18. East Africa from the
Red Sea to Mozambique; also in Madagascar and the Persian Gulf. Common
and a favourite food fish on the Kenya coast.

ALLIED SPECIES:
**773. PLECTORHYNCHUS RETICULATUS** (Günther) 37 cm. Olive brown
with a pattern of dark reticulations on upper parts of body. China, E. Indies, Australia.
**774. P. FLAVOMACULATUS** (C. & V.) 60 cm. Grey with close-set narrow longitudinal orange lines on head and cheeks and orange spots on body and dorsal; orange
markings becoming smaller and duller with age. South and E. Africa, Seychelles and
E. Indies.
**775. P. HARRAWAYI** Smith 105 cm. Grey, with extremely thick lips. Dorsal
orange. Red Sea, E. Africa, Seychelles, Aldabra.
**776. P. PLAGIODESMUS** Fowler 75 cm. Grey with 10–12 oblique transverse
orange red lines alternating with dark lines. Lips orange. Western Indian Ocean.
**777. P. PLAYFAIRI** Pell 50 cm. Grey with 4–5 oblique light grey cross-bars on head
and body. Western Indian Ocean.
**778. P. FAETELA** (Forskål) 50 cm. Olive grey above, silvery below with 8 yellowish
longitudinal lines, some breaking into spots. Lines fewer and darker in juveniles. Red
Sea and E. Africa to E. Indies and Philippines.

Subfamily *Lethrininae*
Emperors, Pig-face Bream, Naked-headed Snappers, Scavengers
Moderate sized carnivorous fishes of shallow coastal waters. Deep bodied and
somewhat compressed, with pointed heads and small mouth. Most of head and
cheeks naked, but operculum scaly. A single dorsal fin. Lateral line complete.
Ventrals with axillary process; tail emarginate. Lips thick; lateral teeth conical
or molar-like, anterior teeth caniniform. Palate toothless. Over 20 Indo-Pacific
species, one species in W. Africa. Mostly excellent eating. The species are very
similar structurally and difficult to identify when dead or preserved, but easily
distinguished in life by colour and pattern.

**779. LETHRINELLA MINIATA** (Bloch & Schneider) 1801
Long-nosed Emperor, Capitaine-longue-gueule (S)
80 cm; D X/9; A III/8; L 1 44–47; tr 4/15–16. Olive above, paler below, 2–3
oblique bluish lines on snout. Most scales with bluish centres. Fins olive with
reddish margins, tail often purplish. Young with irregular silvery blotches on

sides. Red Sea and E. Africa to the E. Indies, Melanesia, Queensland and Polynesia.

ALLIED SPECIES:

**780. LETHRINELLA NEMATACANTHA** (Bleeker) 25 cm. Second dorsal spine prolonged as free filament. Grey green with brown wavy lines on head and dark spot on side, below lateral line, opposite middle of pectoral. Indistinct, irregular darker cross-bands. Dorsal and tail rosy, other fins yellowish. East Indies, Melanesia, Queensland.

**781. L. VARIEGATA** (C. & V.) 60 cm in the Indian Ocean, smaller elsewhere. Young with irregular dark reticulated pattern, adults with 5–7 narrow dark cross-bars. Lips pink. Tail purple in adults, red-edged in young. South and E. Africa to E. Indies, Melanesia and Queensland.

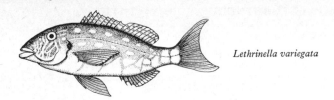

*Lethrinella variegata*

**782. L. MICRODON** (C. & V.) 30 cm. Olive with blue lines from eye, across snout and operculum. Blue spots on scales. Dorsal and tail banded, inside of mouth orange. India, E. Indies, Melanesia.

**783. L. CONCHYLIATA** Smith 75 cm. Silvery with irregular dark markings. Lips, edge of operculum and pectoral base red. Dorsal yellow banded with red. Western Indian Ocean.

**784. L. XANTHOCHEILUS** (Klunzinger) 75 cm. Yellowish brown above, yellow laterally, pinkish below. Head darker. Lips orange yellow, opercular margin and pectoral base red. Fins yellow, soft dorsal and margin of tail red. Red Sea and Western Indian Ocean.

**785. LETHRINUS NEBULOSUS** (Forskål) 1775                    **Pl. 7**
Spangled Emperor, Eclair (S), Morwong (Queensland)
75 cm; D X/9; A III/8; L 1 45–48; tr 5/14–16. As figured, but variable; blue markings may be more extensive. Coral reefs throughout the entire Indo-Pacific including the Red Sea and Queensland, but not in Hawaii.

ALLIED SPECIES:

**786. LETHRINUS KALLOPTERUS** Bleeker 50 cm. Silvery with dark green head and back; tail, soft dorsal and anal with red margins, paired fins rosy or orange. East Africa to Seychelles, E. Indies, Philippines, Melanesia, Queensland and Samoa.

**787. L. RETICULATUS** C. & V. 38 cm. Olive brown, paler below. Juveniles with 7–8 diffuse, irregular cross-bands, often forming a reticulate pattern. A dark spot opposite pectoral tip. Head with 2–3 brown bands above eye; a red mark at upper corner of operculum. Fins pink, dorsal with orange red margin. Ceylon to E. Indies, Philippines, Taiwan, Melanesia, Micronesia, Polynesia and Queensland.

**788. L. HYPSELOPTERUS** Bleeker 42 cm. Olive with purple edge to scales. Head deep violet or violet-brown with orange bar on preorbital. A large blackish spot above pectoral base. Maxilla and inside of mouth red. Fins reddish violet. Indonesia, Philippines and Melanesia.

**789. L. MAHSENA** (Forskål) 42 cm. Olive above, whitish below, head much darker Inside of mouth red. Tail yellow, dorsal and anal bright red, paired fins pink. Entire Indo-Pacific including the Red Sea and Queensland, but not in Hawaii.

**790. L. FLETUS** Whitley 45 cm. Grey green, head and back darker, mottled with olive brown. Bright blue lines radiating from eye across snout and preorbital. Fins pale pink with darker spots and lines. New Guinea and Queensland.

**791. L. RHODOPTERUS** Bleeker 55 cm. Dark olive grey above, paler on sides. A large dark blotch above pectoral tip. Fins yellow or olive, dorsal with rosy margin. Inside of mouth red. East Indies, Melanesia, Queensland. *L. glyphodon* Günther is a form of this species lacking the lateral blotch.

**792. L. ORNATUS** C. & V. 45 cm. Blue green above, with 5–6 longitudinal yellow stripes. Dorsal and tail red with yellow margins, other fins yellow. Eyes, lips and opercular edge red. East Indies, Melanesia, Queensland.

**793. L. OBSOLETUS** (Forskål) 60 cm. Head and back brown, paler below. 3–4 orange red longitudinal stripes. Ventrals hyaline, other fins orange red. Red Sea and E. Africa to E. Indies and Melanesia.

**794. L. LENTJAN** (Lacépède) 30 cm. Greenish grey, paler below, often with pale scale centres. Head brownish mauve. Tail mauve, other fins yellowish or pinkish. Edge of operculum bright red. Common in the entire Indo-Pacific excluding Hawaii.

**795. L. CAERULEUS** C. & V. 45 cm. Silvery yellow; head dark green, becoming violet on operculum. A red spot above eyes, lips red. Pectorals yellow, other fins hyaline with red margins. Western Indian Ocean.

**796. L. BORBONICUS** C. & V. 25 cm. Back olive, sides paler, head very dark olive, pink under chin. Ventrals yellow, other fins and tail orange red. Red Sea and W. Indian Ocean.

**797. L. CROCINEUS** Smith 60 cm. Greenish above, yellow on sides and below, head dark olive. Lips orange. Ventrals and anal hyaline, other fins and tail bright yellow. Western Indian Ocean.

**798. L. ENIGMATICUS** Smith 30 cm. Head bright green, lips blue. Body dull silvery with 7–9 yellow vertical bars which cease at and are connected with a yellow mid-lateral stripe. Fins pinkish, tail and soft dorsal with yellow margins. Bird Island (Seychelles) only.

**799. L. HARAK** (Forskål) 45 cm. Grey green. A large oblong mid-lateral blackish blotch above pectoral tip. Pectorals brown, ventrals hyaline with orange tip, dorsal and anal red; tail red with pale transverse bars. Entire Indo-Pacific excluding Hawaii.

**800. L. SANGUINEUS** Smith 50 cm. Olive above, whitish on sides and below. Each scale with a scarlet margin. Opercular margin and pectoral base scarlet. Ventrals hyaline with some red; other fins and tail red. Western Indian Ocean.

**801. L. CHRYSOSTOMUS** (Richardson) 90 cm. Dark grey with 9–10 irregular whitish cross-bands on body. Some vermilion markings around eye and a prominent red spot at pectoral base. Fins and tail blackish, dorsal with a narrow red margin. Queensland.

**802. L. HAEMATOPTERUS** (Schlegel) 26 cm. Olive brown, head and back darker. Each scale with a dark central spot, forming longitudinal dark lines. Eye yellow. Mauritius, E. Indies, Philippines, Taiwan, Japan, Micronesia and Polynesia.

**803. L. MAHSENOIDES** C. & V. 36 cm. Pale green with a white spot on each scale. Cheeks with numerous white spots. Edge of operculum red, fins and tail greenish. Eye yellow. Red Sea and E. Africa to Madagascar, Ceylon, E. Indies, Philippines, Taiwan and Polynesia.

**804. L. RAMAK** (Forskål) 30 cm. Olive, paler below. Two broad, indistinct yellowish bands from operculum to base of tail. Fins brownish. Entire Indo-Pacific, excluding Queensland and Hawaii.

**805. L. FRENATUS** C. & V. 23 cm. Olive with a large squarish blotch between pectoral and lateral line. Faint irregular dark cross-bars. Scales of upper part of body with a bluish spot. Inside of mouth orange. Dorsal with red margin, pectorals pink, other fins dusky. Ceylon, E. Indies, Philippines.

Family THERAPONIDAE

A small family of small to medium-sized carnivorous fishes confined to the Indo-Pacific. They are found in shallow marine and brackish waters and some species are restricted to fresh water. Scales ctenoid, small to moderate. Lateral line complete, consisting of scales which are smaller than the others. Operculum and cheeks scaly. Two strong opercular spines. A continuous dorsal fin with a notch between spinous and rayed portions. Dorsal spines can be depressed into a groove. Ventrals without axillary process. Teeth villiform. Some species grunt when caught. Edible, but of little economic importance.

### 806. HELOTES SEXLINEATUS (Quoy & Gaimard) 1824
Six-lined Perch

25 cm; D XII/10–11; A III/10–11; L 1 80–87; tr 12/19–20. Tail slightly emarginate. Bluish green above, silvery on sides and below. 4–6 dark longitudinal bands, the middle one from snout through eye to tail base. A large blackish blotch on shoulder. Distal half of dorsal blackish. Tail with basal, median and marginal transverse bands. Estuarine waters in the E. Indies, Melanesia and N. Australia.

### 807. PELATES QUADRILINEATUS (Bloch) 1790
Trumpeter Perch

20 cm; D XII/10; A III/9–10; L 1 68–73; tr 12–14/23. Greenish brown above, silvery on sides and below; marked like 806, but tail unmarked, dorsal with an anterior dark blotch. River mouths and brackish water in India, Ceylon, E. Indies, Philippines, Taiwan, Japan, Melanesia, Queensland and Fiji.

ALLIED SPECIES:

**808. PELATES OXYRHYNCHUS** (Schlegel) 25 cm. Similar to 806 and 807, but diffuse intermediate bands present between main stripes. Tail with several horizontal dark bars. East Indies, Philippines, Taiwan, Japan, Fiji.

### 809. EUTHERAPON THERAPS (C. & V.) 1829
Banded Grunter

20 cm; D XII/10; A III/8–9; L 1 45–49; tr 7–8/14–15. Four longitudinal bands, the topmost mid-dorsal. A dark anterior blotch on spinous dorsal and 2 smaller ones on soft dorsal; a dark blotch in middle of anal. Tail forked with 2 oblique dark bars on each lobe. Bays and estuaries from E. Africa to Ceylon, the E. Indies, Philippines, Taiwan, Melanesia and Queensland.

### 810. THERAPON JARBUA (Forskål) 1775
Crescent Bass, Tiger Bass

25 cm; D XI–XII/10; A III/8–9; L 1 76–99; tr 14–16/23–25. Silvery with 3 slightly oblique dark longitudinal lines. A large black spot on anterior part of spinous dorsal. Tail with 3 horizontal dark lines, the central one being a continuation of the lower body line. Tips of tail blackish. Bays and estuaries, sometimes penetrating rivers. Entire Indo-Pacific excluding Hawaii.

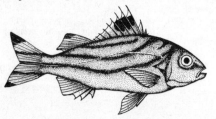

Crescent Bass

ALLIED SPECIES:
**811. THERAPON KNERI** Bleeker 25 cm. Body and tail with indistinct dark spots the size of pupil. Spinous dorsal, ventrals and front of anal blackish. Fiji and Polynesia.
**812. AUTISTHES PUTA** (C. & V.) 17 cm. Very similar to 809, but much more slender. Mid-lateral band reaches middle of tail margin. 2–3 strong preopercular spines. Ceylon, E. Indies, Philippines, Melanesia and Queensland.
**813. MESOPRISTES CANCELLATUS** (C. & V.) 25 cm. 5–6 indistinct dark saddles on back. Three indistinct longitudinal dark lines more or less broken into spots. Fins and tail unmarked. East Indies and Melanesia.
**814. M. ARGENTEUS** (C. & V.) 28 cm. Uniform silvery, juveniles with 3–5 narrow dark bands. Lobes of tail rounded. South and E. Africa. Madagascar, India, E. Indies, Philippines, Melanesia and Queensland. Introduced to Fiji.
**815. AMPHITHERAPON CAUDOVITTATUS** (Richardson) 20 cm. Body and dorsal with numerous small black spots. A prominent broad black subapical bar on each lobe of tail. Melanesia and N. Australia.

Family SPARIDAE **Silver Bream, Sea-bream, Porgies**
Moderate-sized carnivorous fishes which differ from the foregoing families in their molar-like teeth which are used for crushing crustacea. Mostly S. African, but a few species range throughout the Indo-Pacific. Red or silvery, deep-bodied and compressed. Scales large, ctenoid. Lateral line complete, with enlarged scales near its origin. Cheeks and operculum scaly. A single dorsal fin. Second anal spine enlarged, tail emarginate. Pectorals long and pointed; ventrals with scaly axillary process. Front teeth enlarged, caniniform. Palate toothless. Excellent eating.

### 816. ARGYROPS SPINIFER (Forskål) 1775
Redfin (S. Africa), Steamboat Bream (Q.), Long-spined Snapper
60 cm; D XI–XII/10–11; A III/8; L 1 49–53; tr 8/17. Deep-bodied and compressed, dorsal profile humped. First 5 dorsal spines prolonged into long free filaments. Tail emarginate. Silvery with 6 faint pinkish vertical bars which are much more distinct in the young. Lips and opercular margin pink. Tail and dorsal filaments pinkish, other fins whitish. Uncommon, usually around sunken shoals and reefs. Red Sea, E. and S. Africa to Ceylon, India, the E. Indies and Queensland.

ALLIED SPECIES:
**817. ARGYROPS FILAMENTOSUS** (C. & V.) 38 cm. Similar to 816, but profile of head more blunt, only 1 dorsal spine prolonged; generally more pinkish on back and sides, vertical bars absent. South and E. Africa, India.

### 818. RHABDOSARGUS SARBA (Forskål) 1775
Tarwhine, Silver Bream
45 cm, said to attain 12 kg in S. Africa. D XI/13–14; A III/11–12; L 1 62–65; tr 8/13. Tail forked. Bluish head and back, silvery on sides, belly bright yellow. Several golden stripes from operculum to base of tail. Eyes, fins and tail yellow. Red Sea, E. and S. Africa, Seychelles, Ceylon, E. Indies, Philippines, Japan, Taiwan, Melanesia, Australia.

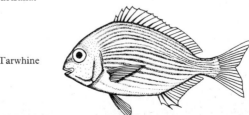

Tarwhine

### 819. ACANTHOPAGRUS BERDA (Forskål) 1775
### =MYLIO BERDA
Black Bream, Pinkey Bream
75 cm; D XI/11–12; A III/8–9; L 1 46–54; tr 4/11–12. Tail forked, pectorals
very long. Generally blackish, but individuals from open waters silvery. Young
olive with dark lines along scale rows. A black spot at pectoral base. Occurs
sparingly in most of the Indo-Pacific including the Red Sea and Queensland,
but not Hawaii.

### 820. ACANTHOPAGRUS BIFASCIATUS (Forskål) 1775
50 cm; D XI/13; A III/10; L 1 49; tr 5/12. Silvery with a black vertical bar
across top of head, through the eyes, to the corners of the mouth. A 2nd black
bar across nape in front of dorsal, along edge of operculum, ending at lower
opercular edge. A mid-dorsal black band from upper lip to dorsal base, crossing
the 2 vertical bars. Dorsal and tail yellow with black margins, pectorals yellow,
ventrals and anal hyaline with black margins. South Africa to the Red Sea,
India and E. Indies.

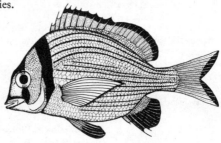

*Acanthopagrus bifasciatus*

ALLIED SPECIES:
### 821. ACANTHOPAGRUS LATUS (Houttuyn) 45 cm. Similar to 820, but lacks
the black bars on head. Ceylon, E. Indies, Taiwan, Japan.

OTHER SPECIES:
### 822. DIPLODUS SARGUS (L.) 40 cm. Silvery with a large black blotch on caudal
peduncle. Fins yellowish, old adults almost black. East Africa, S. Africa and W. Africa.
### 823. D. TRIFASCIATUS (Rafinesque) 45 cm. Young bright yellow, adults silvery.
A blackish vertical bar on head, through eye, 3–4 very wide blackish bars on body and
one on caudal peduncle. East, S. and W. Africa.
### 824. CHRYSOBLEPHUS LATICEPS (C. & V.) 45 cm. Coppery red, occasion-
ally blue, with a large white patch behind eye and a white saddle below spinous dorsal.
South Africa, Madagascar, Mauritius.
### 825. C. ANGLICUS (Gilchrist & Thompson) 105 cm. Deep bodied; profile of head
humped above eye, nearly vertical and slightly concave above mouth. Silvery pink;
dorsal and anal yellow, tail and pectorals pink, ventrals whitish. East Africa.

## Family GERRIDAE Silver-biddies, Silver-bellies
Small silvery fishes of shallow sandy areas, found in all warm seas. Some species
enter fresh water. Often in large schools, they feed on minute marine organisms.
Allied to the family Leiognathidae and included in that family by some authors.
Compressed, elongated to oval, with large thin scales. Cheeks and operculum

scaly. Lateral line complete; a single dorsal fin, dorsal and anal scaly at base. Tail forked, ventrals with axillary process. Mouth small, protractile, forming a long downward directed tube when protruded. Teeth small and sharp, palate toothless. Good eating when fresh, much used for bait.

**826. GERRES FILAMENTOSUS** Cuvier & Valenciennes 1829
Spotted Silver-biddy, Kapas-kapas (E. Indies)
25 cm; D IX/10–11; A III/7–8; L 1 45–48; tr 5–6/12–13. Second dorsal spine prolonged into a very long free filament. Bluish above, silvery on sides; 8–9 vertical series of large bluish spots. Fins yellow, dorsal with blackish margin. Common throughout the Indo-Pacific excluding Hawaii. *G. punctatus* C. & V. 1830 and *G. macracanthus* Bleeker 1854 are probably synonyms.

Spotted Silver-biddy

ALLIED SPECIES:

**827. GERRES OBLONGUS** C. & V. 30 cm. Second dorsal spine moderately prolonged. Plain silvery, purplish olive above. Young with faint cross-bars. Most of the Indo-Pacific excluding Queensland and Hawaii.

**828. G. ABBREVIATUS** Bleeker 23 cm. Second, 3rd and 4th dorsal spines prolonged, but not free. Greenish above, silvery below. Several distinct dark lines along scale rows. Ceylon, E. Indies, Melanesia, Queensland. *G. roppi* Barnard 1927 from Natal is probably a synonym.

**829. G. KAPAS** Bleeker 17 cm. Spinous dorsal slightly elevated, with blackish margin. Adults unmarked, young with irregular dark blotches. Seychelles, E. Indies, Melanesia, Philippines, Micronesia, Polynesia. See 830.

**830. G. ACINACES** Bleeker 25 cm. Similar to 829, but dorsal profile of snout concave, tail lobes much longer, scales smaller. South and E. Africa to E. Indies and Melanesia.

**831. G. POETI** C. & V. 1830 20 cm. Front of dorsal elevated, tail rather short. Deep bodied, dorsal profile somewhat humped at dorsal origin. Fin spines robust. Plain silvery. South and E. Africa, Seychelles, E. Indies, Melanesia. Probably a synonym of *G. oyeana* (Forskål) 1775.

**832. G. OYEANA** (Forskål) 1775 23 cm. L 1 35–38. Similar to 831. Most of the Indo-Pacific excluding Queensland and Hawaii.

**833. G. MACROSOMA** Bleeker 25 cm. L 1 40–43. Similar to 831 and 832, but scales smaller, tail longer. Madagascar, E. Indies, Taiwan, Melanesia, Micronesia, Polynesia.

**834. G. ARGYREUS** (B. & S.) 18 cm. L 1 45–46. Tip of spinous dorsal blackish. Seychelles to E. Indies, Melanesia and Queensland.

**835. G. OVATUS** Günther 25 cm. L 1 36–40. Posterior part of ventrals golden yellow. Australia.

**836. GERREOMORPHA SETIFER** (H.-B.) 13 cm. Ten dorsal spines. Silvery with 4–5 faint dark cross-bands. Fins bright yellow. Ceylon, India, Maldives, Laccadives.

**837. PENTAPRION LONGIMANUS** (Cantor). Anal fin very long, with 5–6 spines. Should probably be placed in the family Leiognathidae. India and Ceylon.

Family MULLIDAE
### Red Mullet, Surmullets, Goatfish, Capucin, Rouget (S)

A large family of small to moderate bottom feeding shallow water fishes of all warm seas. Usually seen in pairs or in small parties. Brightly coloured and easily recognised by the pair of fleshy sensory barbels under the chin. Excellent eating and considered a delicacy in some Mediterranean countries despite the numerous small bones. They do not take bait and are usually caught in traps or gillnets. Oblong; scales large, ctenoid. Lateral line complete, slightly arched. Head blunt, cheeks and operculum scaly. Two widely separated dorsal fins. Mostly red or yellow; some species very variable and capable of startling colour changes in response to circumstances or mood.

**838. UPENEUS TRAGULA** Richardson 1846                    **Pl. 9**
Bar-tailed Goatfish
35 cm; D VII–VIII; I/7–8; A I/6–7; L 1 30–32; tr 2–3/6. Shallow coastal waters. South and E. Africa to the Seychelles, Ceylon, India, the E. Indies, Taiwan, Japan, Melanesia and Queensland.

**839. UPENEUS VITTATUS** (Forskål) 1775                    **Pl. 9**
Yellow-banded Goatfish
30 cm; D VIII; I/8; A I/6–7; L 1 32–36; tr 3/6–7. As figured, but variable, some individuals being more brownish or reddish. Shallow coastal waters in the entire Indo-Pacific excluding Hawaii. See 840.

ALLIED SPECIES:
**840. UPENEUS SULPHUREUS** C. & V. 30 cm. Similar to 839, but only 2 lateral yellow stripes. Tail not banded. Entire Indo-Pacific excluding Hawaii.
**841. U. ARGE** J. & E. 23 cm. Similar to 839 and 840. Two yellow stripes: one from snout through eye to base of tail and one from angle of mouth to base of tail. First dorsal fin hyaline with 2 series of dark dots, 2nd with 5 dark transverse lines; tail with 6–7 dark transverse bars on each lobe. Entire Indo-Pacific including Hawaii, but not in Queensland.
**842. U. BENSASI** (Schlegel) 20 cm. Back dark brown; sides golden, more or less speckled and blotched with red, belly white. First dorsal orange with an indistinct wavy red transverse band. Pectorals pinkish, other fins and tail yellowish with transverse series of dark red spots on the rays. South and E. Africa, E. Indies, Taiwan, Japan, Micronesia and Polynesia as far as Tahiti.
**843. U. TAENIOPTERUS** C. & V. 30 cm. Back reddish, belly white. Both dorsals with 3 brown longitudinal bands. Tail with a large triangular red spot and 6 oblique brown bars across each lobe. Ceylon and India.

**844. MULLOIDICHTHYS AURIFLAMMA** (Forskål) 1775                    **Pl. 9**
Golden-banded Goatfish, Weke-ula (H)
40 cm; D VII; I/8; A I/6–7; L 1 33–38; tr 3/7. Variable. Lateral stripe may be pale yellow, orange, or even red. Cheeks may be spotted with yellow or orange. Fins and tail may be hyaline, pink, yellow, orange or red. Entire Indo-Pacific including Queensland and Hawaii.

**845. MULLOIDICHTHYS PFLUGERI** (Steindachner) 1900                    **Pl. 9**
60 cm. Fin and scale counts as for 844. Usually in rather deep water. Hawaii.
ALLIED SPECIES:
**846. MULLOIDICHTHYS SAMOENSIS** (Günther) 32 cm. Olive above, silvery below. A broad yellow stripe from snout through eye to tail base; often a narrower yellow stripe above it and sometimes several below it. A conspicuous blackish spot between pectoral tip and lateral line. Tail yellow, other fins yellowish or pinkish. Entire Indo-Pacific including Hawaii, but not Queensland.

**847. M. VANICOLENSIS** (C. & V.) 30 cm. Back pale olive brown, sides yellowish to orange, silvery white below. Iris orange; fins uniform pale yellowish, tail with dark margin. East Indies, Philippines, Taiwan, Ryukyu, Melanesia, Micronesia and Polynesia.

**848 PARUPENEUS BIFASCIATUS** (Lacépède) 1802
36 cm; D VIII; I/8; A I–II/6; L 1 28; tr 2–3/6–7. Purplish brown to red above, with paler scale centres; paler below. Three diffuse, variable blackish saddles, one below 1st dorsal, one below 2nd dorsal, one on caudal peduncle. Fins reddish brown, 2nd dorsal and anal with yellowish spots. Most of Indo-Pacific including Hawaii, but not Queensland. See 849.

**849. PARUPENEUS MULTIFASCIATUS** Quoy & Gaimard 1824 **Pl. 9**
30 cm; very variable and similar to 848, but may be distinguished by the presence of a dark saddle *between* the 2 dorsal fins. Hawaii.

**850. PARUPENEUS TRIFASCIATUS** (Lacépède) 1802
Five-barred Goatfish
25 cm; D VIII; I/8; A I/6–7; L 1 27–30; tr 2/6–7. Olive to blue-grey above, paler washed with red or violet below. Five dusky saddles, 1st before spinous dorsal, 2nd below spinous dorsal, 3rd below dorsal interspace, 4th below front half of soft dorsal, 5th on caudal peduncle, the 2nd and 5th being wider than the others. A brown blotch behind eye sometimes extended through eye to snout. Fins mottled dusky and yellow, 2nd dorsal and anal with yellow stripes. Ceylon and India to the E. Indies and Melanesia.

**851. PARUPENEUS BRANDESII** (Bleeker) 1851
30 cm. Red and gold. Several blue lines from eye to snout and blue spots on head and caudal peduncle. A large yellow patch below 2nd dorsal preceded by a diffuse blackish saddle and followed by a similar such saddle. First dorsal, pectorals and ventrals orange. Second dorsal and anal yellow with 3–4 bluish lines; tail yellow, outer rays red. East Africa, Seychelles, E. Indies and Philippines.

**852. PARUPENEUS BARBERINOIDES** (Bleeker) 1852
25 cm. Back reddish brown, sides paler red anteriorly, yellowish posteriorly. A narrow blackish mid-dorsal stripe to end of 2nd dorsal; a broader blackish stripe from snout through eye to below anterior part of 2nd dorsal. A black spot on lateral line just beyond end of 2nd dorsal, preceding a yellowish patch. A large blackish triangular area covering lower part of operculum and pre-operculum, surrounding pectoral base, joining end of mid-lateral stripe and ending abruptly as a straight line from beginning of 2nd dorsal base to a point midway between ventral base and beginning of anal. Dorsal fins with bluish lines. Tail yellow with lower lobe edged with blackish; pectorals orange, ventrals purple-red. East Indies and Melanesia.

**853. PARUPENEUS MACRONEMUS** (Lacépède) 1802 **Pl. 9**
Long-barbelled Goatfish
35 cm; D VIII; I/8; A I/6–7; L 1 29–31; tr 2–3/6. As figured, but ground colour and extent of dark markings variable. South and E. Africa, E. Indies and Melanesia.

**854. PARUPENEUS BARBERINUS** (Lacépède) 1802 **Pl. 9**
Dash and Dot Goatfish
50 cm; D VIII; I/8; A I/6; L 1 28–30; tr 3/6. As figured, but variable, sometimes darker. Shallow coastal waters. Entire Indo-Pacific excluding Hawaii.

ALLIED SPECIES:

**855. PARUPENEUS INDICUS** (Shaw) 40 cm. As figured, but ground colour variable, sometimes much darker; lateral yellow area always conspicuous. Entire Indo-Pacific excluding Hawaii. **Pl. 9**.

**856. P. CYCLOSTOMUS** (Lacépède) 38 cm. Bright rosy red, paler below, washed with orange on caudal peduncle. 4–5 golden stripes along lower scale rows from behind pectoral base. Several narrow purplish lines alternating with yellow lines, radiating from eye, anterior ones reaching snout. Fins red with faint yellow lines, tail red edged with orange. South and E. Africa to the E. Indies and Melanesia.

**857. P. CHRYSEREDROS** (Lacépède) 23 cm. Bright yellow, base of scales blue. A series of narrow longitudinal blue lines on head, some radiating from eye. A prominent brick-red saddle on caudal peduncle. Paired fins yellow, tail yellow with blue rays, 1st dorsal yellow with blue spines; anal and 2nd dorsal yellow with blue longitudinal lines. East Africa, Seychelles, E. Indies, Polynesia and Hawaii.

**858. P. LUTEUS** (C. & V.) 30 cm. Head and back red with darker scale margins, sides and belly pinkish to yellowish. Body scales with a golden spot. Four narrow horizontal blue lines across head and cheeks. Fins pinkish, soft dorsal with 3–4 yellow bands. East Indies, Melanesia and Polynesia as far as Tahiti.

**859. P. JANSENI** (Bleeker) 20 cm. Uniform rosy red, paler below. Fins rosy and yellow, soft dorsal with a faint dark median band. East Indies and Melanesia.

**860. P. SPILURUS** (Bleeker) 32 cm. Red with 3 olive yellow curved stripes from snout to below dorsal. A large black spot on caudal peduncle, preceded by a large yellow blotch. Known from various scattered localities: Red Sea, Andaman islands, Japan, Fiji and Queensland.

**861. PARUPENEUS PORPHYREUS** Jenkins 1902          **Pl. 9**
37 cm. Apparently dimorphic; ground colour red or slaty blue, both colours often represented in the same small school. Black spot preceded by white spot very conspicuous and diagnostic. Shallow water. East Africa, Seychelles, Samoa, Fiji, Hawaii.

ALLIED SPECIES:

**862. PARUPENEUS FRATERCULUS** (C. & V.) 45 cm. Similar to 861, but white spot absent, black saddle larger. A blue line from upper lip to eye. South and E. Africa, Ceylon, E. Indies and Polynesia as far as Tahiti.

**863. P. PLEUROTAENIA** (Playfair) 20 cm. Similar to 862 and treated as its juvenile by some authors, but black saddle absent or smaller, blue line prolonged behind eye, most scales on upper sides, starting from pectoral tip, with a blue basal dot. East Africa to Natal.

**864. P. PLEUROSPILUS** (Bleeker) 35 cm. Back reddish brown, snout bright rosy red, sides golden, belly yellowish white. Eye red. Three blue lines from snout to eye, middle one continued to tail base as a rather diffuse, broad blue stripe. Traces of a second blue stripe from below opercular angle. A dark red spot between the two blue stripes, behind pectoral. Fins pinkish orange, soft dorsal with 2 bluish lines, tail with 5 faint reddish cross-bars on each lobe. East Africa to the E. Indies. See 865.

**865. P. PLEUROSTIGMA** (Bennett) 30 cm. Very similar to 864, but dark red spot further back, below interdorsal space. Most of Indo-Pacific including Hawaii, but not in Queensland.

**866. P. CINNABARINUS** (C. & V.) 25 cm. Bright orange red. A large purplish blotch on operculum. Silvery scale centres forming 4 lines, 2 above lateral line, 2 below. Fins reddish with yellow spines and rays. Upper tail lobe orange, lower lobe red. Ceylon and India, E. Indies and Polynesia as far as Bora Bora.

**867. P. CHRYSONEMUS** (J. & E.) 22 cm. Red, silvery pinkish on sides and below. Paired fins and 1st dorsal red. Tail yellow, 2nd dorsal and anal yellow with 3–4 darker longitudinal lines. Hawaii.

**868. P. TAENIATUS** (Kner) 12 cm. Reddish brown above, much paler on sides and below. A pale stripe from eye to upper part of caudal peduncle. A 2nd pale stripe from operculum above pectoral base to tail base. Fins unmarked. Fiji and S. China.

**869. P. SIGNATUS** (Günther) 45 cm. Red, clouded with brown on back; a dusky band from operculum to below end of soft dorsal. A large black saddle preceded by a pink blotch on caudal peduncle. Philippines, Japan, Queensland, Lord Howe island, Fiji.

**870. PARUPENEUS SEYCHELLENSIS** (Smith) 1963                    **Pl.9**
25 cm  Differs from other species in having 6+18 gillrakers. Seychelles only, where it is very common.

Family SCIAENIDAE
**Croakers, Drummers, Kingfish, Jewfish (A), Kabeljou (S. Africa), Corvinas (Mozambique)**
Predatory fishes found in the coastal waters of all warm seas, but absent from oceanic islands; especially well represented and numerous in Australian and S. African waters. Fierce and very active predators of sandy shores which often ascend rivers in pursuit of their prey. Excellent sport and good eating if not too large. Called croakers or drummers because of their ability to produce loud drumming noises under water by contracting and expanding their swimming bladders. Also called jewfish (corruption of dewfish) because of the beautiful silvery grey colour of some species. Robust, compressed and oblong. Scales thin and adherent. Lateral line complete and somewhat arched. Cheeks and operculum scaly, operculum with 2 flat spines. A single dorsal fin, usually notched between spinous and rayed portions. Anal short based, with 1 or 2 spines. Tail rounded. Teeth villiform, outer and anterior ones often enlarged.

**871. SCIAENA DUSSUMIERI** (Cuvier & Valenciennes) 1833
25 cm. D X/I/23–26; A II/7; L 1 50–52; tr 6–7/16–17. Dark coppery brown, paler below; fins reddish brown, spinous dorsal tinged with black; ventrals yellow. South and E. Africa, Ceylon, E. Indies and Melanesia.

ALLIED SPECIES:
**872. SCIAENA MACROPTERA** (Bleeker) 23 cm. Tail wedge-shaped. Silvery grey, speckled with black. India and Ceylon to E. Indies and Melanesia.
**873. S. SINUATA** (Day) 50 cm. 9–10 oblique dark stripes, the lower ones almost horizontal. South and E. Africa to India.

**874. JOHNIUS DUSSUMIERI** (Cuvier & Valenciennes) 1830
20 cm; D X/I/27–32; A II/7–8; L 1 48–50; tr 5/10–12. Tail wedge-shaped. Greenish grey above, silvery below, speckled all over with brown. A black mark on operculum and a blackish spot in pectoral axil. Fins dusky, dorsal black. Ceylon, India, E. Indies and Melanesia.

ALLIED SPECIES:
**875. JOHNIUS BELENGERI** (C. & V.) 30 cm. Dark grey, a black spot on operculum, unpaired fins black. East Indies and Melanesia.
**876. J. ANEUS** Bloch 23 cm. Tail rounded. Silvery grey, white below. Paired fins and anal yellowish, other fins tipped with grey. India and Ceylon.
**877. J. COIBOS** (H.-B.) 90 cm. Tail rounded in young, wedge-shaped in adults. Silvery with paler lines along scale rows. A dark blue mark on operculum. Spinous dorsal black, soft dorsal grey, other fins yellow. India and Ceylon.
**878. J. OSSEUS** (Day) 18 cm. Grey-brown above, white below. Operculum bluish black. India and Ceylon.

**879. J. MACULATUS** B. & S. 30 cm. Silvery grey with gold wash. Five broken black bands on back. India and Ceylon.

**880. PSEUDOSCIAENA PAMOIDES** Munro 12 cm. Brown, paler below. A dusky blotch on operculum and dusky speckles all over. Gulf of Papua.

**881. P. SOLDADO** (Lacépède) 75 cm. Green above, grey laterally, white below. Distal margin of fins dark, ventrals white. South and E. Africa, India, E. Indies, Melanesia and Queensland.

**882. P. SINA** (C. & V.) 25 cm. Brown above, silvery washed with gold below. Spinous dorsal black, other fins grey. South and E. Africa to India, E. Indies and Melanesia.

**883. P. AXILLARIS** (C. & V.) 26 cm. Silvery, purplish above. A black spot in pectoral axil. Spinous dorsal black. India, Ceylon, E. Indies and Melanesia.

**884. P. GOLDMANNI** (Bleeker) 19 cm. Brownish above, silvery white below. Spinous dorsal dusky, other fins brownish. East Indies and Melanesia.

**885. P. CARUTTA** (Bloch) 30 cm. Head and back purplish, sides and belly golden. Spinous dorsal darker. Ceylon and India, E. Indies, Queensland.

**886. P. DIACANTHUS** (Lacépède) 150 cm. Operculum with 2 spines. Greyish brown above, silvery below, head purplish, fins dotted with black. Ceylon, India, E. Indies, Queensland.

**887. PAMA PAMA** (Hamilton-Buchanan) 1822

150 cm; D X/I/40–45; A II/7; L l 47–55; tr 9/8. Tail wedge-shaped. Light brown above, whitish below; golden and purplish reflections on head. Distal half of dorsal and tail grey, remainder of fins yellow. Estuaries in India, E. Indies and Melanesia.

**888. OTOLITHUS ARGENTEUS** Cuvier & Valenciennes 1830

Silver Teraglin

80 cm; D X/I/27–31; A II/7; L l 48–54; tr 7–8/9–12. A pair of large anterior canines on each jaw. Tail wedge-shaped. Silvery, darker above, with bluish and pinkish reflections. A dark patch on operculum. Anal and paired fins orange. Coastal waters and river mouths in Ceylon, India, E. Indies, Melanesia and Queensland. Excellent eating.

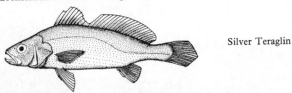

Silver Teraglin

ALLIED SPECIES:

**889. OTOLITHUS MACULATUS** C. & V. 45 cm. Grey above, golden below; 5–6 rows of black spots on body, extending to tail. Ceylon, India and E. Indies.

**890. O. RUBER** (B. & S.) 75 cm. Brownish red above, silvery gold below. Fins yellow, soft dorsal and anal with grey margin, spinous dorsal edged with black. South and E. Africa to India, Ceylon and the E. Indies.

Family SILLAGINIDAE **Whiting, Smelts, Pescadinhas (Mozambique)**
A small family of small fishes of sandy shores and estuarine waters confined to the Indo-Pacific. Bottom dwellers which feed by rooting for worms and crustacea with their long conical snout. Excellent eating; usually caught in seine nets, but some species will take suitable bait. Elongated, tapering at both ends. Scales ctenoid on body, cycloid on operculum. A small opercular spine. Dorsal divided by a very deep notch between spines and rays. Two weak anal spines. Tai

emarginate or truncate. Lateral line complete. Ventrals without axillary process. Mouth small, terminal, protrusible. The species are very similar and rather difficult to distinguish.

### 891. SILLAGO SIHAMA (Forskål) 1775
Silver Whiting, Northern Whiting (A), Peche Madame (S), Pescadinha (P)
30 cm; D X–XI; I/20–23; A II/22–24; L 1 69–73; tr 5–6/10–12. Silvery, olive grey above; a broad but rather diffuse silvery yellow mid-lateral band. Soft dorsal with dark spots. Skips on surface of water if alarmed; taken on small hooks in sandy areas. Red Sea, S. and E. Africa, Seychelles, Ceylon, India E. Indies, Melanesia, Queensland.

Silver Whiting

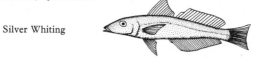

ALLIED SPECIES:
**892. SILLAGO MACROLEPIS** Bleeker 20 cm. L 1 54–56. Yellowish with a diffuse mid-lateral silvery stripe. East Indies and Melanesia.
**893. S. CILIATA** C. & V. 50 cm. Adult uniform silvery, young with black lateral blotches. A black mark at pectoral base. Soft dorsal spotted with black, pectorals, ventrals and anal bright yellow. East Indies, Melanesia, Queensland.
**894. S. MACULATA** Q. & G. 30 cm. Silvery with irregular elongated oblique black spots. A black mark at pectoral base and a well defined silvery mid-lateral band. Dorsal greenish with brown spots; pectorals, ventrals and anal yellow. Burrows and hides in holes in the sand or mud of the bottom when alarmed. Ceylon and India to E. Indies, Melanesia and Queensland.
**895. S. CHONDROPUS** Bleeker 35 cm. Dusky above, a silvery mid-lateral band, pearly below. Fins hyaline, dorsal with dusky tips. South and E. Africa, E. Indies, Melanesia.
**896. S. JAPONICA** T. & S. 23 cm. Olive brown above, white below, with a diffuse mid-lateral silvery stripe. Fins hyaline. East Indies, Philippines, Taiwan, Japan, Melanesia.

### Family MALACANTHIDAE Blanquillos, False Whiting, Maka'a (H)
Small inshore carnivorous fishes of the Indo-Pacific. Elongate, nearly cylindrical, with small scales. Similar to the Sillaginidae, but differ in having long undivided dorsal and anal fins and a prominent opercular spine. Lateral line complete, lips fleshy, mouth terminal.

### 897. MALACANTHUS LATOVITTATUS (Lacépède) 1802
Blue Blanquillo
38 cm; D IV/43–46; A I/38–40; L 1 120–130; tr 10/45. Head and back blue, belly white. Blue and white areas separated by a broad black mid-lateral band which starts behind operculum and terminates at tail margin. Dorsal blue with yellowish margin. Upper rays of tail blue or greenish, remainder of tail black. Pectorals blue, ventrals and anal hyaline. Shallow coastal waters, entering rivers. Rare. South and E. Africa, Seychelles, India, Ceylon, E. Indies, Melanesia.

Blue Blanquillo

### 898. MALACANTHUS HOEDTI Bleeker 1859
Banded Blanquillo, Maka'a (H)
30 cm; D V/54–57; A I/48–52; L 1 166–175; tr 7–8/24–28. Light olive above, silvery below; 20 oblique dark bars on back. Dorsal pink with narrow yellow edge. Other fins yellow, outer parts of tail lobes black. Shallow coastal waters in the E. Indies, Melanesia, Polynesia and Hawaii. Rare.

Family MONODACTYLIDAE **Silver Batfish, Moonfish**
Small deep-bodied, very compressed fishes of coastal and brackish waters, often ascending rivers. Two species, one in the Indo-Pacific and one in W. Africa.

### 899. MONODACTYLUS ARGENTEUS (Linnaeus) 1758
Silver Batfish, Fingerfish, Butter-bream (Q), Moony, Moonfish, Kite-fish (S. A.), Breton (S), Gedabang (Malay)
23 cm; D VII–VIII/28–31; A III/28–30; L 1 50–65; tr 14–15/44–45. Brilliant silvery all over. Juveniles with 2 vertical black bars across head, lost with age. Tip of dorsal orange in young individuals. Usually in small schools among rocks, in lagoons, sandy areas and in mangrove creeks. Edible, but of little economic importance, except as an aquarium fish. Common throughout the Indo-Pacific, but absent from Hawaii.

Silver Batfish

Family PEMPHERIDAE
**Sweepers, Bullseyes, Beach-salmon, Helicopter-fish**
A small family of small to moderate Indo-Pacific fishes. Oblong to ovoid, strongly compressed. Lateral line complete, extending onto tail. Eyes large. Mouth oblique, slightly protractile. Members of the genus *Pempheris* are very similar and difficult to distinguish. When small they occur in very large dense schools, usually stationary in shady places under overhanging coral heads. As they grow they tend to move to deeper water.

### 900. PEMPHERIS OUALENSIS Cuvier & Valenciennes 1831
18 cm; D V–VI/9–10; A III/39–43; L 1 50–65; tr 6–7/15–16. Bright metallic coppery with a black spot at pectoral base. This is the most widespread and frequently seen species. Red Sea, S. and E. Africa, Seychelles, India, E. Indies, Philippines, Melanesia, Micronesia and Polynesia as far as Tahiti.

*Pempheris oualensis*

ALLIED SPECIES:

**901. PEMPHERIS VANICOLENSIS** C. & V. 18 cm. Brownish, lacking black pectoral spot. Pectorals yellow, ventrals orange. India and Ceylon to E. Indies, Melanesia, Polynesia.

**902. P. MOLUCA** C. & V. 15 cm. Pectoral base blackish, vertical fins reddish. South and E. Africa, India, Ceylon, E. Indies and Melanesia.

**903. P. MACROLEPIDOTUS** (B. & S.) 20 cm. Seychelles to the Pacific.

**904. P. SCHWENCKI** Bleeker East Indies; dubiously recorded from S. Africa.

**905. PARAPRIACANTHUS GUENTHERI** (Klunzinger) 8 cm. Not as deep-bodied as *Pempheris*, anal fin shorter. Silvery with yellow sheen and black spots. Rather deep water. East Africa.

**906. LEPTOBRAMA MULLERI** Steindachner 30 cm. More elongated and slender than 905. Steel blue above, silvery below. Fins yellow, dorsal with a black blotch. Beaches and river mouths in Melanesia and Queensland.

## Family TOXOTIDAE **Archerfish, Riflefish**
Small fishes of the C. Indo-Pacific which inhabit brackish waters, river mouths and mangrove creeks. They are able to catch insects by rising to the surface and shooting drops of water at them. Favourite aquarium subjects.

### 907. TOXOTES JACULATOR (Pallas) 1766
25 cm; D IV/12–14; A III/15–16; L 1 28–30; tr 4/9–10. Olive above, silvery on sides and below. Five triangular black saddles. Posterior part of anal and distal part of dorsal blackish. India, Andamans, E. Indies, Philippines, China, Melanesia, N. Australia, Queensland, Fiji and Polynesia.

ALLIED SPECIES:

**908. TOXOTES CHARTAREUS** (H.-B.) 30 cm. Similar to 907, but with 6–7 unequal black blotches on upper sides. India and Ceylon, E. Indies, Philippines, Melanesia and Queensland.

## Family KYPHOSIDAE
**Drummers, Rudderfish, Chub, Bluefish (S. Africa), Poisson d'ail (S)**
Small to moderate fishes of all warm seas. Usually found in small schools about coral reefs and rocks, where they feed on algae and weeds. Rather heavily built, smoothly oval fishes with moderate ctenoid scales which are smaller on back, head and breast and cover basal portions of the vertical fins. Lateral line complete, slightly arched. Cheeks and operculum scaly. 1–2 blunt opercular spines. A single dorsal, sometimes slightly notched. Ventrals with a scaly axillary process. Tail emarginate. Mouth small, horizontal, terminal. Sometimes follow ships, hence the name 'Rudderfish'. Edible, but of poor quality.

### 909. KYPHOSUS CINERASCENS (Forskål) 1775
Topsail Drummer, Ashen Drummer, Nenue, Manaloa (Hawaii)
45 cm; D XI/14; A III/12–13; L 1 50–55; tr 11–13/16–19. Silvery, darker above. Golden lines along horizontal scale rows, a silver band below eye. Fins blackish. Entire Indo-Pacific including the Red Sea, Queensland, Hawaii.

*Toxotes jaculator*

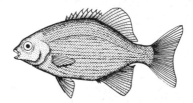

Topsail Drummer

ALLIED SPECIES:

**910. KYPHOSUS LEMBUS** (C. & V.) 35 cm. Silvery; 2 bluish bands below eye; fins grey. East Indies and Melanesia.

**911. K. VAIGIENSIS** (Q. & G.) 40 cm. Silvery bluish with bronzy horizontal stripes. Fins violet grey. Red Sea, S. and E. Africa, Seychelles, India, E. Indies, Melanesia, Micronesia, Polynesia and Queensland.

**912. K. BIGIBBUS** Lacépède 75 cm. Dark grey, dusky or golden, with pale lines along scale rows. South and E. Africa, Seychelles, Ceylon, E. Indies.

**913. SECTATOR AZUREUS** J. & E. 38 cm. More slender than previous species. Steel blue above, yellowish laterally, white below. A blue mid-lateral stripe from mouth to base of tail. Tail forked. Very rare, Hawaii.

## Family PLATACIDAE Batfish, Leaf-fish

Highly compressed, deep-bodied fishes with almost round bodies which are known only from the Indo-Pacific. The young have extremely elongated and elevated dorsal and anal fins which become shorter as they mature. Usually in shallow water among weeds, sea-grass or coral. The young are often coloured like dead leaves and when alarmed slowly sink into the vegetation, becoming extremely difficult to see. Small specimens of *Platax* are very popular aquarium subjects.

**914. PLATAX PINNATUS** (Linnaeus) 1758                          **Pl. 6**
Angel-fish, Sea-bat (S. Africa), Poule d'eau (S), Tudong Priok (Malay),
65 cm; D V/28–38; A III/24–29; L 1 50; tr 20 above arched part of lateral line. Dorsal spines almost concealed. Extremely variable when young; sometimes reddish or coppery, looking precisely like a dead leaf. Some individuals have a red stripe from snout to dorsal origin continued on anterior margin of dorsal, as well as a red margin to the ventrals and anal. Throughout the entire Indo-Pacific excluding Hawaii. *Platax teira* (Forskål) 1775, *P. orbicularis* (Forskål) 1775 **(Pl. 6)** and *P. vespertilio* (Bloch) 1790, all from the C. Indo-Pacific, have been treated as good species by some authors and as forms, phases or synonyms of *P. pinnatus* by others.

ALLIED SPECIES:

**915. PLATAX BATAVIANUS** C. & V. 50 cm. Differs from 914 in developing a large hump above the eye with advancing age. East Indies, Melanesia and Queensland.

**916. P. NOVEMACULEATUS** McCulloch 14 cm. Differs from 914 and 915 in having 9 dorsal spines (very short and almost embedded) and in acquiring the adult shape at a very early stage. Known from N. Queensland only.

**917. TRIPTERODON ORBIS** Playfair 1866
Spadefish
75 cm; D IX/19–21; A III/15–17; L 1 43–45; tr 12/24; 3rd and 4th dorsal spines much prolonged. Silvery with 8 dark cross-bands on head and body. Dorsal and tail yellowish, ventrals and anal blackish. East Africa, from Natal to Kenya.

Spadefish

*Platax batavianus*

## Family DREPANIDAE **Sicklefish**

A family consisting of a single wide-spread species which resembles the *Platacidae*, but differs in the structure of the dorsal fin and in having long sickle-like pectoral fins.

### **918. DREPANE PUNCTATA** (Linnaeus) 1758

Spotted Batfish, Sicklefish, Concertinafish (S. Africa)

45 cm; D VI–VII/29–32; A III/21–23; L 1 70; tr 14–15/33–35. Silvery with pinkish wash. Eight irregular vertical rows of dark dots. Fins yellowish, dorsal faintly spotted. Coastal waters and sandy bays throughout most of the Indo-Pacific excluding Hawaii; also known from tropical W. Africa.

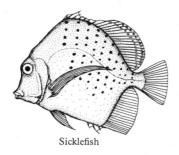

Sicklefish

## Family SCATOPHAGIDAE **Scats, Butterfish**

A small family of deep-bodied highly compressed Indo-Pacific fishes intermediate between the Platacidae and the Chaetodontidae. Scales minute, extending onto head and vertical fins. A single dorsal fin, deeply notched between spinous and rayed parts. Anal with 4 spines. Lateral line, complete, arched. Head small, mouth small, square, terminal, non-protrusible. Fishes of brackish water; scavengers, often feeding on excrement. Edible when absolutely fresh, but generally despised because of their foul feeding habits. Excellent aquarium fishes when small.

### **919. SCATOPHAGUS ARGUS** (Linnaeus) 1766

Spotted Scat, Ketang (Malay)

30 cm; D XII/16; A IV/16; L 1 90; tr 26–83. Olive green, darker above, with numerous irregular large black spots which are larger on back. Fins and tail dusky. Juveniles bright orange red on back with a few irregular black crossbands. India, Ceylon, E. Indies, Philippines, Melanesia and Queensland.

Spotted Scat

ALLIED SPECIES:
**920. SCATOPHAGUS TETRACANTHUS** (Lacépède) 18 cm. Yellowish with blackish head and back. Three broad, distinct, light yellowish cross-bars. Fins and tail dark dusky. South and E. Africa to the E. Indies.
**921. SELENOTOCA MULTIFASCIATA** (Richardson) 40 cm. Similar to 919, but snout more acute, dorsal spines somewhat produced. Bright silvery, greenish above. 10–12 irregular vertical black bars breaking into spots below lateral line. East Indies, Melanesia, N. Australia, New Caledonia.

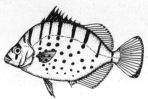

*Selenotoca multifasciata*

Family SCORPIDIDAE
A small family of Indo-Pacific fishes which are included in the *Chaetodontidae* by some authors. They differ from that family in having smaller scales.

**922. MICROCANTHUS STRIGATUS** (Cuvier & Valenciennes) 1831
Stripey, Convict-fish, Footballer                                             **Pl. 15**
15 cm; D XI/17; A III/13; L 1 42–45; tr 12–13/22–27. As figured, but old individuals may be more yellowish. Usually in small schools where the surf is breaking on the coral; the young in tidal rock pools. Taiwan, China, Japan, the Philippines, Hawaii, Australia.

Family CHAETODONTIDAE **Butterflyfishes and Angelfishes**
A large family of deep-bodied, highly compressed small to moderate fishes of all tropical waters. Colourful and graceful, they are typical coral-reef fishes and very popular with aquarists.

Subfamily *Chaetodontinae*
Coralfish, Butterflyfish, Papillons (S), Kikakapu, Kapuhili, Lauhau (Hawaii)
Very attractive small fishes of shallow coral reefs. When alarmed they usually take refuge in crevices in the coral and wedge themselves in by erecting their dorsal and anal spines and are then almost impossible to dislodge. Mostly various shades of white, yellow and orange with black markings, very often with a black stripe through the eye. The markings of some species change considerably with age. Scales ctenoid, moderate to large, smaller on head and fins. Unpaired fins densely scaled. Lateral line complete, strongly arched. Head small, mouth terminal, small; snout prolonged in some species. Teeth very small, setiform (the name of the family means bristle-teeth). Sedentary, solitary, in pairs or occasionally in small schools, they feed on small invertebrates. Mostly fishes of shallow water and coral pools, but a few venture down to about 30 m. Many Indo-Pacific species, a few in the Caribbean and tropical Atlantic. The large genus *Chaetodon* has been split into other genera by some authors; in this work these genera are treated as subgenera and follow the name *Chaetodon* in brackets.

**923. FORCIPIGER LONGIROSTRIS** (Broussonet) 1782        **Pl. 10**
Long-snouted Coralfish, Lau-wiliwili-nukunuku-oioi (Hawaii)
18 cm; D XI–XIII/22–24; A III/17–18; Sc 60–75; tr 12–14/29–31. Able to
search corals and cracks and holes in rocks for minute organisms. Usually seen
in pairs or in groups of 5–6. Entire Indo-Pacific including the Red Sea, Australia
and Hawaii, as far as the Revillagigedo islands off Mexico.

**924. CHELMON ROSTRATUS** (Linnaeus) 1758        **Pl. 10**
Beaked Coralfish, Kerepek (Malay)
17 cm; D IX/26–31; A III/17–21; L 1 43–46; tr 9–10/21–24. As figured, but
orange bands much darker in some specimens. Habits and behaviours similar to
923. Red Sea to India, Ceylon, E. Indies, China, Taiwan, Philippines, Melanesia
and Australia.

ALLIED SPECIES:
**925. CHELMONOPS TRUNCATUS** (Kner) 20 cm. Snout produced, rear of soft
dorsal angular. Silvery, orange on back with 6 vertical black stripes, 1st through eye,
6th on caudal peduncle, 3 inner ones wider; tail orange. A large ocellus on soft dorsal in
juveniles. South Queensland, New South Wales, Lord Howe island.

*Chelmonops truncatus*

**926. HENIOCHUS VARIUS** Cuvier & Valenciennes 1829        **Pl. 10**
Hunchbacked Coralfish
18 cm; D X–XII/21–25; A III/17–18; L 1 40–45; tr 10–11/22–27. East Indies,
Melanesia, Queensland, Fiji.

**927. HENIOCHUS ACUMINATUS** (Linnaeus) 1758        **Pl. 10**
Pennant Coralfish, Coachman, Pavillon (S)
25 cm; D XI–XII/24–27; A III/16–19; L 1 44–46; tr 10–11/22–26. The
commonest and one of the most beautiful of the genus. Usually seen in pairs or
small parties poking about among coral branches. Entire Indo-Pacific including
the Red Sea, Queensland and Hawaii. Should not be confused with *Zanclus
canescens* (1515).

**928. HENIOCHUS PERMUTATUS** Cuvier & Valenciennes 1831
**=H. CHRYSOSTOMUS** (Bleeker)        **Pl. 10**
Horned Coralfish
15 cm; D XII/21–23; A III/17–19; L 1 47–54; tr 10–11/22–26. In young
specimens the pale area of the anal fin may be light blue. India, E. Indies,
Philippines, Melanesia, Queensland, Micronesia and Polynesia.

**929. HENIOCHUS MONOCERUS** Cuvier & Valenciennes 1831    **Pl. 15**
23 cm. Develops a horn on forehead with age. East Africa and Seychelles to
the E. Indies, Taiwan, Japan, Micronesia and Polynesia as far as Tahiti.

ALLIED SPECIES:

**930. HENIOCHUS SINGULARIUS** Smith & Radcliffe 15 cm. Similar to 929, but horn black surrounded by a white area, ocular band angled forward below eye, snout white, lips black. Second black vertical band from ventral base to dorsal origin, including first two dorsal spines; 4th spine prolonged. Philippines, Taiwan, Borneo, Celebes, Gilolo.

**931. H. EXCELSA** Jordan 5 cm. Known from a single specimen brought to the surface in Hawaii by a lava flow in 1919. The only species of the genus with a large black, pale-ringed ocellus on soft dorsal.

**932. PARACHAETODON OCELLATUS** (Cuvier & Valenciennes) 1831
Six-spined Butterflyfish                                      **Pl. 10**
18 cm; D VI/28–29; A III/19–20; L 1 39–42; tr 14–15/27–28. Ceylon, India, E. Indies, Taiwan, Philippines, New Guinea, Queensland, N. Australia, Fiji and Polynesia as far as Tahiti.

**933. HEMITAURICHTHYS ZOSTER** (Bennett) 1831          **Pl. 10**
15 cm. As figured, but the extent of golden brown on the head variable. East Africa, Seychelles, E. Indies, Philippines, Micronesia, Melanesia, Hawaii. *H. polylepis* Bleeker 1857 is probably a synonym.

ALLIED SPECIES:

**934. HEMITAURICHTHYS THOMPSONI** Fowler Uniform dark brown. A rare deep water species known from Hawaii only.

**935. CORADION MELANOPUS** Cuvier & Valenciennes 1831
Two-eyed Coralfish
12 cm; D X/24–26; A III/19; L 1 44; tr 10/19. Silvery white with a narrow black ocular band, a very broad dark central vertical band divided above pectoral base, and a narrow dark band from soft dorsal to anal, ending in a rounded ocellus on each fin. Ventrals blackish. East Indies and Melanesia.

ALLIED SPECIES:

**936. CORADION CHRYSOZONUS** (C. & V.) 15 cm. Similar to 935, but post-ocular vertical bands golden brown. One ocellus only, on dorsal and a pale edged black ring on caudal peduncle. East Indies, Melanesia, Philippines and China.

**937. C. FULVOCINCTUS** Tanaka 12 cm. Very similar to 936; vertical bands blackish, 2nd band divided above pectoral. A single very large blue-ringed black ocellus on soft dorsal. Japan, Taiwan.

**938. C. ALTIVELIS** McCulloch 13 cm. Similar to 935 and 936, but has 8 dorsal spines, very high dorsal and anal fins and no ocelli. Known from 2 specimens from S. Queensland.

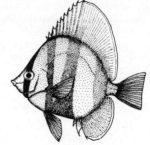

Two-eyed Coralfish                              *Coradion altivelis*

### 939. GONOCHAETODON TRIANGULUM
(Cuvier & Valenciennes) 1831                              **Pl. 10**
Triangular Coralfish, Herringbone Coralfish
12 cm; D XI/22–28; A III/20–23; Sc 30–33; tr 7-8/15–19. East Indies, Philippines, Melanesia, Queensland and Fiji.

ALLIED SPECIES:
**940. GONOCHAETODON LARVATUS** Ehrenberg. Treated by some authors as
a geographical subspecies of 939. Red Sea. **Pl. 10.**
**941. G. KARRAF** (C. & V.) Similar to 940, but has a dark ocular band. Intermediate
between 940 and 939 and possibly a variety of 940. Red Sea.

### 942. MEGAPROTODON STRIGANGULUS (Gmelin) 1789     **Pl. 12**
=CHAETODON TRIFASCIALIS Quoy & Gaimard 1824
Chevroned Coralfish
15 cm; D XIV–XV/15–17; A IV–V/15–16; L 1 21–25; tr 8-9/10–14. As figured,
but young tend to have much darker soft dorsal and anal and a wider ocular band.
Common throughout most of the Indo-Pacific, but absent from Hawaii.

### 943. CHAETODON (TETRACHAETODON) PLEBEIUS
Gmelin 1789                                              **Pl. 14**
Two-spot Coralfish
12 cm; D XIII–XIV/17–19; A IV–V/15–17; Sc 43–45; tr 6-7/13–14. As
figured, but in old individuals the blue lateral area is much duller, often reduced
to greenish lines between the scale rows, and the black ocellus on the caudal
peduncle may be much narrower. Andaman islands, E. Indies, Philippines,
Melanesia, Queensland, Fiji.

### 944. CHAETODON (RHABDOPHORUS) TRIFASCIATUS
Mungo Park 1797                                          **Pl. 14**
12 cm; D XIII/21–23; A III/19–20; Sc 38–40; tr 5-7/13–14. Common throughout the Indo-Pacific including Queensland, Hawaii and Tahiti.

ALLIED SPECIES:
**945. CHAETODON (RHABDOPHORUS) MELAPTERUS** Guichenot.
Similar in shape and markings to 944; orange yellow with reddish lines along scale
rows. Fins and tail broadly black, snout black. Ocular band outlined by two narrow
yellow marginal lines. Arabia, Somalia, Socotra, Réunion.

**946. C. (R.) AUSTRIACUS** Rüppell. Similar to 944; lemon yellow; dorsal white
with broad posterior black margin; tail black with narrow hyaline margin, anal black
with narrow yellow margin. Red Sea only.

*Chaetodon melapterus*

*C. austriacus*

**947. CHAETODON BENNETTI** Cuvier & Valenciennes 1831 **Pl. 14**
18 cm; D XIV/17–18; A III/15–16; Sc 38–46; tr 9–10/18–20. Rare. East
Africa, Seychelles, E. Indies, Philippines, Melanesia and Polynesia as far as
the Society islands.

**948. CHAETODON UNIMACULATUS** Bloch 1787 **Pl. 14**
15 cm. Ceylon and India to the E. Indies, Philippines, Hawaii and Tahiti.

**949. CHAETODON SPECULUM** Cuvier & Valenciennes 1831 **Pl. 14**
15 cm; D XIV/17–18; A III/15–16; Sc 40–44; tr 9–12/17–20. Moluccas, New
Guinea, Philippines and Taiwan.

ALLIED SPECIES:
**950. CHAETODON ZANZIBARIENSIS** Playfair 1867; 15 cm. Identical with
949, but scale count said to differ. East Africa and Seychelles.

**951. CHAETODON EPHIPPIUM** Cuvier & Valenciennes 1831 **Pl. 12**
Saddled Coralfish
30 cm; D XII–XIII/22–26; A III/21–22; L 1 32–34; tr 9–11/15–17. Unmistakable in all stages; very young individuals have no dorsal filament. A
most beautiful fish. East Indies, Philippines, Melanesia, Queensland and
Polynesia as far as the Society islands and Hawaii. Also on the west coast of
C. America. Usually in pairs.

**952. CHAETODON SEMEION** Bleeker 1855 **Pl. 12**
Dotted Coralfish
15 cm; D XIII–XIV/24–27; A III/21–24; L 1 28–32; tr 6–9/13–15. As figured,
but juveniles have a black bar on caudal peduncle and no dorsal filament.
Usually seen in pairs, rather rare. East Indies, Melanesia and Polynesia as
far as the Society islands.

**953. CHAETODON OCTOFASCIATUS** (Bloch) 1787 **Pl. 11**
Eight-banded Coralfish
10 cm; D X–XI/18–20; A III/16–17; Sc 42–46; tr 9–11/20–23. India, E. Indies,
Philippines, Moluccas, New Guinea.

**954. CHAETODON RAINFORDI** McCulloch 1923 **Pl. 11**
Rainford's Coralfish
15 cm; D XI/21; A III/18; L 1 45. Variable, often more yellow, less orange
than figured. North Queensland.

**955. CHAETODON AUREOFASCIATUS** Macleay 1878 **Pl. 11**
Golden-striped Coralfish
12 cm; D XIII–XV/20–22; A III/16–18; Sc 40–45; tr 8/9. Queensland and
New Guinea.

**956. CHAETODON (ANISOCHAETODON)
SEMILARVATUS** Ehrenberg 1831
=**C. MELANOPOMA** Günther 1865
12 cm. Orange yellow with 12 vertical
red and violet lines. Ocular band replaced by a large black spot around eye
and on cheek. Zanzibar to Aden and the
Red Sea.

*Chaetodon semilarvatus*

**957. CHAETODON ORNATISSIMUS** Cuvier & Valenciennes 1831
Ornate Coralfish **Pl. 11**
18 cm; D XII/25; A III/21; Sc 43–50; L 1 23–43; tr 10–12/21–25. East Indies, Philippines, Moluccas, Melanesia, Samoa, Fiji, Tahiti, Hawaii.

**958. CHAETODON MEYERI** Bloch & Schneider 1801 **Pl. 11**
Meyer's Coralfish
18 cm; D XII–XIII/23–25; A III–IV/18–21; L 1 32–38; tr 8–11/22–28. East Africa, Seychelles, E. Indies, Melanesia.

ALLIED SPECIES:
**959. CHAETODON BLACKBURNII** Desjardins 12 cm. Similar to 958, but no black bands on snout; radiating black bands do not connect together before pectoral base, dorsal, anal and tail black. Rare; South-east Africa, Madagascar, Mauritius.

**960. CHAETODON FREMBLI** Bennett 1829 **Pl. 12**
Blue-lined Coralfish
12 cm. Hawaiian Archipelago, where it is common among coral.

**961. CHAETODON MELANOTUS** Bloch & Schneider 1801
Black-backed Coralfish **Pl. 11**
17 cm; D XII/19–20; A III/17–18; L 1 25–26; tr 6–8/13–16. As figured, but old specimens duller in colour, black ocellus at anal base sometimes reduced to a patch of black-centred scales, black ring on caudal peduncle broken into a dorsal saddle and a ventral spot. Common. East Africa, Seychelles, India, E. Indies, Philippines, Taiwan, Melanesia, Queensland, Fiji, Samoa.

**962. CHAETODON (ANISOCHAETODON) LINEOLATUS**
Cuvier & Valenciennes 1831 **Pl. 11**
New Moon Coralfish
30 cm; D XII/24–28; A III/20–21; L 1 17–26; tr 6–8/15–16. The largest of the butterflyfishes. Common throughout the entire Indo-Pacific including the Red Sea, Queensland and Hawaii.

**963. CHAETODON (ANISOCHAETODON) FALCULA**
Bloch 1795 **Pl. 13**
Pig-faced Coralfish
20 cm; D XII/24–27; A III/19–22; L 1 24–25; tr 6–7/13–15. Red Sea, S. and E. Africa, Seychelles, E. Indies, Melanesia, Queensland, Fiji and Polynesia as far as Tahiti and Borabora.

**964. CHAETODON (ANISOCHAETODON) VAGABUNDUS**
Linnaeus 1758 **Pl. 11**
Vagabond Coralfish
20 cm; D XII–XIII/22–25; A III/20–22; L 1 31–34; tr 5–8/14–16. Entire Indo-Pacific excluding Hawaii; common. *C. vagabundus pictus* Forskål differs from the typical Pacific subspecies in having broader marginal yellow bands, black dorsal spines and a reddish transverse line on the tail. Gulf of Aden and Red Sea.

**965. CHAETODON ADIERGASTOS** Seale 1910
5 cm. Ocular band very broad around eye, but interrupted above it, forming a black horseshoe on nape. Silvery with 18 oblique parallel lines along scale

rows, directed backwards and upwards. Dorsal and anal orange yellow edged with black. Tail orange yellow with submarginal black band and hyaline margin. Pectorals hyaline, ventrals yellow. Juveniles brighter, with a complete ocular band and a black spot on soft dorsal. Philippines, Taiwan, S. Japan.

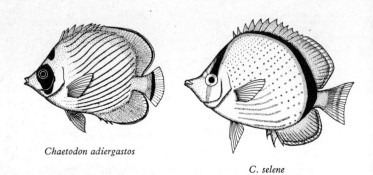

*Chaetodon adiergastos*

*C. selene*

### 966. CHAETODON SELENE Bleeker 1853
15 cm. Ocular band black above eye, yellow below it. Body silvery white with rows of yellow spots on upper and posterior parts and 7 continuous yellow lines from pectoral base to above anal spines. A black stripe edged proximally with yellow from beginning of dorsal base, across base of caudal peduncle to mid-anal base. Paired fins hyaline, vertical fins orange yellow, tail with a hyaline border. Philippines, Celebes, Moluccas, W. Irian.

### 967. CHAETODON GARDINERI Norman
15 cm. Similar to 966 and possibly a subspecies of it. Pale blue with orange-yellow scale centres. A large dark purplish patch before caudal peduncle. Ocular band with bright yellow posterior margin above eye. Dorsal grey-blue with yellow margin; tail orange with hyaline margin, anal yellow with blue submarginal line. Gulf of Aden.

### 968. CHAETODON (ANISOCHAETODON) AURIGA
Forskål 1775 = C. SETIFER Bloch 1797                                    Pl. 1
Threadfin Coralfish
23 cm; D XII–XIII/23–24; A III/20–21; L 1 26–30; tr 6–8/15–18. One of the commonest and best known species. Juveniles lack the dorsal filament. Coral reefs and tidal pools throughout the entire Indo-Pacific including the Red Sea, Hawaii and Queensland.

### 969. CHAETODON AUREUS Temminck & Schlegel 1842
15 cm. Head silvery white with a complete black ocular band and black lips. Body dark golden yellow with darker lines along the scale rows. Dorsal and anal with a light yellow submarginal band and black margin. Tail with a narrow black submarginal line and hyaline border. Pectorals hyaline, ventrals golden. Juveniles with large black ocellus on soft dorsal. Taiwan and S. Japan.

**970. CHAETODON WIEBELI** Kaup 1863

15 cm. Very similar to 969, but ocular band more irregular, dorsal ocellus lacking in juveniles and replaced by an ill-defined black ocellus on caudal peduncle. Treated as a synonym of 971 by some authors. Philippines, Taiwan, S. Japan.

**971. CHAETODON LUNULA** Lacépède 1801     **Pl. 12**

20 cm; D XII/23–25; A III/18–20; L 1 38. As figured, but juveniles with an ocellus on soft dorsal. One of the commonest and best known butterflyfishes. Coral reefs and rock pools in the entire Indo-Pacific. See 970, 972 and 973

ALLIED SPECIES:

**972. CHAETODON FASCIATUS** Forskål Similar to 971, but scales much larger. Treated as a senior synonym of that species by some authors. Originally described from Arabia; confined to the Red Sea and the Gulf of Aden.

**973. C. BELLA-MARIS** Seale. Another probable synonym of 971. Philippines Taiwan and S. China.

**974. CHAETODON QUADRIMACULATUS** Gray 1831     **Pl. 12**

15 cm. Shallow coral reefs in S. Japan, Micronesia and Polynesia. Fairly common in Hawaii.

**975. CHAETODON TINKERI** Schultz 1951     **Pl. 12**

15 cm. Named in honour of Spencer W. Tinker, Director of the Waikiki Aquarium. Only known from rather deep water in Hawaii.

**976. CHAETODON MODESTUS** Temminck & Schlegel 1842

12 cm. Very similar to *Coradion fulvocinctus* (937), but central cross-band undivided, dorsal ocellus smaller, snout more pointed. Philippines, Taiwan, China, S. Japan.

**977. CHAETODON MARLEYI** Regan 1929

18 cm; D XI/22–26; A III/16–19; L 1 40–45. Silvery with a yellow spot on each scale. Ocular band narrow and rather pale below eye. A golden brown band from 4th–6th dorsal spines to ventral axil, enclosing pectoral base. A further golden band from mid-dorsal base, surmounted by a white-ringed ocellus, tapering to anal base at 4th–7th ray. A faint dark band on caudal peduncle. Ventrals orange brown, other fins hyaline with orange yellow base. Ocellus placed further back in juveniles. Among estuarine weeds, down to 100 m, in Madagascar and S. Africa.

*C. marleyi*

### 978. CHAETODON (RHABDOPHORUS) XANTHOCEPHALUS
Bennett 1832        **Pl. 14**
Yellow-headed Coralfish
20 cm; D XIII–XIV/25–27; A III/23–24; L 1 40. As figured, but juveniles have broader ocular band and blackish dorsal and anal fins. East Africa, Seychelles, Ceylon and India. See 979.

ALLIED SPECIES:
**979. CHAETODON CARENS** Seale 1910 Very similar to 978, possibly an eastern subspecies. Very rare, Philippines only.

### 980. CHAETODON LEUCOPLEURA Playfair 1866     **Pl. 14**
15 cm. East Africa and the Seychelles, rare.

### 981. CHAETODON FLAVIROSTRIS Günther 1873
Similar to 978, but body darker, ventral fins blackish. Queensland and the S.-W. Pacific.

ALLIED SPECIES:
**982. CHAETODON NIPPON** Steindachner & Doderlein 14 cm. Adults dull olive with blackish dorsal, anal and caudal peduncle. Head darker, without ocular band. Tail yellowish at base, hyaline distally. Juveniles pinkish with a faint ocular band, yellow ventrals and an imperfect ocellus on dorsal. South Japan and Philippines.
**983. C. GUNTHERI** Ahl 10 cm. Silvery; ocular band terminating at isthmus. Scale centres on upper sides and back darker. Paired fins and tail hyaline. Dorsal, anal and caudal peduncle orange yellow. Soft dorsal and anal with a black submarginal line and a narrow bluish margin. Philippines, Taiwan, Japan, Celebes, Ceram and Amboina.

### 984. CHAETODON DAHLI Ahl 1923
3 cm; D XIII/23; A III/19–20; Sc 32; tr 5/13. Yellowish, darker above, ocular band not reaching isthmus. Soft dorsal and anal with a blackish submarginal line and narrow white margin; a black transverse line on tail; soft dorsal with an imperfect dark ocellus. New Guinea and Queensland.

### 985. CHAETODON COLLARIS Bloch 1787     **Pl. 13**
Collared Coralfish
15 cm; D XII/25–27; A III/20–22; L 1 30; tr 8/15. India, Ceylon, E. Indies, Philippines, China.

### 986. CHAETODON RETICULATUS Cuvier & Valenciennes 1831
Reticulated Coralfish
15 cm; D XII–XIII/26–28; A III/20–25; L 1 35–42; tr 8–10/21–24. Very similar to 985, but generally duller, profile more blunt; snout uniform grey, silvery band behind eye wider and more diffuse, dorsal whitish, caudal peduncle blackish, no red on tail; Micronesia, Fiji, Samoa, Tahiti, Hawaii.

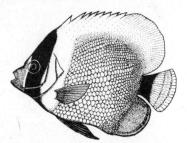

*Chaetodon reticulatus*

### 987. CHAETODON (ANISOCHAETODON) RAFFLESI
Bennett 1830       **Pl. 13**
Raffles' Coralfish
12 cm; D XIII/22–23; A III/19–20; L 1 26–27; 5–7/12–14. Ceylon and India,
E. Indies, Philippines, Melanesia, Queensland, Micronesia and Polynesia.
Very common in Fiji and Samoa.

### 988. CHAETODON (ANISOCHAETODON) KLEINI Bloch 1790
Klein's Coralfish       **Pl. 13**
13 cm; D XIII/22–23; A III/17–19; L 1 32–34; tr 7–8/12–15. East Africa,
Seychelles, E. Indies, Philippines, China, Taiwan, Melanesia, Caroline islands,
Queensland, Fiji and Samoa.

### 989. CHAETODON CORALLICOLA Snyder 1904
10 cm. Rather like a smaller, duller version of 988. Hawaii only, usually below
30 m.

### 990. CHAETODON CITRINELLUS Cuvier & Valenciennes 1831
Citron Coralfish       **Pl. 13**
11 cm; D XIII–XV/20–21; A III/15–17; L 1 32–33; tr 8–9/16–17. East Indies,
Philippines, Melanesia, Micronesia, Queensland, Polynesia as far as the Tuamotu
islands and Hawaii.

### 991. CHAETODON MILIARIS Quoy & Gaimard 1824     **Pl. 13**
Millet-seed Coralfish
15 cm; D XIII/20–23; A III/18–20; Sc 44; tr 6/20. Common throughout most
of the Indo-Pacific. Absent from the Barrier Reef, but common in Hawaii.

### 992. CHAETODON PELEWENSIS Kner 1868       **Pl. 13**
Dot-and-dash Coralfish
12 cm. Queensland and Polynesia as far as the Tuamotu and Society islands.

### 993. CHAETODON PUNCTATOFASCIATUS
Cuvier & Valenciennes 1831
= **C. MULTICINCTUS** Garrett 1863
10 cm. Very similar to 992, but rows of spots vertical, not oblique. East Indies,
Philippines, Melanesia, Taiwan, S. Japan; common in Hawaii.

*C. punctatofasciatus*

### 994. CHAETODON GUTTATISSIMUS Bennett 1832     **Pl. 13**
Spotted Coralfish
12 cm; D XII/25–27; A III/20–22; L 1 30; tr 8/15. East Africa, the Red Sea,
India, Ceylon and the Seychelles.

### 995. CHAETODON (LINOPHORA) MERTENSI
Cuvier & Valenciennes 1831                                          **Pl. 14**
15 cm; D XII–XIII/21–22; A III/16–18; L I 33. Very similar to the following
two species, with which it has been confused. There is some doubt about the
range of this species, as many of the published records for *C. mertensi* may
apply to 996 and 997. Ceylon and India to the E. Indies, Philippines, Micronesia,
Fiji and Polynesia as far as the Tuamotu islands.

### 996. CHAETODON (LINOPHORA) CHRYSURUS Desjardins 1833
15 cm. Differs from 995 in having a clearly defined black mark edged with
white on the nape. Probably confined to the E. Coast of Africa, the Seychelles
and Madagascar. The Red Sea race (*C. chrysurus paucifasciatus* Ahl) differs in
having an orange brown ocular band edged with black.

### 997. CHAETODON (LINOPHORA) XANTHURUS
Bleeker 1857
15 cm. Spot on nape as in 996, but scales larger, the ones on sides and back
clearly edged with black. Probably confined to the Philippines, Taiwan and
S. Japan.

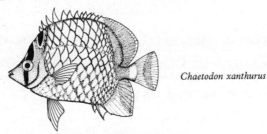

*Chaetodon xanthurus*

### 998. CHAETODON ARGENTATUS Smith & Radcliffe 1911
12 cm. Closely related to the above 3 species, but lacks all traces of orange.
Silvery white; scales very large, edged with black. Ocular band irregular and
somewhat diffuse, fading out below eye. A diffuse black vertical band from nape
to level of eye and one from mid-dorsal to behind pectoral base. A broader,
better defined black band from edge of soft dorsal across peduncle, to posterior
edge of anal. Tail with 2 transverse bands. Philippines, Taiwan and Okinawa.

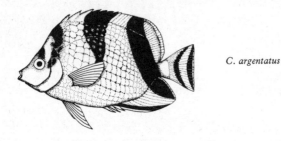

*C. argentatus*

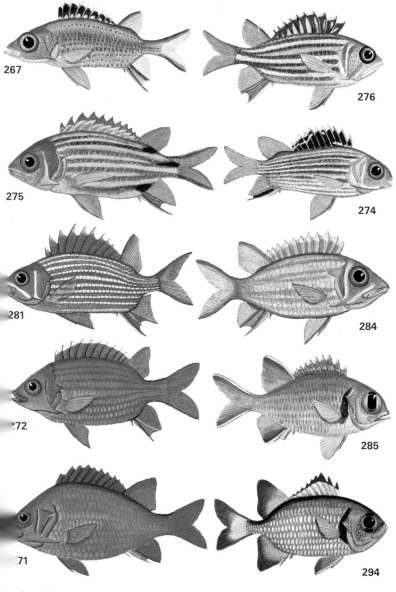

**1**

## late 1

67 *Kutaflammeo sammara*
75 *Holocentrus cornutus*
81 *Holocentrus xantherythrus*
72 *Holocentrus violaceus*
71 *Holocentrus spinifer*

**276** *Holocentrus ruber*
**274** *Holocentrus diadema*
**284** *Holocentrus ensifer*
**285** *Myripristis murdjan*
**294** *Myripristis adustus*

2

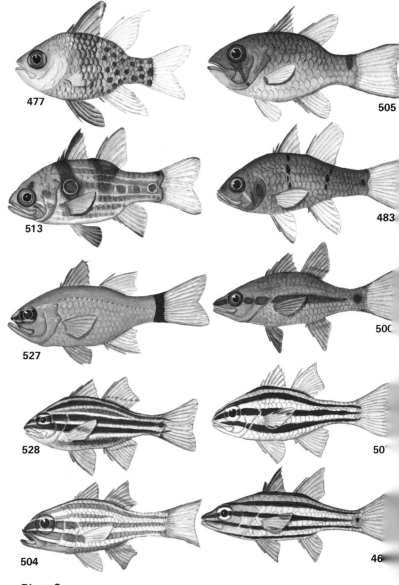

**Plate 2**

477 *Sphaeramia orbicularis*
513 *Apogonichthys nigripinnis*
527 *Ostorhinchus aureus*
528 *Ostorhinchus endekataenia*
504 *Gronovichthys cyanosoma*

505 *Gronovichthys bandanensis*
483 *Apogon taeniatus*
500 *Pristiapogon fraenatus*
507 *Lovamia novemfasciata*
462 *Paramia quinquelineata*

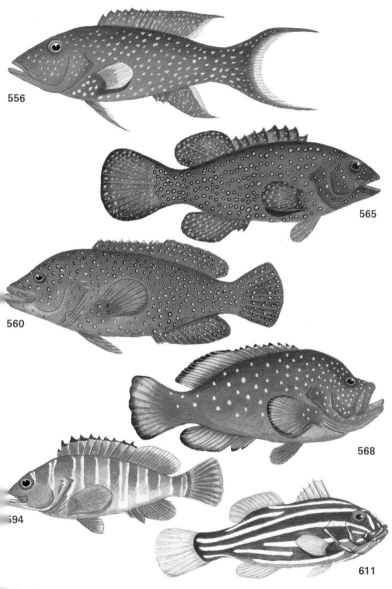

**4**

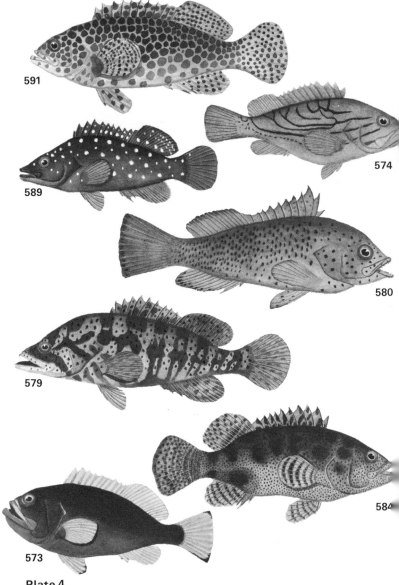

## Plate 4

**591** *Epinephelus merra*
**589** *Epinephelus coeruleopunctatus*
**579** *Epinephelus tauvina*
**573** *Epinephelus flavocaeruleus*

**574** *Epinephelus morrhua*
**580** *Epinephelus fario*
**584** *Epinephelus fuscoguttatus*

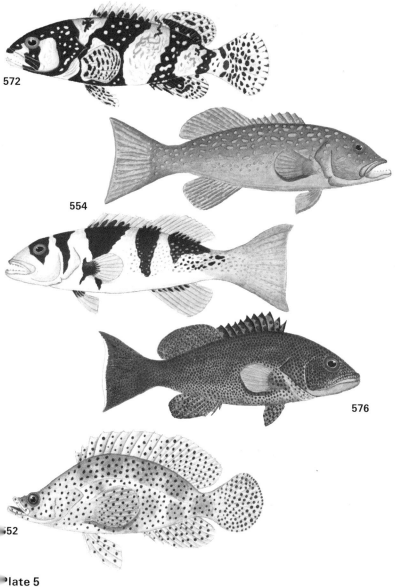

5

572

554

576

552

Plate 5

572 Promicrops lanceolatus
554 Plectropoma maculatum
  (2 forms)
552 Cromileptes altivelis

576 Epinephelus areolatus

**6**

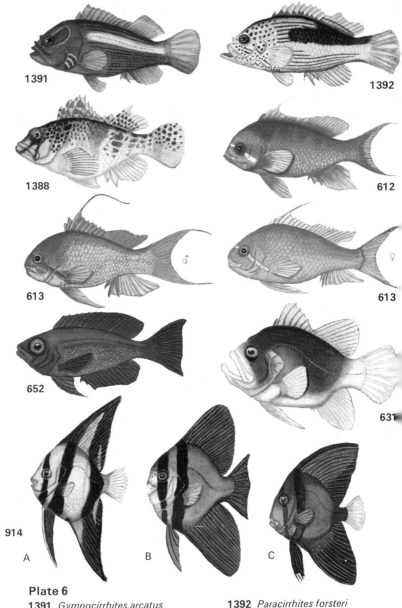

**Plate 6**

**1391** *Gymnocirrhites arcatus*
**1388** *Cirrhitichthys oxycephalus*
**613** *Anthias squamipinnis*
**652** *Priacanthus hamrur*
**914** *Platax pinnatus*: A, juvenile; B, adult; C, "orbicularis"

**1392** *Paracirrhites forsteri*
**612** *Anthias huchti*
**631** *Diploprion bifasciatum*

7

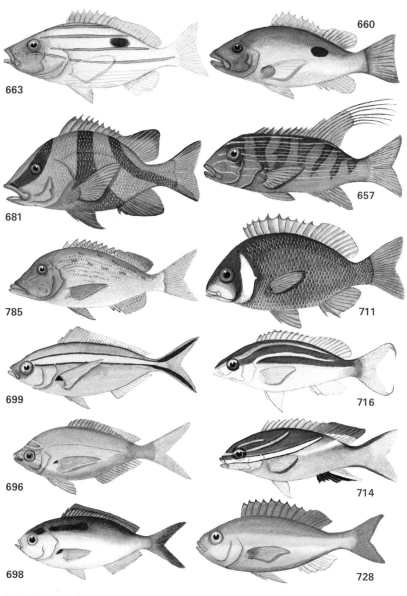

**Plate 7**

663 *Lutjanus kasmira*
681 *Lutjanus sebae*
785 *Lethrinus nebulosus*
699 *Caesio coerulaureus*
696 *Caesio cuning*
698 *Caesio lunaris*

660 *Lutjanus fulviflamma*
657 *Symphorus nematophorus*
711 *Scolopsis vosmeri*
716 *Scolopsis frenatus*
714 *Scolopsis bilineatus*
728 *Parascolopsis eriomma*

**8**

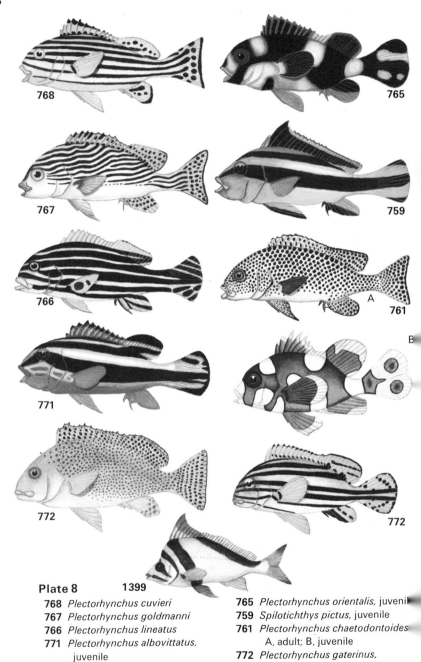

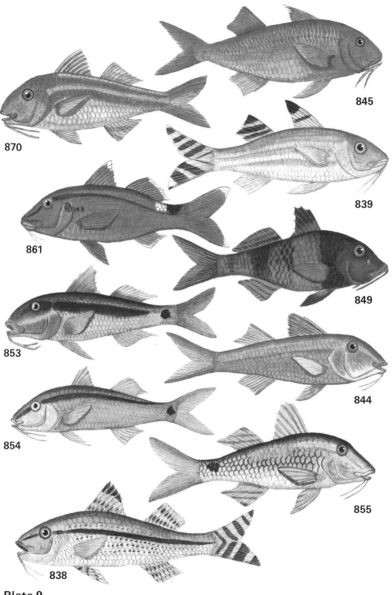

9

## Plate 9

870 *Parupeneus seychellensis*
861 *Parupeneus porphyreus*
853 *Parupeneus macronemus*
854 *Parupeneus barberinus*
838 *Upeneus tragula*

845 *Mulloidichthys pflugeri*
839 *Upeneus vittatus*
849 *Parupeneus multifasciatus*
844 *Mulloidichthys auriflamma*
855 *Parupeneus indicus*

10

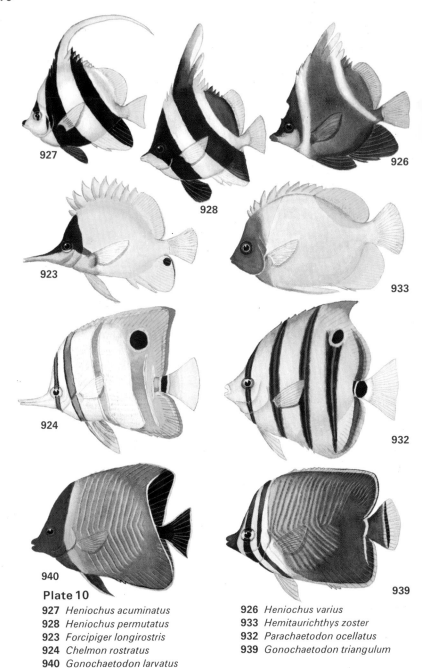

**Plate 10**

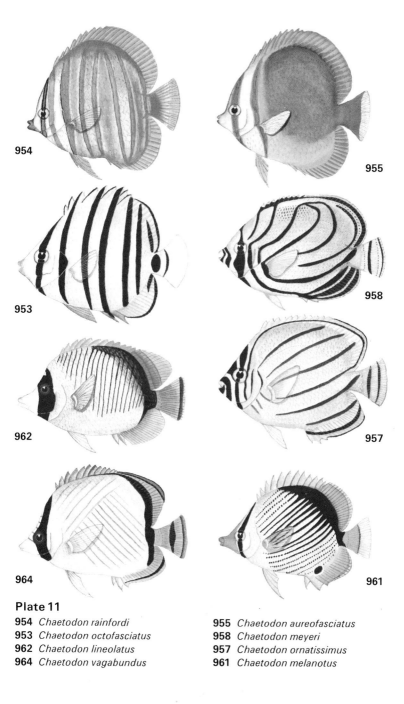

**Plate 11**

954 *Chaetodon rainfordi*
953 *Chaetodon octofasciatus*
962 *Chaetodon lineolatus*
964 *Chaetodon vagabundus*

955 *Chaetodon aureofasciatus*
958 *Chaetodon meyeri*
957 *Chaetodon ornatissimus*
961 *Chaetodon melanotus*

12

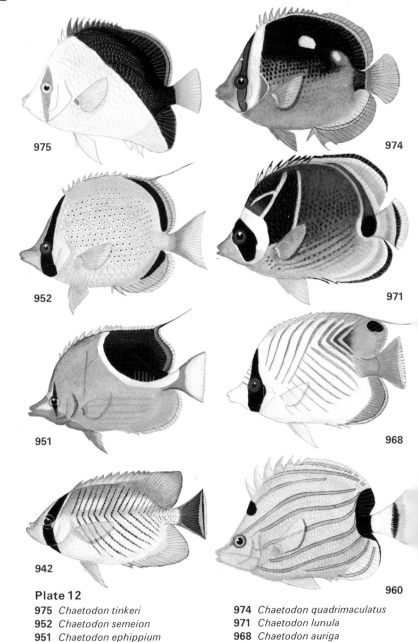

975

974

952

971

951

968

942

960

**Plate 12**
**975** *Chaetodon tinkeri*
**952** *Chaetodon semeion*
**951** *Chaetodon ephippium*
**942** *Megaprotodon strigangulus*

**974** *Chaetodon quadrimaculatus*
**971** *Chaetodon lunula*
**968** *Chaetodon auriga*
**960** *Chaetodon frembli*

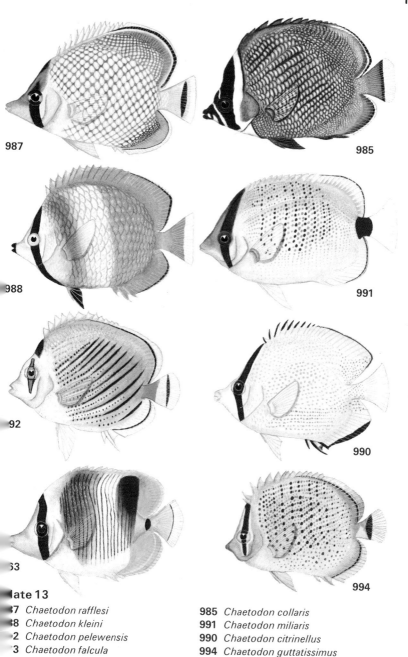

987

985

988

991

92

990

63

994

Plate 13

987 *Chaetodon rafflesi*
988 *Chaetodon kleini*
92 *Chaetodon pelewensis*
3 *Chaetodon falcula*

985 *Chaetodon collaris*
991 *Chaetodon miliaris*
990 *Chaetodon citrinellus*
994 *Chaetodon guttatissimus*

**14**

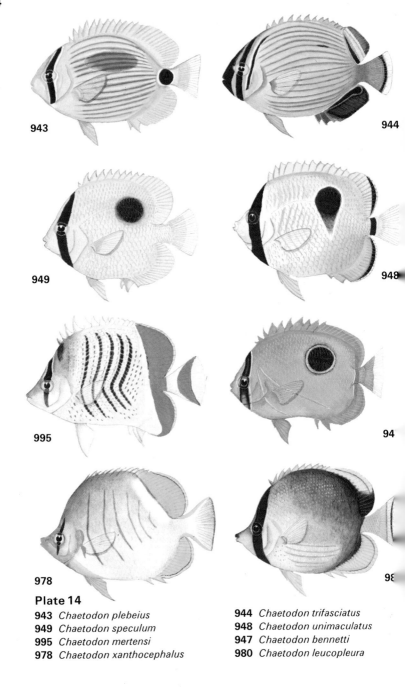

943

944

949

948

995

94

978

98

**Plate 14**

943 *Chaetodon plebeius*
949 *Chaetodon speculum*
995 *Chaetodon mertensi*
978 *Chaetodon xanthocephalus*

944 *Chaetodon trifasciatus*
948 *Chaetodon unimaculatus*
947 *Chaetodon bennetti*
980 *Chaetodon leucopleura*

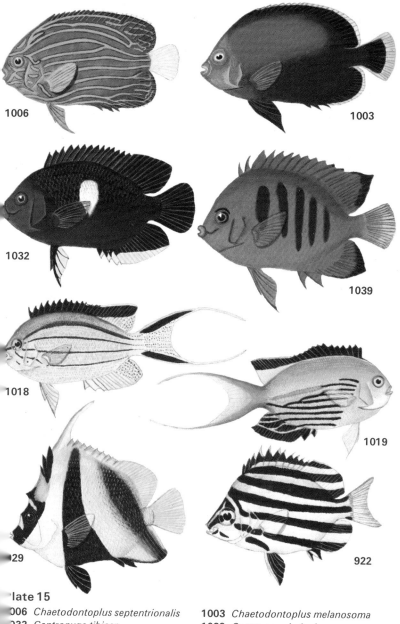

**Plate 15**

1006 *Chaetodontoplus septentrionalis*
1032 *Centropyge tibicen*
1018 *Genicanthus lamarcki*, ♀
1029 *Heniochus monoceros*

1003 *Chaetodontoplus melanosoma*
1039 *Centropyge loriculus*
1019 *Genicanthus watanabei*, ♂
922 *Microcanthus strigatus*

**16**

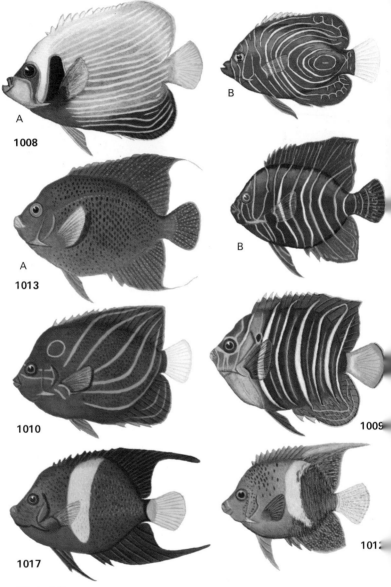

**Plate 16**

**1008** *Pomacanthodes imperator:*
    A, adult; B, juvenile
**1013** *Pomacanthops semicirculatus:*
    A, adult; B, juvenile
**1010** *Pomacanthodes annularis*
**1017** *Arusetta asfur*

**1009** *Pomacanthodes chrysurus*
**1012** *Pomacanthops maculosus*

**17**

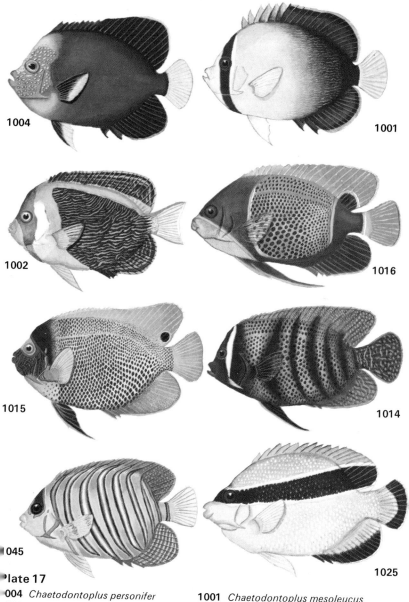

**Plate 17**

1004  *Chaetodontoplus personifer*
1002  *Chaetodontoplus douboulayi*
1015  *Euxiphipops xanthometopon*
1045  *Pygoplites diacanthus*

1001  *Chaetodontoplus mesoleucus*
1016  *Euxiphipops navarchus*
1014  *Euxiphipops sexstriatus*
1025  *Apolemichthys arcuatus*

**18**

**Plate 18**

1029 *Centropyge flavissima*
1038 *Centropyge potteri*
1042 *Centropyge fisheri*
1026 *Apolemichthys trimaculatus*

1031 *Centropyge bicolor*
1037 *Centropyge bispinosus*
1034 *Centropyge vroliki*
1023 *Apolemichthys xanthurus*

19

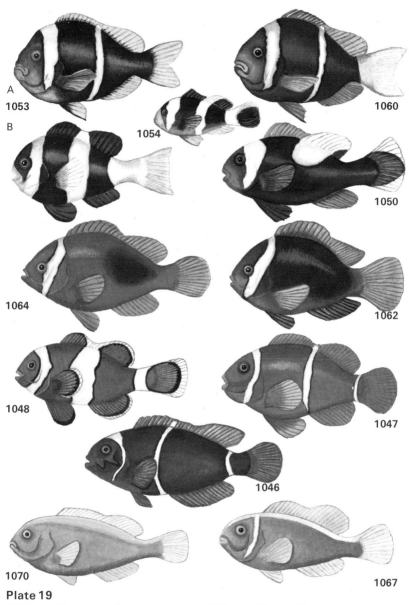

## Plate 19

1053  *Amphiprion clarkii:*
　　　A, Singapore; B, Guadalcanal
1054  *Amphiprion allardi,* juvenile
1064  *Amphiprion rubrocinctus*
1048  *Amphiprion ocellaris*
1070  *Amphiprion akallopisos*

1060  *Amphiprion akindynos*
1050  *Amphiprion polymnus*
1062  *Amphiprion melanopus*
1047  *Amphiprion tricinctus*
1046  *Premnas biaculeatus*
1067  *Amphiprion perideraion*

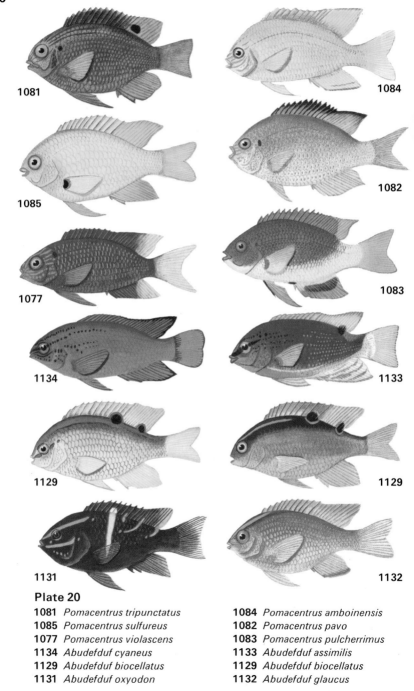

**Plate 20**

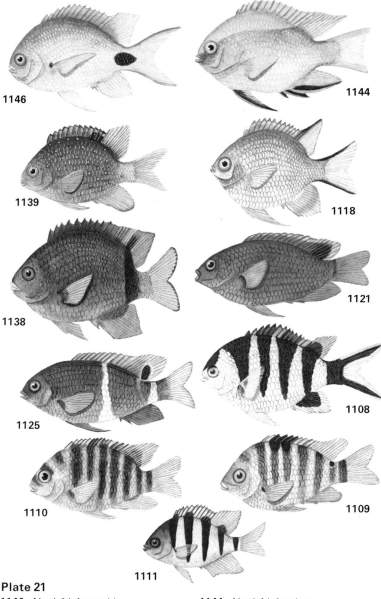

**Plate 21**

1146 *Abudefduf sparoides*

1139 *Abudefduf lacrymatus*

1138 *Abudefduf dicki*

1125 *Abudefduf xanthozona*

1110 *Abudefduf septemfasciatus*

1111 *Abudefduf saxatilis*

1144 *Abudefduf melanopus*

1118 *Abudefduf leucogaster*

1121 *Abudefduf zonatus*

1108 *Abudefduf coelestinus*

1109 *Abudefduf sordidus*

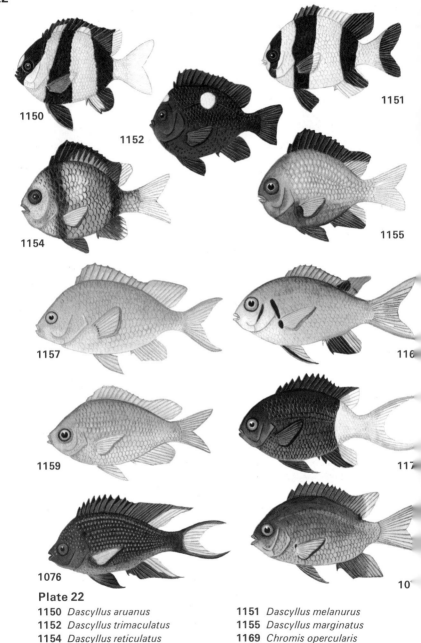

**22**

1150

1152

1151

1154

1155

1157

116

1159

117

1076

10

## Plate 22

1150 *Dascyllus aruanus*
1152 *Dascyllus trimaculatus*
1154 *Dascyllus reticulatus*
1157 *Chromis caeruleus*
1159 *Chromis ovalis*
1076 *Pomacentrus taeniurus*

1151 *Dascyllus melanurus*
1155 *Dascyllus marginatus*
1169 *Chromis opercularis*
1174 *Chromis dimidiatus*
1074 *Eupomacentrus nigricans*

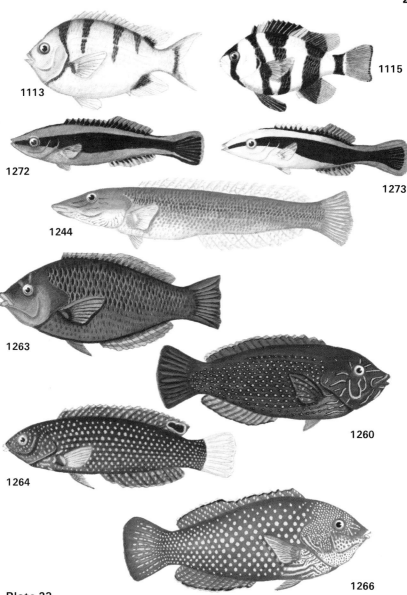

23

## Plate 23

1113 *Abudefduf abdominalis*
1272 *Labroides dimidiatus*
1244 *Cheilio inermis*
1263 *Anampses diadematus*
1264 *Anampses meleagrides*

1115 *Abudefduf annulatus*
1273 *Labroides phthirophagus*
1260 *Anampses caeruleopunctatus*
1266 *Anampses cuvieri*

**24**

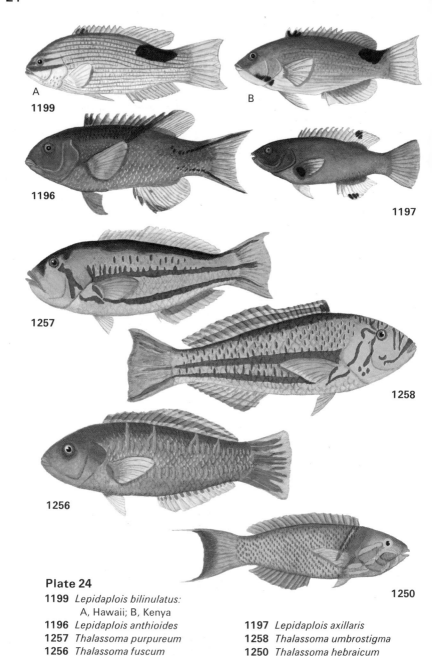

A
1199

B

1196

1197

1257

1258

1256

1250

## Plate 24
**1199** *Lepidaplois bilinulatus:*
    A, Hawaii; B, Kenya
**1196** *Lepidaplois anthioides*
**1257** *Thalassoma purpureum*
**1256** *Thalassoma fuscum*

**1197** *Lepidaplois axillaris*
**1258** *Thalassoma umbrostigma*
**1250** *Thalassoma hebraicum*

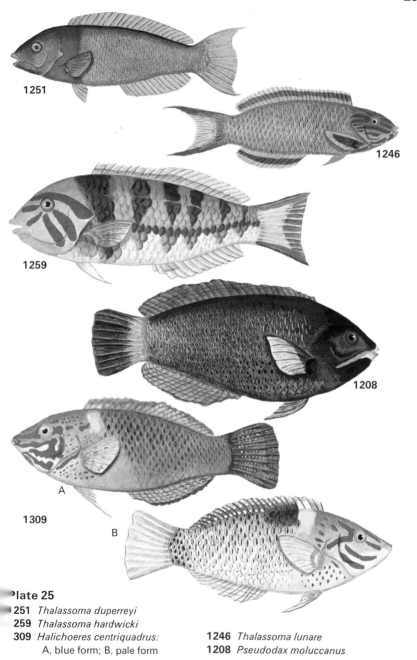

1251

1246

1259

1208

A

1309

B

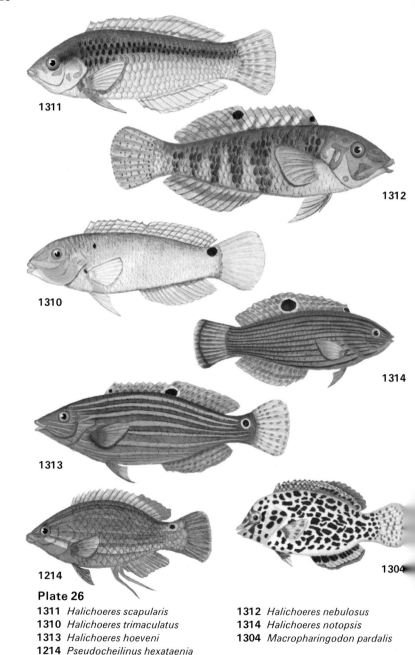

**26**

1311

1312

1310

1314

1313

1214

1304

### Plate 26

1311 *Halichoeres scapularis*
1310 *Halichoeres trimaculatus*
1313 *Halichoeres hoeveni*
1214 *Pseudocheilinus hexataenia*

1312 *Halichoeres nebulosus*
1314 *Halichoeres notopsis*
1304 *Macropharingodon pardalis*

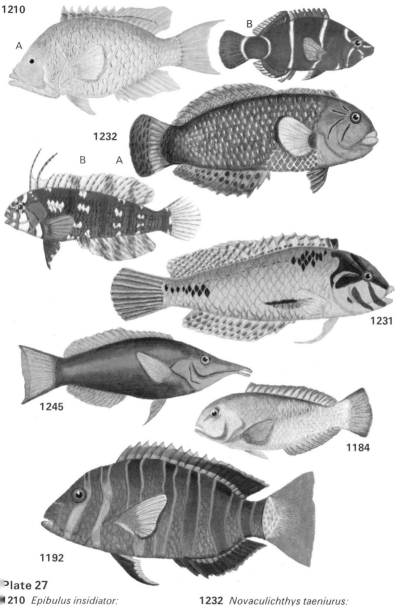

Plate 27

1210 *Epibulus insidiator:*
   A, adult; B, juvenile
1245 *Gomphosus varius*
1192 *Lienardella fasciata*

1232 *Novaculichthys taeniurus:*
   A, adult; B, juvenile
1231 *Novaculichthys macrolepidotus*
1184 *Choerodon robustus*

**28**

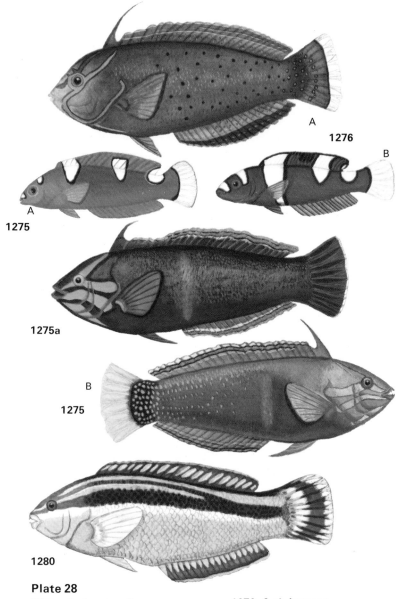

**Plate 28**

**1275** *Coris gaimardi:*
    A, juvenile; B, adult
**1275a** *Coris gaimardi africana*
**1280** *Coris flavovittata*

**1276** *Coris formosa:*
    A, adult; B, juvenile

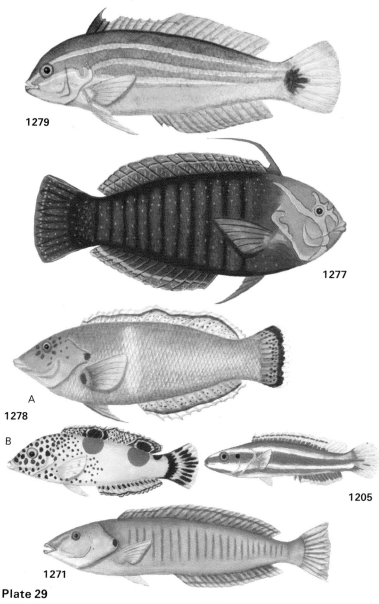

29

**Plate 29**

1279 *Coris caudimacula*
1278 *Coris aygula:*
    A, adult, B, juvenile
1271 *Hologymnosus semidiscus*

1277 *Coris frerei*
1205 *Verriculus opercularis*

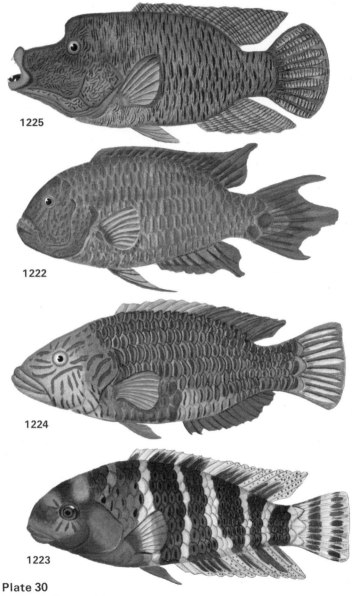

1225

1222

1224

1223

## Plate 30
**1225** *Cheilinus undulatus*
**1222** *Cheilinus trilobatus*
**1224** *Cheilinus diagramma*
**1223** *Cheilinus fasciatus*

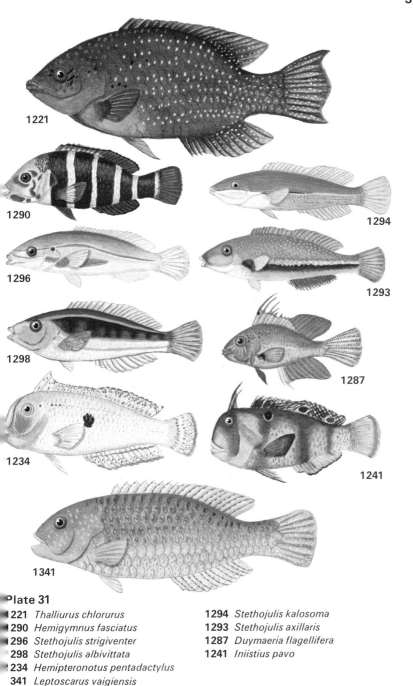

**Plate 31**

1221  *Thalliurus chlorurus*
1290  *Hemigymnus fasciatus*
1296  *Stethojulis strigiventer*
1298  *Stethojulis albivittata*
1234  *Hemipteronotus pentadactylus*
341  *Leptoscarus vaigiensis*

1294  *Stethojulis kalosoma*
1293  *Stethojulis axillaris*
1287  *Duymaeria flagellifera*
1241  *Iniistius pavo*

32

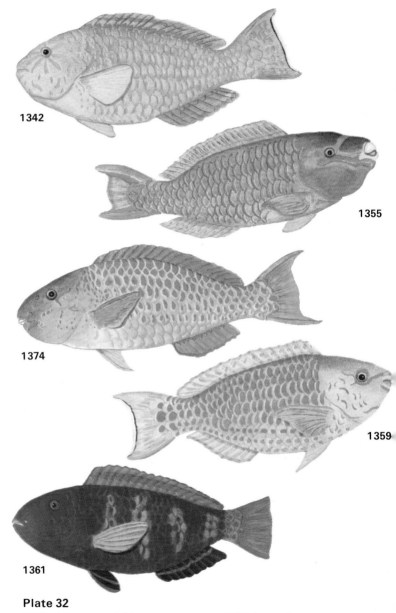

1342

1355

1374

1359

1361

**Plate 32**

1342 *Calotomus spinidens*
1374 *Scarus ghobban (f. apridentatus)*
1361 *Scarus rhoduropterus*

1355 *Scarus formosus*
1359 *Scarus forsteri*

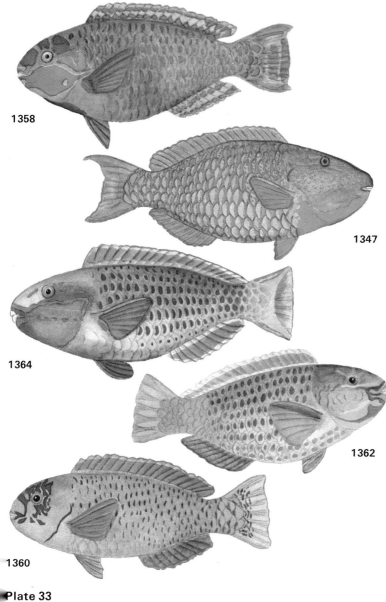

33

1358

1347

1364

1362

1360

**Plate 33**
**1358** *Scarus taeniurus*
**1364** *Scarus capistratoides*
**1360** *Scarus enneacanthus*

**1347** *Bolbometopon bicolor,* ♀
**1362** *Scarus sordidus*

34

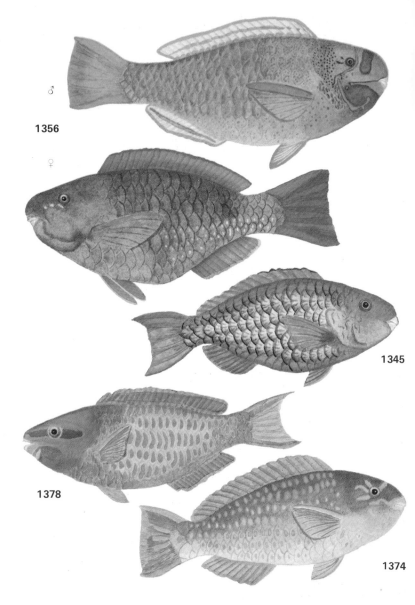

♂

1356

♀

1345

1378

1374

## Plate 34
**1356** *Scarus perspicillatus*
**1378** *Scarus cyanognathos*

**1345** *Scarops rubroviolaceus,* ♀
**1374** *Scarus ghobban*

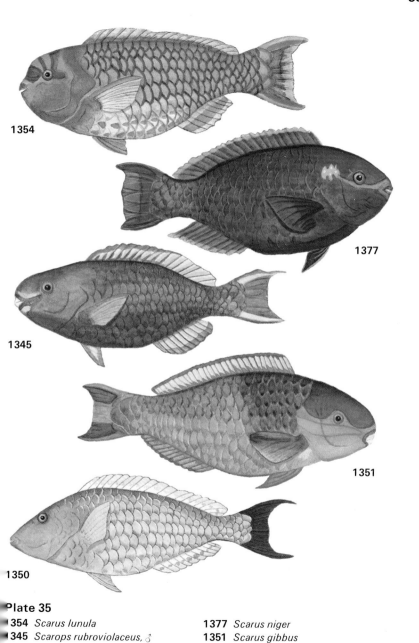

**Plate 35**

1354  *Scarus lunula*
1345  *Scarops rubroviolaceus,* ♂
1350  *Scarus harid vexillus*

1377  *Scarus niger*
1351  *Scarus gibbus*

36

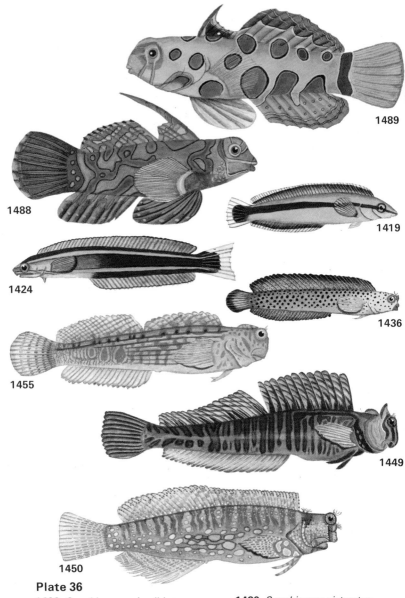

**Plate 36**

1488 *Synchiropus splendidus*
1424 *Runula rhinorhynchos*
1455 *Istiblennius andamanensis*
1450 *Salarias fasciatus*

1489 *Synchiropus picturatus*
1419 *Aspidontus tractus*
1436 *Laiphognathus multimaculatus*
1449 *Lophalticus kirki*

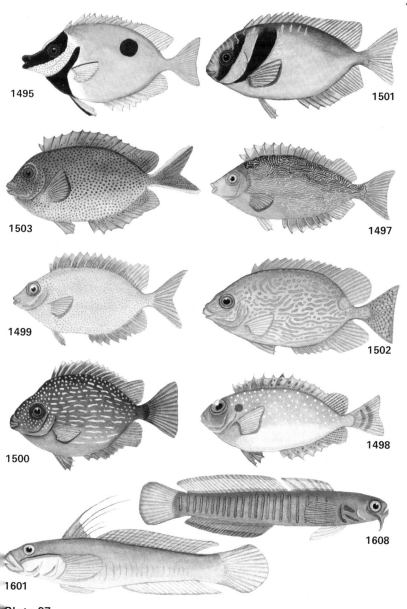

## Plate 37

| | |
|---|---|
| **1495** *Lo vulpinus* | **1501** *Siganus virgatus* |
| **1503** *Siganus stellatus* | **1497** *Siganus spinus* |
| **1499** *Siganus corallinus* | **1502** *Siganus lineatus* |
| **1500** *Siganus javus* | **1498** *Siganus oramin* |
| **1601** *Eleotriodes strigatus* | **1608** *Pogonoculius zebra* |

**38**

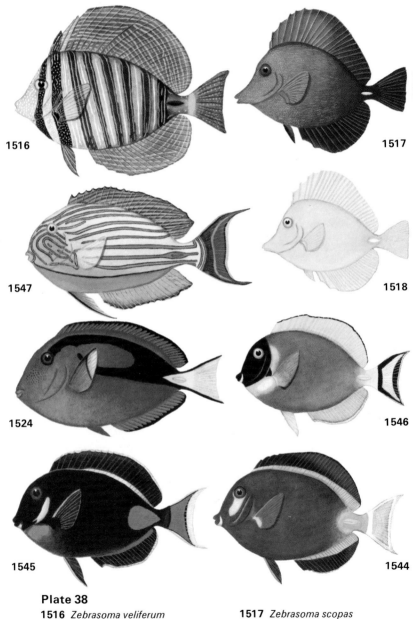

**1516**

**1517**

**1547**

**1518**

**1524**

**1546**

**1545**

**1544**

Plate 38

1516 *Zebrasoma veliferum*
1547 *Acanthurus lineatus*
1524 *Paracanthurus hepatus*
1545 *Acanthurus achilles*

1517 *Zebrasoma scopas*
1518 *Zebrasoma flavescens*
1546 *Acanthurus leucosternon*
1544 *Acanthurus aliala*

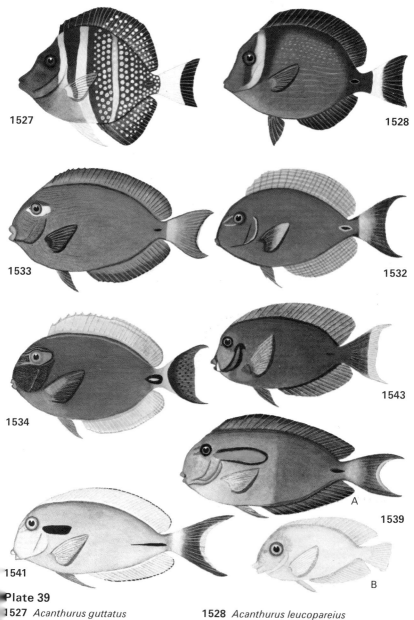

**Plate 39**

1527 *Acanthurus guttatus*
1533 *Acanthurus mata*
1534 *Acanthurus dussumieri*
1541 *Acanthurus nigricans*

1528 *Acanthurus leucopareius*
1532 *Acanthurus fuliginosus*
1543 *Acanthurus pyroferus*
1539 *Acanthurus olivaceus:*
   A, adult; B, juvenile

**40**

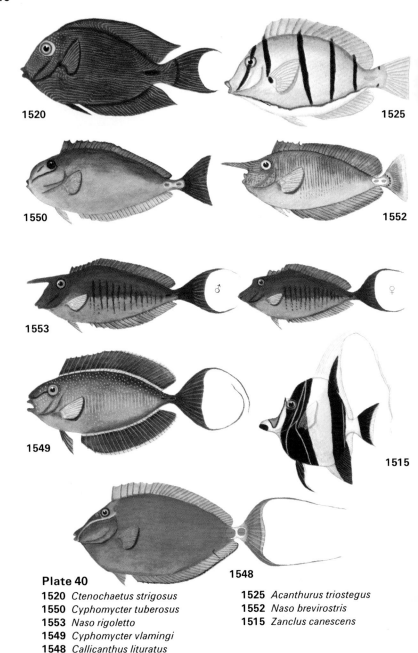

**Plate 40**

1520 *Ctenochaetus strigosus*
1550 *Cyphomycter tuberosus*
1553 *Naso rigoletto*
1549 *Cyphomycter vlamingi*
1548 *Callicanthus lituratus*

1525 *Acanthurus triostegus*
1552 *Naso brevirostris*
1515 *Zanclus canescens*

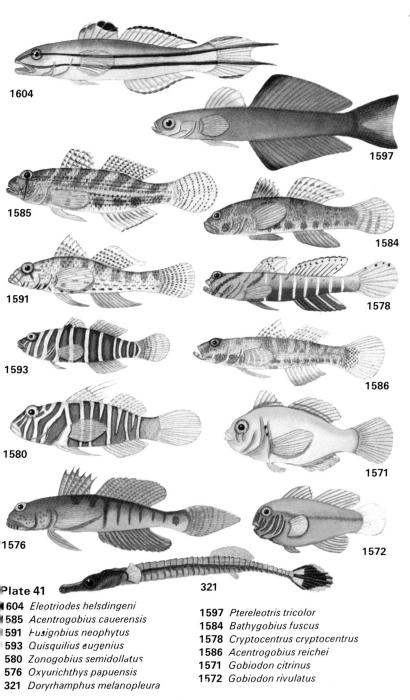

**41**

42

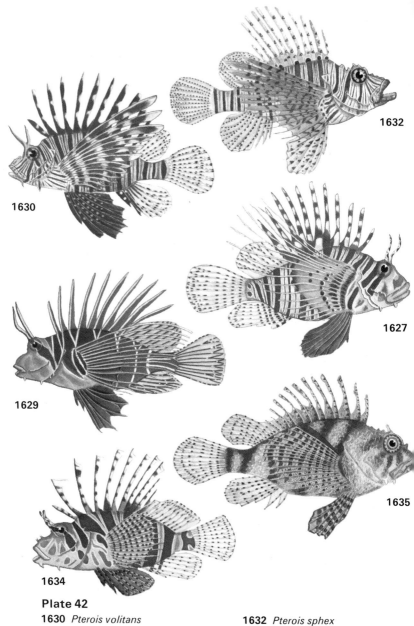

1632

1630

1627

1629

1635

1634

**Plate 42**

1630 *Pterois volitans*
1629 *Pteropterus radiatus*
1634 *Brachirus zebra*

1632 *Pterois sphex*
1627 *Pteropterus antennatus*
1635 *Brachirus brachypterus*

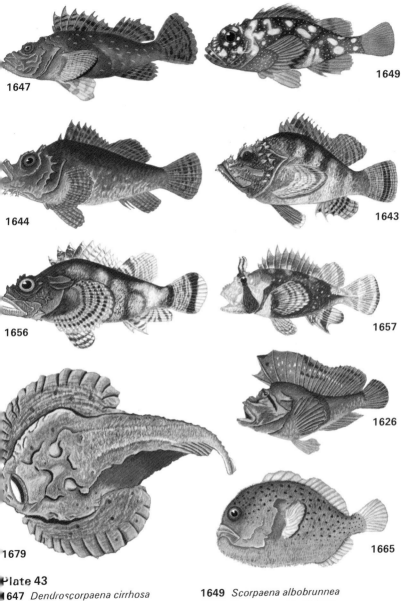

43

44

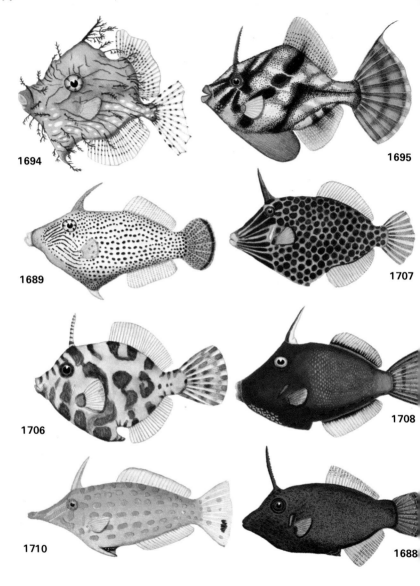

1694

1695

1689

1707

1706

1708

1710

1688

**Plate 44**

1694 *Chaetoderma penicilligera*
1689 *Pervagor spilosoma*
1706 *Amanses pardalis*
1710 *Oxymonacanthus longirostris*

1695 *Monacanthus mylii*
1707 *Cantherines sandwichensis*
1708 *Cantherines howensis*
1688 *Pervagor melanocephalus*

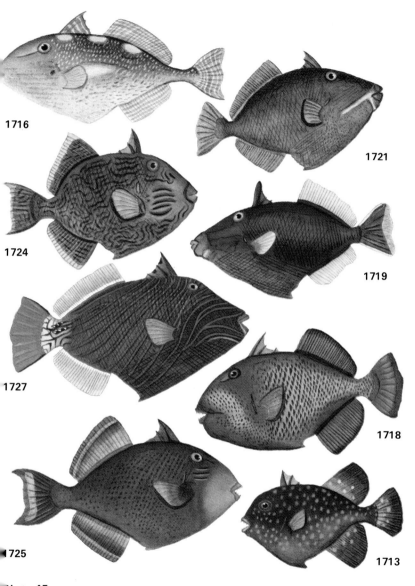

1716

1721

1724

1719

1727

1718

1725

1713

46

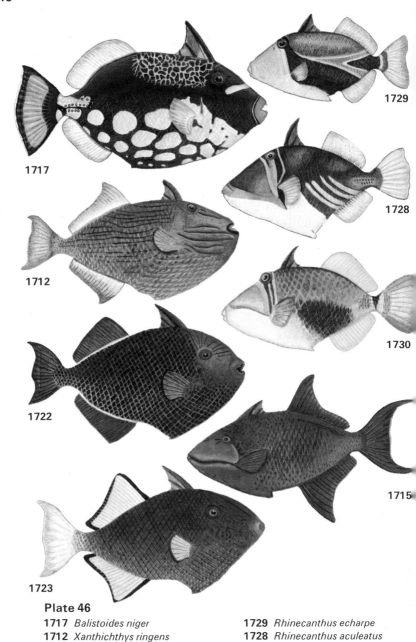

**Plate 46**

1717 *Balistoides niger*
1712 *Xanthichthys ringens*
1722 *Melichthys buniva*
1723 *Melichthys vidua*

1729 *Rhinecanthus echarpe*
1728 *Rhinecanthus aculeatus*
1730 *Rhinecanthus verrucosus*
1715 *Odonus niger*

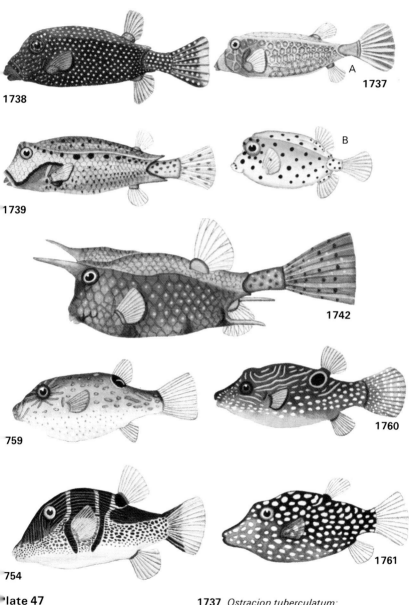

Plate 47

1738  *Ostracion lentiginosum*, ♀
1739  *Rhynchostracion nasus*
1759  *Canthigaster bennetti*
1754  *Canthigaster cinctus*

1737  *Ostracion tuberculatum:*
       A, adult; B, juvenile
1742  *Lactoria cornuta*
1760  *Canthigaster margaritatus*
1761  *Canthigaster jactator*

48

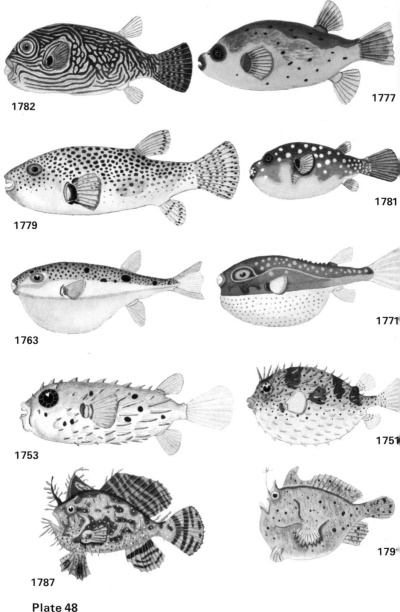

1782

1777

1779

1781

1763

1771

1753

1751

1787

1791

**Plate 48**

1782 *Arothron reticularis*
1779 *Arothron stellatus*
1763 *Gastrophysus sceleratus*
1753 *Diodon jaculiferus*
1787 *Histrio histrio*

1777 *Arothron citrinellus*
1781 *Arothron hispidus*
1771 *Amblyrhinchotes hypselogene*
1751 *Diodon hystrix*
1791 *Antennarius oligospilos*

**999. CHAETODON TRIVIRGATUS** Weber & Beaufort 1936
Very similar to 998. Known from Amboina only.

**1000. CHAETODON DAEDALMA** Jordan & Fowler 1902
A silvery fish with all the scales heavily outlined in black and no ocular band.
South Japan only.

The subfamily also includes the following Indo-Pacific species:
*Chaetodon leucopygus* Ahl 1923, Dar-es-Salaam.
*C. howensis* Waite 1903, Lord Howe Island.
*C. mitratus* Günther 1860, Mauritius.
*C. trichrous* Günther 1874, Society islands.
*C. maculatus* Sauvage 1891, Madagascar.
*C. notophthalmus* Ahl 1923, ? locality.
*C. tricinctus* Waite 1901, Lord Howe Island.
*C. reinwardti* Günther 1860, Moluccas.
*C. ocellicauda* C. & V. 1831, Amboina, New Guinea, Philippines.
*C. nigropunctatus* Sauvage 1880, Mascate, Madagascar.
*C. oxycephalus* Bleeker 1853, Ternate.
*C. dixoni* Regan 1904, New Hebrides.
*C. fowleri* Klausewitz 1956, Java.
*C. frenatus* Fowler 1935, Thailand.

Subfamily *Pomacanthinae* Angelfishes
Small to moderate brilliantly coloured fishes of all warm seas. Similar in habits
and structure to the *Chaetodontinae* from which they differ in having a strong
spine at the angle of the preoperculum. Angelfishes are subject to startling
changes of colour and pattern as they grow; immature individuals of *Pomacanthodes*, *Pomacanthops* and *Euxhiphipops* are marked with pale cross-stripes
or rings. In the genus *Chaetodontoplus* the scales are small and scarcely visible.
Favourite aquarium fishes, especially when small. Sedentary, solitary or in
pairs; they feed by scraping small organisms off corals and rocks.

**1001. CHAETODONTOPLUS MESOLEUCUS** (Bloch) 1787    **Pl. 17**
15 cm; D XII/17; A III/16; Sc 70–85; tr 12–13/23–28. As figured, but tail
orange in some individuals. Malay peninsula, E. Indies, Philippines, Taiwan,
Okinawa and Melanesia.

**1002. CHAETODONTOPLUS DUBOULAYI** (Günther) 1867    **Pl. 17**
20 cm; D XI/22; A III/21. As figured, but juveniles with better defined ocular
band, no light vermiculations on body and reduced yellow dorsal band. North
Queensland and N.-W. Australia.

**1003. CHAETODONTOPLUS MELANOSOMA** Bleeker 1853    **Pl. 15**
16 cm; D XIII/17–19; A III/17–19; Sc 115. Adult as figured; juvenile, originally described as *C. dimidiatus* Bleeker 1877, black with a yellow band from
nape to just behind ventrals and a broad yellow margin to dorsal and posterior
part of anal; tail yellow with a broad black transverse band and hyaline margin.
Indonesia, Melanesia and Philippines.

**1004. CHAETODONTOPLUS PERSONIFER** (McCulloch) 1914
**Pl. 17**
30 cm. As figured, but tail black with yellow margin in some individuals.
Queensland.

162 ANGELFISHES

**1005. CHAETODONTOPLUS CONSPICILLATUS** (Waite) 1900
25 cm; D XIII/18; A III/18. Head yellowish; body rich coffee brown, jaws, chin and chest darker. Eye enclosed by a dark ring which is produced in front. Margin of dorsal yellow, anal dark brown; pectorals black with yellow base and margin; tail yellow, posterior third black, narrowly margined yellow. Lord Howe island and Capricorn islands, off Australia.

**1006. CHAETODONTOPLUS SEPTENTRIONALIS**
Schlegel 1844 **Pl. 15**
21 cm; D XIII/18–19; A III/16–17; Sc 140. Adult as figured, juvenile black and yellow, similar to that of 1003, but yellow dorsal margin very narrow, base of tail black. Taiwan, S. China and S. Japan.

**1007. CHAETODONTOPLUS CHRYSOCEPHALUS** (Bleeker) 1854
17 cm. Dark orange brown shading to blackish brown posteriorly. Head and nape with broad irregular blue vermiculations; lips blue. Soft dorsal with a narrow orange margin; anal with a narrow yellow margin, tail yellow; paired fins blackish. Indonesia and S. Japan.

**1008. POMACANTHODES IMPERATOR** (Bloch) 1787 **Pl. 16**
=CHAETODON NICOBARIENSIS Schneider 1801 (juvenile)
Imperial Angelfish
38 cm; D XIII–XIV/18–21; A III/18–21; Sc 76–90. This most beautiful fish occurs throughout the entire Indo-Pacific including the Red Sea, Queensland and Hawaii, but is nowhere common.

**1009. POMACANTHODES CHRYSURUS**
(Cuvier & Valenciennes) 1831 **Pl. 16**
20 cm; D XIII–XIV/18–19; A III/19; L 1 80. Uncommon; usually seen in shady spots under overhanging coral rocks. East Africa, Seychelles and Madagascar.

**1010. POMACANTHODES ANNULARIS** (Bloch) 1787 **Pl. 16**
Ringed Angelfish, Babi (Malay)
25 cm; D XIII/20–21; A III/20; L 1 70. Adult as figured, juvenile with transverse light bands. Indian Ocean only: E. Africa, India and Ceylon, E. Indies.

**1011. POMACANTHODES STRIATUS** (Rüppell) 1835
30 cm; D XI–XII/22–24; A III/21–22; scales very small. Tail truncate, dorsal and anal angular, but not prolonged. Adult, described as *Holacanthus rhomboides* Gilchrist & Thompson 1908, dark greyish brown, posterior third of body abruptly paler in some specimens; larger scales with a black centre. Tail and fins black. Juvenile black with 15–17 alternating narrow and wide transverse bluish white stripes and yellowish tail. East Africa, Natal, Red Sea, Arabia and Seychelles.

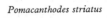
*Pomacanthodes striatus*

**1012. POMACANTHOPS MACULOSUS** (Forskål) 1775     **Pl. 16**
=**P. FILAMENTOSUS** Smith 1955
28 cm; D XII–XIII/21; A III/19–20; L 1 75. Yellow lateral band appears in juveniles before the transverse blue-white lines are lost. In very old specimens the anal becomes produced as well as the dorsal (*P. filamentosus* Smith). Red Sea, E. Africa, Aldabra. See 1017.

**1013. POMACANTHOPS SEMICIRCULATUS**
(Cuvier & Valenciennes) 1831 (juvenile)     **Pl. 16**
=**HOLACANTHUS LEPIDOLEPIS** Bleeker 1853 (adult)
Blue Angelfish
38 cm; D XIII/20–23; A III/18–20; Sc 65–75. The commonest and best known species of the group; the very beautiful juveniles are often seen in shallow tidal pools. The blue markings on the tail resemble Arabic script and are occasionally thought to represent verses of the Koran, such specimens being the object of great veneration among Moslem fishermen. Entire Indo-Pacific, excluding Hawaii.

**1014. EUXIPHIPOPS SEXSTRIATUS** (Cuvier & Valenciennes) 1831
Six-banded Angelfish     **Pl. 17**
50 cm; D XIII–XIV/16–18; A III/16–18; Sc 46–52. Adult as figured, juvenile with 8 transverse white stripes and blue markings better developed. E. Indies, Philippines, Taiwan, Okinawa, Melanesia, Queensland, N.-W. Australia and Palau island.

**1015. EUXIPHIPOPS XANTHOMETOPON** (Bleeker) 1853     **Pl. 17**
Blue-faced Angelfish
38 cm; D XIII–XIV/16–18; A III/16–18; Sc 46–52; tr 7/20–21. Adult as figured, juvenile with 10–12 narrow white transverse lines. Ceylon, Andaman Islands, E. Indies, Philippines, Taiwan, Okinawa, Melanesia and Queensland.

**1016. EUXIPHIPOPS NAVARCHUS** Cuvier & Valenciennes 1831
Blue-girdled Angelfish     **Pl. 17**
20 cm; D XIII–XIV/17–18; A III/16–18; Sc 45–50; tr 6/20–21. Striped juvenile pattern lost when the fish is still very small. Indonesia, Philippines and Melanesia.

**1017. ARUSETTA ASFUR** (Forskål) 1775     **Pl. 16**
15 cm; D XII/20–21; A III/19; Sc 50. Often confused with 1012; however it differs from that species in having the yellow transverse band in front of the anal base; in *P. maculosus* it ends above the middle of the anal fin base. East Africa, Red Sea and Persian Gulf.

**1018. GENICANTHUS LAMARCKI** (Lacépède) 1802     **Pl. 15** (♀)
Swallow-tailed Angelfish
2 cm; D XV/15–16; A III/16–17; Sc 50. Width and number of longitudinal stripes variable; specimens without dark margins to the tail are probably males. East Indies, Philippines, Okinawa and New Guinea, Aldabra, E. Africa.

**1019. GENICANTHUS WATANABEI** (Yasuda & Tominaga) 1969
    **Pl. 15** (♂)
10 cm. ♂ as figured. ♀ lacks black and orange stripes on body, but has a pattern of wide blue-edged black bands on snout and above eyes; outer caudal rays and distal half of dorsal and anal black. South Japan and Okinawa.

## 1020. GENICANTHUS MELANOSPILUS (Bleeker) 1857

18 cm; D XV/16; A III/18; Sc 48–50. Yellowish with 15 irregular dark vertical bands on sides; in some specimens the bands are restricted to the upper half of the body (G. semicinctus (Waite) 1900). G. caudovittatus (Günther) 1860, without body-bands, but with black outer caudal rays, is almost certainly the ♀. East Indies, Mauritius, Madagascar, E. Africa and the Red Sea.

ALLIED SPECIES:

1021. GENICANTHUS SEMIFASCIATUS Kamohara 12 cm. Light green above, white below; back and upper sides marked with numerous irregular brown cross-bands which merge with a very irregular orange band which starts from above eye and tapers to a mid-lateral point above anal origin. Dorsal and tail lined and spotted with brown and orange, other fins white. South Japan, apparently rare.

1022. G. FUCOSUS (Yasuda & Tominaga) 13 cm. Whitish, light olive above. Eye ringed with blue and surmounted by a large black blotch. Operculum white with black posterior edge and a black line from behind eye to base of preopercular spine. Tail deeply forked, black with white margin. Rare, S. Japan.

## 1023. APOLEMICHTHYS XANTHURUS (Bennett) 1832          Pl. 18

15 cm; D XIV/19; A III/16; L 1 45–48. As figured. India and Ceylon, not uncommon.

## 1024. APOLEMICHTHYS XANTHOTIS Fraser-Brunner 1950

15 cm. Known from a single specimen from the Gulf of Aden. The description, original figure and scale and fin counts seem to agree with 1023.

## 1025. APOLEMICHTHYS ARCUATUS (Gray) 1831          Pl. 17

17 cm; D XIII/18; A III/18; Sc 50. Hawaii only, uncommon.

## 1026. APOLEMICHTHYS TRIMACULATUS

Cuvier & Valenciennes 1831                              Pl. 18
26 cm; XIV/16–17; A III/17–18; Sc 48. East Africa, Mauritius, Aldabra and Seychelles to E. Indies, New Guinea and Okinawa. Common in the Seychelles.

ALLIED SPECIES:

1027. APOLEMICHTHYS ARMITAGEI Smith 20 cm. Very similar to 1026 but yellow-green, posterior part of dorsal fin black. Known from the Seychelles only.
1028. A. VENUSTUS (Yasuda & Tominaga) 8 cm. Dull yellow, darker posteriorly a broad bright blue band above eyes, across nape, ending in a point at pectoral base Back and upper sides from dorsal origin and caudal peduncle blackish with a large bright blue spot in the centre of each scale. Dorsal, anal and tail blackish, irregularly spotted, lined and edged with bright blue. Pectorals yellow, ventrals yellow with bright blue anterior margin. Described in 1969 from Izu-Oshima, in S. Japan.

## 1029. CENTROPYGE FLAVISSIMA (Cuvier & Valenciennes) 1831

Lemonpeel                                              Pl. 1
11 cm; D XIV/15; A III/16; Sc 45. Adult as figured. Juvenile with a large black spot in middle of side, below lateral line. South Pacific, from Queenslan to the New Hebrides, Fiji and Samoa and Tahiti. Also in Taiwan and th Pescadore islands.

ALLIED SPECIES:

1030. CENTROPYGE HERALDI Woods & Schultz 8 cm. Very similar to 1029 but lacks the blue ring round the eye and the blue markings on the operculum and fins Japanese waters.

**1031. CENTROPYGE BICOLOR** Bloch 1787     **Pl. 18**
Black and Gold Angelfish
15 cm; D XIV–XV/15–17; A III/17–18; Sc 45–48; tr 7–8/20–22. East Indies, Philippines, Okinawa, New Guinea, Queensland, Solomon islands, New Hebrides, Fiji and Samoa.

**1032. CENTROPYGE TIBICEN** (Cuvier & Valenciennes) 1831   **Pl. 15**
Black Angelfish
13 cm; D XIV/16–17; A III/16–17; Sc 45–48. East Indies, Philippines, Taiwan, S. Japan, New Guinea, New Hebrides and Lord Howe island.

**1033. CENTROPYGE NOX** (Bleeker) 1853
Brown Angelfish
12 cm; D XIV–XV/15–17; A III/16–18; Sc 38–43; tr 7–8/22–23. Dorsal and anal pointed posteriorly, tail rounded. Blackish brown, paler on breast, which may be yellowish. Tail black with narrow white edge. East Indies, Melanesia, Queensland.

**1034. CENTROPYGE VROLIKI** (Bleeker) 1853     **Pl. 18**
Pearly-scaled Angelfish
12 cm; D XIV–XV/15–16; A III/16–17; Sc 42–48; tr 7/19–20. Adult as figured, juvenile with a dark ocular band. Philippines, China Sea, Okinawa, Moluccas, New Guinea and Solomon islands; common, sometimes in very shallow water. Doubtfully recorded from the Red Sea.

**1035. CENTROPYGE MULTIFASCIATUS** (Smith & Radcliffe) 1911
12 cm; D XIII/17–18; A III/17–18. Pale brown, paler below; 7–10 dark regular transverse bands as wide as interspaces extending on to soft dorsal and anal. Tail with several narrow transverse bars; a dark ocular band, diffuse below eye. Rare; Borneo, Buru and Philippines.

**1036. CENTROPYGE MULTISPINIS** (Playfair) 1866
14 cm; D XIV/15–17; A III/16–17; Sc 45–48. Blackish with blue scale centres. A large black blotch on sides, above pectoral base. Numerous regular dark vertical bands on sides; preopercular spines, lips and fin margins bright blue; tail with a white margin. South and E. Africa, Seychelles, Aldabra and Ceylon

**1037. CENTROPYGE BISPINOSUS** (Günther) 1860     **Pl. 18**
11 cm; D XIV–XV/16–18; A III/17–18; Sc 43–46. As figured, but juveniles darker, with less red. Known from a number of scattered localities: Kenya, Pemba, Seychelles, Amboina, New Hebrides, Samoa, Fiji and Tahiti.

**1038. CENTROPYGE POTTERI** (Jordan & Metz) 1912     **Pl. 18**
10 cm. Hawaii only, not rare, usually in less than 20 m of water.

**1039. CENTROPYGE LORICULUS** (Günther) 1874     **Pl. 15**
=**C. FLAMMEUS** Woods & Schultz 1953
12 cm. Johnston Island and Hawaii, rare.

**1040. CENTROPYGE FERRUGATUS** Randall & Burgess 1972
7 cm; D XIV/17; A III/17–18; Sc 43–45. Anal and dorsal angular, tail truncate. Rusty red with numerous black spots on body and fins. Dorsal and anal with narrow pale blue margin, tail hyaline. Ryukyu, Okinawa and Amami-Oshima islands in S. Japan; rather deep water.

**1041. CENTROPYGE NIGRIOCELLUS** Woods & Schultz 1953
5 cm. A round black spot at pectoral base and another on soft dorsal. Known from a single specimen taken at Johnston Island, Hawaii.

**1042. CENTROPYGE FISHERI** (Snyder) 1904 **Pl. 18**
8 cm; D XIV/15; A III/17; Sc 40. Rare, rather deep water in Hawaii.

ALLIED SPECIES:

**1043. CENTROPYGE ACANTHOPS** (Norman) 4 cm. Almost certainly a synonym of 1042. Natal and E. Africa.

**1044. CENTROPYGE FLAVICAUDA** Fraser-Brunner 5 cm. Very similar to 1042, but more elongated; blue colour more extensive, extending to back and dorsal. South China and Japan; also recorded from Durban. Very rare.

**1045. PYGOPLITES DIACANTHUS** (Boddaert) 1772 **Pl. 17**
23 cm; D XIII–XIV/17–22; A III/17–19; Sc 45–57; tr 7/22. As figured, but Indian Ocean specimens often more orange. A most beautiful fish. Throughout the entire Indo-Pacific excluding Hawaii, but nowhere common. Usually solitary, in shallow water.

The following species of *Pomacanthinae* have also been described from the Indo-Pacific: *Chaetodontoplus niger* Chan 1969 (S. China), *Genicanthus macclesfieldensis* Chan 1969 (S. China), *Centropyge eibli* Klausewitz 1963 (Nicobar islands).

Family HISTIOPTERIDAE **Boarfish**
Deep-bodied fishes of deep waters. The majority of species are found in cool waters off S. Australia and S. Africa, but one species (*Histiopterus typus* Temminck & Schlegel, 1844) is known from Japan, Hawaii and New Guinea. Quadrangular or triangular and elevated, strongly compressed. Scales small and rough. Lateral line arched. Dorsal profile concave before nape, snout produced, cheeks scaly, operculum with rough exposed bony plates, preoperculum serrated. A single dorsal fin, rayed portion greatly elevated. Three anal spines. Pectorals long, pointed. Ventrals large, tail emarginate. Chin with small barbels in some species. Fig., p. 24.

Family AMPHIPRIONIDAE **Anemone-fish, Clownfish**
Small brightly coloured perch-like fishes which live in association with the large *Stoichactis* Sea-anemones. Confined to and widespread throughout the Indo-Pacific, but absent from the Hawaiian Archipelago. Elongate-oval, compressed. Scales small and ctenoid, extending forward to the eyes. Lateral line interrupted below dorsal rays, resumed on caudal peduncle. Opercular bones scaly, except preopercular flange. Other opercular bones with numerous comb-like spines and lower edge of suborbital with several small spines in *Amphiprion*; comb-like spines lacking, suborbital with 2 large spines in *Premnas*. Dorsal fin continuous, sometimes notched, with 9–12 spines. Anal with 2 spines. Mouth small, with thick lips. Females larger than males, in some species very much so. In nature anemone-fishes are always found in close association with large Sea-anemones, in shallow water on coral. The number of these fishes associated with each anemone seems to depend on the size of the host, but usually there is only one large fish, presumably a female, accompanied by a varying number of smaller fish. Clownfishes exude a mucous substance which protects them from the stings of the anemone; when alarmed they immediately

take shelter among the tentacles of the anemone, to venture forth into the open again as soon as the danger has passed, but never straying far. In return the anemone presumably benefits by obtaining scraps from the fish's meals. In captivity clownfishes are able to live without their host, but they fare better and live longer if a suitable anemone is placed in their tank. They swim with an odd rising and falling waddling, wriggling motion which has earned them the name of clownfishes. They are among the most popular of marine aquarium fishes, and among the very few species which have been bred in captivity. Most of the species are very similar, variable and confusing and the synonymy of the commoner species is tangled and voluminous. They have been revised by Allen (1972) and his treatment is followed in this work.

 *Premnas*     *Amphiprion*

Heads of Amphiprionidae (Adapted from Munro 1967)

### 1046. PREMNAS BIACULEATUS (Bloch) 1790          Pl. 19
Tomato Clownfish
15 cm; D X/17–18; A II/14–15; L 1 44–49; Sc 78–80; tr 8–11/33–36. East Indies, Philippines, Melanesia and Queensland.

### 1047. AMPHIPRION TRICINCTUS Schultz & Welander 1955     Pl. 19
Three-banded Clownfish
10 cm. Variable: brown, red or blackish, tail the same colour as body. Third white band occasionally lost with age. Marshall islands only according to the literature, but seen by the author at Port Moresby (Papua, New Guinea).

### 1048. AMPHIPRION OCELLARIS Cuvier & Valenciennes 1830
Orange Clownfish                                          Pl. 19
8 cm. One of the commonest and best known clownfishes; usually confused with *A. percula*. East Indies, Philippines, Ryukyu islands, India, Ceylon, Andaman islands and N. Australia (Darwin).

### 1049. AMPHIPRION PERCULA (Lacépède) 1802
Black-finned Orange Clownfish
8 cm; D X–XII/14–18; A II/11–13; L 1 29–38; Sc 51–56; tr 5–6/22–26. Almost identical with 1048, but differs in having a black spinous dorsal, much black on back between 1st and 2nd white band and more black on pectoral and tail. Queensland and Melanesia.

### 1050. AMPHIPRION POLYMNUS (Linnaeus) 1758          Pl. 19
=A. LATICLAVIUS (C. & V.) 1830
White-saddled Clownfish
12 cm. As figured, but amount of red or brown on snout and chin variable. Philippines, Vietnam, China, Ryukyu, Moluccas, New Guinea, Solomons and Queensland.

**1051. AMPHIPRION SEBAE** Bleeker 1853
Yellow-tailed Clownfish
12 cm; D X–XI/14–15; A II/13–14; L 1 34–40; Sc 49–52; tr 5–7/18–19.
Brownish black with 2 white cross-bands, 2nd band bent backwards and extending on to upper third of soft dorsal. Base of pectoral, caudal peduncle and
tail bright yellow. Arabia, India, Ceylon, Maldives, Laccadives, Andamans and
Indonesia.

**1052. AMPHIPRION LATEZONATUS** Waite 1900
10 cm. All black with 3 white bands and white margin to tail. Very rare. Lord
Howe island and New South Wales.

**1053. AMPHIPRION CLARKII** (Bennett) 1830                    **Pl. 19**
=**A. XANTHURUS** (C. & V.) 1830
=**A. PAPUENSIS** Macleay 1883
=**A. JAPONICUS** (T. & S.) 1842
=**A. MELANOSTOLUS** (Richardson) 1842
Clark's Clownfish
15 cm; D X/15–17; A II/13–14; L 1 40; Sc 50; tr 5/20. Extremely variable;
generally dark with 2 white bands; caudal peduncle often white. Tail white or
yellow, with a large black blotch in juveniles. Anal and ventrals generally
black. Often imported as *A. sebae*. Persian Gulf, Ceylon, Maldives, Indonesia,
Philippines, S. China, Ryukyu, Japan, Melanesia, Micronesia, Australia.

**1054. AMPHIPRION ALLARDI** Klausewitz 1970          **Pl. 19** (Juv.)
East African Clownfish
12 cm; D X–XI/13–14; A II/12–13; L 1 35; Sc 55; tr 5/20. Juvenile as figured;
adult with yellow tail and reddish brown underparts and snout; colour of fins
variable. East coast of Africa, from Natal to Kenya. See 1055, 1056.

**1055. AMPHIPRION BICINCTUS** Rüppell 1828
Red Sea Clownfish
Similar to 1054, but scale and fin counts said to differ. Red Sea only.

**1056. AMPHIPRION FUSCOCAUDATUS** Allen 1972
Seychelles Clownfish
Very similar to 1054, but tail black with upper rays white. Seychelles and
Aldabra.

**1057. AMPHIPRION CHRYSOGASTER** Cuvier & Valenciennes 1830
=**A. FUSCIVENTER** Bennett 1831
=**A. MAURITIENSIS** Schultz 1953
Mauritius Clownfish; Debouetteur (Mauritius)
Mauritius only.

**1058. AMPHIPRION LATIFASCIATUS** Allen 1972
Colours in life unknown. Two pale bands, tail pale. Madagascar only, rare.

**1059. AMPHIPRION CHRYSOPTERUS** Cuvier & Valenciennes 1830
Golden-finned Clownfish
12 cm; D X/15–16; A II/13–14; L 1 31–37; tr 5/19–20. Micronesia, Fiji,
Samoa, Gilbert islands and Tahiti.

**1060. AMPHIPRION AKYNDINOS** Allen 1972     **Pl. 19**
White-tailed Clownfish
12 cm. Variable, juveniles often with a 3rd white band on peduncle and dark blotch on tail. Queensland and New Caledonia.

**1061. AMPHIPRION CHAGOSENSIS** Allen 1972
Similar to 1060, but very rare. Known only from the Chagos Archipelago in the Indian Ocean.

**1062. AMPHIPRION MELANOPUS** Bleeker 1862     **Pl. 19**
Black Clownfish
11 cm; D X–XI/15–17; A II/13–14; L 1 35–38; Sc 48–51; tr 4–6/19–21. Adult as figured, but variable. Juveniles often with a 2nd white band. Indonesia, Melanesia, Micronesia, Samoa, New Caledonia. Very common in Queensland. See 1063.

**1063. AMPHIPRION MACCULLOCHI** Whitley 1929
Very similar to 1062, but differs structurally. Lord Howe island only.

**1064. AMPHIPRION RUBROCINCTUS** Richardson 1842     **Pl. 19**
Richardson's Clownfish
12 cm; D X–XI/15–18; A II/15–18; L 1 32–41; Sc 49–57; tr 4–6/19–21. Adult as figured, but juvenile with a 2nd white band and occasionally with traces of a 3rd; black lateral blotch variable in size, often absent. This species and 1065 are commonly sold as *A. ephippium*. North-West Australia, Queensland, New Guinea, Fiji, Tonga, Samoa and Tahiti.

**1065. AMPHIPRION FRENATUS** Brevoort 1856
=**A. POLYLEPIS** Bleeker 1877
Bridled Clownfish
Very similar to 1064, but adults often develop a larger black lateral blotch and occasionally lose the white band, thus strongly resembling 1066. Distribution more northerly than in 1064. South China, Taiwan, Ryukyu, Okinawa, S. Japan and Korea. Very doubtfully recorded from S. Africa.

**1066. AMPHIPRION EPHIPPIUM** (Bloch) 1790
Black-backed Clownfish
12 cm. Bright tomato red, usually with a large black lateral blotch. White stripes absent at all stages. Nicobar islands, Malaya, Sumatra, Thailand.

**1067. AMPHIPRION PERIDERAION** Bleeker 1855     **Pl. 19**
Salmon Clownfish
8 cm. More elongated than foregoing species. East Indies, Philippines, Thailand, Palau islands, Eniwetok, Bikini, Hong Kong, Amami, Taiwan, New Guinea, New Hebrides, Queensland.

**1068. AMPHIPRION CALLIOPS** Schultz 1966
Superficially resembles 1067. Indian Ocean; no other data available.

**1069. AMPHIPRION NIGRIPES** Regan 1908
Black-footed Clownfish
Very similar to 1067, but ventrals always black, anal occasionally black. Maldive islands.

**1070. AMPHIPRION AKALLOPISOS** Bleeker 1853              **Pl. 19**
White-backed Clownfish
9 cm; D IX–X/18–20; A II/12–14; L 1 37–42; Sc 53–57; tr 4–6/18–19. White
dorsal stripe tapers and ceases above eyes. Indonesia, Andamans, Madagascar,
Comoros, Seychelles; very common in E. Africa. See 1071.

**1071. AMPHIPRION SANDARACINOS** Allen 1972
Allen's Clownfish
Very similar to 1070, but dentition and scale counts differ and white dorsal
stripe starts at upper lip. Philippines.

Family POMACENTRIDAE **Damselfish and Sergeant-majors**
A very large family of small, agile, often brightly coloured fishes which occur
in all warm seas. Closely related to the clownfishes from which they differ in
having much larger scales. Usually in small schools, sometimes solitary, sedentary. Difficult to capture because of their ability to take cover among coral
branches. Many species, some very brilliant and favourite aquarium specimens.
Only the commoner species are well known; many species are variable, much
confused in the literature and often known from a few specimens only. Numerous
new species have been described in recent years and intensive collecting with
explosives and anaesthetics in almost any suitable locality is certain to yield
many more.

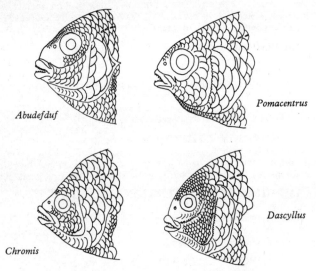

Heads of Pomacentridae (Adapted from Munro 1967)

DEMOISELLES 171

Subfamily *Pomacentrinae* Demoiselles, Damselfish
Small, compressed, perch-like fishes of coral reefs and rocky shores. Scales
large (36 or less longitudinally), ctenoid, extending to nostrils and onto unpaired fins. Lateral line ends below soft dorsal, sometimes continued several
scale rows lower down on caudal peduncle. Cheeks and operculum scaly,
preoperculum margin serrated. Dorsal fin continuous, comprising 12–14 weak
spines; 2 anal spines. Tail forked or emarginate, ventrals with scaly axillary
process. Mouth small, slightly protractile, lips fleshy. 1–2 rows of slender
incisor-like teeth in jaws.

**1072. DAYA JERDONI** (Day) 1873
Jerdon's Demoiselle
15 cm; D XIII/13; A II/14; L 1 19; Sc 30; tr 5/10. Tail emarginate. Back and
head pale blue-green, sides silvery; snout and cheeks with blue spots. Most
scales below lateral line with blue centres. A black dot above pectoral axil.
Tail and fins dusky with blue spots. Ceylon, India, E. Indies, Melanesia,
Queensland.

**1073. EUPOMACENTRUS LIVIDUS** (Bloch & Schneider) 1801
Leaden Demoiselle
16 cm; D XI–XII/13–16; A II/13–14; L 1 16–18/7–9; tr 2/9–10. Tail lobes
rounded. Blackish violet with a blue spot on each body scale. Head and breast
bluish grey. A black spot, surrounded by a white ring in juveniles, on posterior
dorsal rays. Pectorals brown, tail yellowish, other fins blackish. Coastal reefs
throughout the Indo-Pacific excluding Hawaii.

**1074. EUPOMACENTRUS NIGRICANS** (Lacépède) 1803     **Pl. 22**
Dusky Demoiselle
15 cm; D XII/14–17; A II/12–13; L 1 18–21/8–10; tr 2/9–10. One variety
(*Pomacentrus albofasciatus* Schlegel & Müller, 1844) has a broad pale band
from middle of dorsal to anal fin. Coastal reefs in E. Africa, Madagascar, the
E. Indies, Philippines, Taiwan, Ryukyu, Melanesia, Micronesia and Polynesia.

**1075. POMACENTRUS CYANOMOS** Bleeker 1856
Violet Demoiselle
10 cm; D XIII/11; A II/11; Sc 26; tr 3/10. Tail forked, lobes prolonged into
filaments. Silvery violet, darker above. A blackish spot at origin of lateral line
and a triangular brown spot at pectoral base. Fins dark violet, dorsal with a
whitish basal patch. Tail hyaline, outer rays dark violet. Melanesia, E. Indies,
India and Ceylon.

**1076. POMACENTRUS TAENIURUS** Bleeker 1856     **Pl. 22**
Swallow-tailed Demoiselle
11 cm; D XIII/10–11; A II/10–11; Sc 25–33; tr 2/9. Coral reefs, but occasionally
in brackish water. East Africa, Seychelles, E. Indies, Melanesia.

**1077. POMACENTRUS VIOLASCENS** (Bleeker) 1848     **Pl. 20**
Yellow-tailed Demoiselle
8 cm; D XIII/10–11; A II/10–11; L 1 16–18/6–9; tr 2/9. Coral reefs in the E.
Indies, Philippines, Melanesia and Fiji.

ALLIED SPECIES:
**1078. POMACENTRUS MELANOCHIR** Bleeker 10 cm. Blackish with bright
blue lines and spots on head; each body scale with a bright blue vertical streak. Tail

yellow, lobes less prolonged than in 1077; anal and dorsal violet, posterior part yellow in some specimens. East Indies, Melanesia, Micronesia and Polynesia.
**1079. P. LITTORALIS** C. & V. 13 cm. Tail lobes rounded. Blackish brown, tail paler. A black spot at origin of lateral line. East Indies, Melanesia, Queensland, Mauritius.
**1080. P. COELESTIS** Jordan & Starks 8 cm. Blue with a dark blue vertical streak on each body scale. A black spot at origin of lateral line. Ventrals, anal and tail dusky orange. South Japan, Marshall islands.

### 1081. POMACENTRUS TRIPUNCTATUS Cuvier & Valenciennes 1830
Three-spot Demoiselle                                                                 **Pl. 20**
13 cm; D XIII–XIV/13–15; A II/13–15; L 1 15–18/7–11; tr 2/9. As figured, but variable, all or any of the black spots may be absent. Coral reefs, occasionally entering brackish waters. East Africa, Seychelles, Ceylon, E. Indies, Philippines, Melanesia, Queensland.

### 1082. POMACENTRUS PAVO (Bloch) 1787                    Pl. 20
Peacock Demoiselle
11 cm; D XIII/12–14; A II/13–15; L 1 16–21/8–10. Very variable, some specimens being much yellower than the one figured, others almost completely blue with yellow anal and tail. South and E. Africa, Seychelles to E. Indies, Melanesia, Queensland and Polynesia as far as Tahiti and the Tuamotu islands.

### 1083. POMACENTRUS PULCHERRIMUS Smith 1960       Pl. 20
Blue Demoiselle
8 cm. Coral reefs in the W. Indian Ocean; very common in the Seychelles.

### 1084. POMACENTRUS AMBOINENSIS Bleeker 1868       Pl. 20
Amboina Demoiselle
11 cm; D XIII/14–16; A II/15–16; L 1 16–18/8–10. East Indies, Melanesia, Queensland and Fiji.

### 1085. POMACENTRUS SULFUREUS Klunzinger 1871       Pl. 20
Sulphur Demoiselle
10 cm. Coral reefs down to deepish water. Red Sea and W. Indian Ocean. Very common in the Seychelles.

ALLIED SPECIES:
**1086. POMACENTRUS MOLUCCENSIS** Bleeker 8 cm. Brownish orange with pale pinkish spots and lines on snout, chin and cheeks. Anal with a pale submarginal line and dark brown edge. A small black spot at origin of lateral line and another above pectoral base. East Indies, Philippines, Okinawa, Melanesia and Marshall islands.
**1087. P. LUTEOBRUNNEUS** Smith 10 cm. Anal and tail lobes rounded. Dark purplish brown; posterior dorsal rays and tail orange, pectoral pale yellow. Islands of Astove and Aldabra, in the Indian Ocean.
**1088. P. TRICHOURUS** Günther 10 cm. Blackish grey; a black spot at origin of lateral line, pectoral base black. Tail emarginate, pale yellow with black margin. Dorsal and anal blackish with pale longitudinal lines, ventrals blackish, pectorals yellow. East Africa.
**1089. P. SUFFLAVUS** Whitley 8 cm. Tail lobes rounded. Yellowish brown, olive above; pink spots on cheeks and operculum and a row of pink spots along ventral profile, continued on anal. A black spot in pectoral axil. Melanesia and Queensland.
**1090. P. MELANOPTERUS** Bleeker 11 cm. Caudal lobes rounded. Uniform brownish olive, paler on head, breast and caudal peduncle. A black spot at origin of lateral line and a black bar at base of pectoral. Fins blackish, tail pale brown. Mauritius, E. Indies and Melanesia.

**1091. P. NIGROMANUS** Weber 8 cm. Tail emarginate. Brown; head and anterior back contrastingly darker than remainder. A large black spot at pectoral base. Fins paler than body, but anterior part of ventrals and of anal black. Melanesia, E. Indies.

## 1092. POMACENTRUS NOTOPHTHALMUS Bleeker 1853
Yellow Demoiselle
15 cm. Caudal lobes rounded. Bright yellow, upper part of head and anterior part of back violet brown. Two bluish lines on snout; head and operculum with large bluish spots; a black spot at origin of lateral line. Juveniles have a white-ringed black ocellus on dorsal fin and 2 whitish cross-bars. Ceylon, India, E. Indies, Philippines and Melanesia.

## 1093. POMACENTRUS BREVICEPS (Schlegel & Müller) 1841
10 cm. Tail deeply forked, lobes prolonged. Light brown, whitish on belly, with silvery spots on scales of operculum and body. Soft dorsal brown with white spots; other fins and tail yellow, often with white spots. Juveniles with 3–4 dark cross-bars. East Indies, Philippines and Melanesia.

## 1094. POMACENTRUS PERSPICILLATUS
Cuvier & Valenciennes 1830
Four-spot Demoiselle
20 cm. Tail lobes pointed. Pale yellowish, top of head darker. Pale violet blue lines on head and around eyes; a pale lavender vertical streak on each body scale. A dark blotch on nape, a 2nd dark blotch at base of spinous dorsal and one at base of posterior dorsal rays. A 4th dark spot surrounding vent. Fins and tail yellowish to pinkish, anal and tail dusky distally. East Indies and Melanesia.

## 1095. POMACENTRUS PROSOPOTAENIA Bleeker 1852
Masked Demoiselle
18 cm; D XIII/13–15; A II/12–15; L 1 17–18/8–9; tr 2/10. Tail lobes rounded. Olive brown, paler below. Narrow whitish lines across snout and chin and around eyes. Body scales with vertical whitish streaks. A large white-ringed black ocellus inside pectoral axil. Vent surrounded by a blue-ringed black spot. 2–3 indistinct dark saddles on back. Fins yellow or olive. Juveniles with white-ringed ocellus on dorsal and pale cross-bands on body. India, E. Indies and Melanesia.

## 1096. POMACENTRUS CHRYSOPOECILUS Schlegel & Müller 1841
Yellow-spot Demoiselle
15 cm. Tail lobes rounded. Olive brown, yellowish below. Scales of head and body with pale vertical streaks; narrow pale lines on snout and below eye. A round yellow spot below spinous dorsal base and a black spot at origin of lateral line. Fins brown, anal and ventrals blackish. East Indies and Melanesia.

## 1097. POMACENTRUS SEMIFASCIATUS Günther 1881
Half-banded Demoiselle
5 cm. Tail lobes pointed. Reddish with a silvery vertical band across back below 5th–7th dorsal spines. Dorsal reddish with a white blotch on posterior rays. Anal and ventrals black, remaining fins hyaline. Melanesia.

## 1098. POMACENTRUS BIFASCIATUS Bleeker 1854
Double-banded Demoiselle
6 cm. Tail lobes rounded. Dull yellow with a dark saddle on nape and one

on back continued on posterior spinous dorsal. A narrow blue line before eye.
Fins yellow. East Indies and Melanesia.

### 1099. POMACENTRUS VAIULI Jordan & Seale 1905

8 cm. Lips yellow, iris yellow. Purple brown to blue with bright blue lines on
snout and around eyes; several bright blue longitudinal lines on body. Pectoral
base reddish orange; dorsal dark basally, yellow distally, with black margin.
A black spot enclosed by blue ring on soft dorsal. Tail bright golden yellow.
Fiji, Samoa, Marshall islands.

### 1100. POMACENTRUS JENKINSI Jordan & Everman 1903

8 cm. Dark purplish brown. Distinct transverse narrow dark lines on sides,
following scale margins. Base of vertical fins purplish black; distal margin of
tail, soft dorsal and anal pale, otherwise fins blackish. Solitary, living in holes.
Hawaii, Samoa, Marshall islands, Ryukyu islands.

### 1101. POMACENTRUS TRACEYI Schultz 1953

Dark reddish brown. Dorsal scales with a round blue basal spot, lateral scales
with vertical blue streak. A large black spot at dorsal base, $\frac{2}{3}$ from origin.
Caudal peduncle bright yellow, dorsal, tail and posterior half of anal yellow.
Marshall islands.

### 1102. POMACENTRUS SINDENSIS (Day) 1873

12 cm. Green, whitish below. Dark purple streaks below eye and on operculum
and 5 series of purple spots along mid-lateral scale rows. Eye golden with a
vertical blackish bar through pupil. Lips and pectorals yellow. Dorsal and anal
green with yellow posterior rays. Tail forked, green with yellow distal margin.
Weedy rock pools from India to E. Africa and Mozambique.

### 1103. POMACENTRUS APICALIS (De Vis) 1885

Orange-tipped Demoiselle

10 cm. Body, fins and tail blackish brown. Anterior part of dorsal black, basal
$\frac{2}{3}$ blackish brown, distal $\frac{1}{3}$ orange with a blue submarginal line. Anal spines
violet blue, tip of upper tail lobe bright orange. Rather rare. North Queensland
and Torres Straights.

### 1104. POMACENTRUS FLAVICAUDA Whitley 1928

Yellow-tailed Demoiselle

9 cm. Dark brown with bright yellow tail. Tail emarginate. North Australia
and N. Queensland.

The following species of *Pomacentrus* have also been described from the Indo-Pacific:
*P. caeruleus* Q. & G. 1824 described from Mauritius, but also found in the Philippines
and in Polynesia, very similar superficially to certain forms of *P. pavo* (Bloch) and of
*Abudefduf assimilis* (Günther); *P. smithi* Fowler & Bean 1928 (Philippines); *P. gram-
morhynchus* Fowler 1918 (Philippines); *P. lepidogenys* Fowler & Bean 1928 (Philippines);
*P. reidi* Fowler & Bean 1928 (E. Indies and Philipines); *P. stigma* Fowler & Bean 1928
(Philippines); *P. pristiger* C. & V. 1833 (Mauritius and E. Indies); *P. fasciatus* C. & V.
1830 (Java); *P. ovoides* Cartier 1874 (Philippines); *P. beauforti* Fowler & Bean 1928
(Philippines); *P. inornatus* Herre 1934 (Hong Kong); *P. aureus* Fowler 1927 (Howland
island); *P. wardi* Whitley 1927 (Queensland); *P. formosanus* Fowler & Bean (Taiwan);
*P. notatus* De Vis 1884 (New Britain); *P. nomiatus* De Vis 1884 (South Seas); *P.
trifasciatus* De Vis 1884 (South Seas); *P. madagascariensis* Sauvage 1882 (Madagascar);
*P. pingi* Wang 1941 (Hainan); *P. hainanensis* Wang 1941 (Hainan).

Subfamily *Abudefdufinae* (=*Glyphisodontinae*) Sergeant-majors
A very large group of small colourful coral fishes which occur in all warm seas.
Very similar in appearance, structure and habits to the demoiselles, from which
they differ in having a smooth preopercular margin. Favourite aquarium fishes.

### 1105. HEMIGLYPHIDODON PLAGIOMETOPON (Bleeker) 1852
Purple-spotted Sergeant-major
18 cm; D XIII/12–14; A II/13–15; L 1 14–18/5–10; tr 4–5/9–10. Tail slightly
emarginate, lobes rounded. Dark slaty grey with purple-blue spots and vertical
lines on scales of head and body. Purple-blue lines on snout and around eyes;
a black blotch at pectoral base. Fins brownish orange with dark margins.
Coral reefs in the E. Indies and Melanesia.

### 1106. PLECTROGLYPHIDODON NITIDUS Smith 1955
6 cm. Tail emarginate. Green; chin, breast and belly pale blue. Snout, operculum and preoperculum marked with broad purple lines and spots. A purple
basal spot on each scale above lateral line; 10 vertical purple lines below lateral
line on posterior part of body, not extending below level of pectoral base. A
purple line from lower angle of operculum to anal origin, continued to end of
3rd anal ray. A large black kidney-shaped area from base of soft dorsal to base
of anal. Dorsal brownish orange with a blue basal line and a blue submarginal
line from origin to last spines. Posterior anal rays brownish orange. Tail golden
yellow, pectorals light yellow, ventrals pale blue. Western Indian Ocean, rare.

### 1107. PLECTROGLYPHIDODON JOHNSTONIANUS
Fowler & Ball 1924
8 cm. Lips thick. Purplish brown with diagonal dark lines along transverse
scale rows. A large black band in front of peduncle, from soft dorsal to anal.
Hawaii and Marshall islands.

### 1108. ABUDEFDUF COELESTINUS Cuvier & Valenciennes 1830
?=SEXFASCIATUS auct., nec Lacépède     **Pl. 21**
Six-banded Sergeant-major, Boeteur Carreaux (S)
16 cm; D XIII/12–13; A II/12–13; L 1 19–21/3–8; tr 3/11. As figured; markings
tend to become indistinct with age. Very common in shallow coastal waters and
tidal pools throughout the Indo-Pacific excluding Hawaii.

### 1109. ABUDEFDUF SORDIDUS (Forskål) 1775     **Pl. 21**
Grey-banded Sergeant-major, Boeteur Roche (S), Kupipi (Hawaii)
23 cm; D XIII/14–16; A II/14–16; L 1 21–23/7–8; tr 3/13–14. As figured,
but colours dull and markings indistinct in old individuals. Usually in pairs or
small parties in rock pools. Very common and widespread throughout the
Indo-Pacific including the Red Sea and Hawaii.

### 1110. ABUDEFDUF SEPTEMFASCIATUS
Cuvier & Valenciennes 1830     **Pl. 21**
Seven-banded Sergeant-major
22 cm; D XIII/12–13; A II/12–13; L 1 20–22/7–10; tr 3/11–12. Almost identical with 1109, but lacks ocellus on peduncle. Rock pools. Common throughout
most of the Indo-Pacific, but absent from Queensland and Hawaii.

### 1111. ABUDEFDUF SAXATILIS (Linnaeus) 1758     **Pl. 21**
Five-banded Sergeant-major; Kepal Batu (Malay)

18 cm. The young are usually found in small schools in tidal pools, but the adults often congregate in enormous shoals in shallow coastal waters. Common in all warm seas; the typical form was described from the tropical Atlantic; the Indo-Pacific race is *vaigiensis* Q. & G. 1824. Apparently not recorded from Hawaii.

### 1112. ABUDEFDUF BENGALENSIS (Bloch) 1787
Narrow-banded Sergeant-major
16 cm. Tail forked with rounded lobes. Yellowish, light olive-grey on back with 7 dark cross-bands, much narrower than interspaces. Fins yellowish grey, darker terminally. Pectorals with a blackish basal spot. East Indies, S. Japan, Philippines and Melanesia.

### 1113. ABUDEFDUF ABDOMINALIS (Quoy & Gaimard) 1824　　Pl. 23
Maomao (H)
24 cm. Usually in quiet shallow waters; known only from Hawaii.

### 1114. ABUDEFDUF PALMERI (Ogilby) 1913
Palmer's Sergeant-major
18 cm; D XIII/14; A II/14; L l 28; tr 5/18. Tail lobes rounded. Greenish grey, belly silvery. Seven black cross-bands, narrower than pale interspaces. Fins blackish, tail dusky greenish. Queensland.

### 1115. ABUDEFDUF ANNULATUS (Peters) 1855　　　　　　Pl. 23
8 cm; D XIII/12; A II/12; Sc 26; tr 2/9. Tropical east coast of Africa south to Knysna. Rare.

### 1116. ABUDEFDUF THORACOTAENIATUS Fowler & Bean 1928
8 cm. Grey-blue, cheeks and breast silvery, posterior part of body, tail and vertical fins dark. A black vertical band from eye to eye across isthmus; a 2nd black band from upper corner of operculum continuing across breast to opposite side. A 3rd broad black bar from below origin of lateral line, through pectoral base to just below it. Coral reefs and weedy places in the Philippines.

### 1117. ABUDEFDUF CURACAO (Bloch) 1787
Black-snouted Sergeant-major
12 cm; D XIII–XIV/11–13; A II/12–14; L l 14–17/8–12; tr 2–3/9–10. Head and back green; chin, breast and belly silvery white. A blackish green dorsal band from snout to tail. Five blackish green triangular saddles: 1st on head, enclosing eye, 5th on caudal peduncle. Tail green, blackish basally; anal bluish with blackish margin; dorsal and ventrals green, pectorals hyaline. Common among coral from the E. Indies and Philippines to Melanesia, Queensland, Micronesia and Polynesia.

### 1118. ABUDEFDUF LEUCOGASTER (Bleeker) 1847　　　　Pl. 21
White-bellied Sergeant-major
13 cm; D XIII/11–14; A II/13–14; L l 15–16/8–9; tr 2–3/10. East Africa, the Seychelles, E. Indies, Philippines, Melanesia, Queensland, Micronesia and Polynesia as far as the Society islands.

### 1119. ABUDEFDUF MELAS Cuvier & Valenciennes 1830
Black Sergeant-major; Boeteur noir (S)
18 cm; D XIII/14; A II/13–14; L l 16–18/8–10; tr 3/10. Tail lobes rounded. Uniform blackish brown; fins and tail sometimes darker. Solitary, often living in holes among dead coral rubble. Entire Indo-Pacific excluding Hawaii.

**1120. ABUDEFDUF BEHNI** (Bleeker) 1847
12 cm. Tail lobes pointed. Dark brown, peduncle and tail sometimes paler.
Opercular margin dark and a dark area behind preoperculum. A large black
triangle at pectoral base. Ventrals and anal blackish. East Indies, Philippines,
Melanesia and Polynesia.

**1121. ABUDEFDUF ZONATUS** (Cuvier & Valenciennes) 1830    **Pl. 21**
9 cm; D XIII/13; A II/13; L 1 15–17/2; tr 3/9. Solitary, usually in tidal pools.
Entire Indo-Pacific excluding Hawaii and Queensland.

**1122. ABUDEFDUF AMABILIS** (De Vis) 1884
6 cm. Elongated, tail emarginate, lobes pointed. Brown; a narrow white transverse bar from nape to breast, incorporating pectoral base which is always pale.
A white transverse stripe from mid-dorsal base to vent and a white ring on
anterior caudal peduncle. Basal 3rd of tail black. Japan, Philippines, Micronesia,
Polynesia and Queensland. See 1123.

**1123. ABUDEFDUF ALBOFASCIATUS** (Hombron & Jacquinot) 1853
7 cm. Similar to 1122, but with a 4th pale ring on posterior peduncle, base of
tail yellowish and some blue spots on head, back and anal base. Philippines,
Japan, Micronesia and Polynesia.

**1124. ABUDEFDUF SINDONIS** (Jordan & Everman) 1903
12 cm; D XII/19; A II/15. Deep-bodied, tail forked. Dark brown with 2 pale
cross-bands. Tail blackish. Young without pale bars and with a prominent
white-ringed black ocellus on soft dorsal. Restricted to surge areas among lava
rocks in Hawaii.

**1125. ABUDEFDUF XANTHOZONA** (Bleeker) 1853    **Pl. 21**
10 cm; D XIII/11–13; A II/11–13; L 1 18/10; tr 3/9. As figured, but markings
less distinct in old individuals. Solitary in coral pools. East Africa, Seychelles,
E. Indies, Philippines, Solomon islands, Fiji, Samoa and Tahiti.

**1126. ABUDEFDUF PHOENIXENSIS** Schultz 1943
6 cm. Similar to 1125, but 3–4 pale transverse lines; 1st from nape across
operculum; 2nd from 6th dorsal spine, 3rd from soft dorsal origin to vent, 4th
on anterior peduncle, followed by a black ring. Blue ring of dorsal ocellus lost
with age. Tail white or yellowish. Hawaii, Phoenix and Marshall islands.

**1127. ABUDEFDUF LEUCOZONUS** (Bleeker) 1859
8 cm; D XII/15–17; A II/12–14; L 1 20/8; tr 4/10. Dark olive brown with a
pearly blue spot or streak on each body scale. Fins and tail brown; a large blue-
ringed black ocellus on posterior spines and anterior rays of dorsal fin. Blue
ring fades and ocellus becomes indistinct with age. Red Sea, E. Indies, Melanesia, Micronesia and Polynesia.

**1128. ABUDEFDUF CINGULUM** (Klunzinger) 1871
8 cm. Tail forked, lobes rounded. Uniform dark olive, eye golden. A large
black ocellus surrounded by a pale ring which is yellow in front and blue
behind on last spines of dorsal fin. Red Sea and W. Indian Ocean.

**1129. ABUDEFDUF BIOCELLATUS** Quoy & Gaimard 1824    **Pl. 20**
Ocellated Sergeant-major
10 cm; D XIII/11–13; A II/12–14; L 1 15–17/7–9; tr 2/9. Very variable; old
individuals usually darker and duller with blue colour reduced to small spots

on head and back and to pale ring surrounding posterior ocellus. Sometimes with 1 or 2 white vertical bands. Very common in tidal pools throughout the entire Indo-Pacific excluding Hawaii.

## 1130. ABUDEFDUF LEUCOPOMUS Lesson 1830

7 cm. Elongated, tail lobes rounded. Slaty blue, paler below. A blue stripe from snout to above eye, wider behind eye, continued to base of soft dorsal where it surrounds a black ocellus. A black spot at dorsal margin of tail base at all ages. Fins dusky blue, dorsal base darker. Andamans, E. Indies, Philippines, Taiwan, Ryukyu, Japan, Micronesia, Melanesia and Polynesia as far as the Tuamotu islands.

## 1131. ABUDEFDUF OXYODON (Bleeker) 1858                    Pl. 20
Blue-banded Sergeant-major

8 cm; D XII/14; A II/13; L 1 14/9; tr 4/7. East Indies, Philippines and Taiwan. A favourite aquarium fish.

## 1132. ABUDEFDUF GLAUCUS Cuvier & Valenciennes 1830       Pl. 20
Slaty Sergeant-major

9 cm; D XIII/12; A II/12; L 1 17–20/6–8; tr 2–3/8–9. As figured, but old specimens duller in colour. Very common in shallow reef pools throughout the Indo-Pacific excluding Hawaii.

## 1133. ABUDEFDUF ASSIMILIS (Günther) 1862                 Pl. 20
## =GLYPHISODONTOPS UNIOCELLATUS Bleeker 1877
Sapphire Sergeant-major

6 cm; D XIII/11–13; A II/12–14; L 1 15–17/7–9; tr 2/9. As figured, but amount of orange on tail and belly variable, some specimens being almost completely blue. A most beautiful and very common fish of shallow coral reefs and rock pools. Ceylon, E. Indies, Philippines, Micronesia, Melanesia, Polynesia and Queensland. Very common in Fiji and Samoa. A favourite aquarium fish.

## 1134. ABUDEFDUF CYANEUS (Quoy & Gaimard) 1824            Pl. 20
## =GLYPHISODON HEDLEYI Whitley 1927
Cornflower Sergeant-major

7 cm; D XIII/11–12; A II/11–13; L 1 16–17/6–8; tr 3/9–10. Tail may be orange as figured, yellow or blue; northern populations tend to have blue tails, southern populations an orange tail. East Indies, Philippines, Taiwan, Ryukyu, Melanesia, Polynesia and Queensland. See 1135.

## 1135. ABUDEFDUF SAPPHIRUS Jordan & Richardson 1908
## =A. PARASEMA Fowler 1918
6 cm; D XIII/11; A II/12; L 1 13–15/8–9; tr 2–3/8–9. Similar to 1134 but deeper bodied, blue colour slightly violet, posteroventral part of peduncle and basal half of tail bright orange, distal half hyaline. A black spot on upper part of pectoral base and a black line from snout to eyes. Philippines, Taiwan.

## 1136. ABUDEFDUF ANABATOIDES (Bleeker) 1847
10 cm. Tail deeply forked, lobes often produced. Blue green; scales of head and body with blue spots. Tail yellowish with a dark submarginal band at upper and lower margins. Dorsal dusky with blue spots; other fins yellowish. A black spot at pectoral base. East Indies and Melanesia.

**1137. ABUDEFDUF BANKIERI** (Richardson) 1846
8 cm. Tail deeply forked, lobes prolonged. Tips of anal and dorsal also prolonged. Dark slaty with pale spots on head and pale vertical bars on body
scales. A black spot at pectoral base and sometimes a black ocellus at origin of
lateral line. Anterior parts of dorsal and anal black, posterior rays of dorsal and
anal cadmium yellow. East Indies, Philippines, China and Melanesia. Very
common in N. Queensland.

**1138. ABUDEFDUF DICKI** (Lienard) 1839                    **Pl. 21**
10 cm. As figured, but variable; juveniles more reddish with a black spot on
anterior part of dorsal. Coral reefs of entire Indo-Pacific excluding Queensland
and Hawaii.

**1139. ABUDEFDUF LACRYMATUS** (Quoy & Gaimard) 1824    **Pl. 21**
10 cm; D XII/16–17; A II/13; L l 19/7; tr 3/9–10. Entire Indo-Pacific excluding
Queensland and Hawaii.

**1140. ABUDEFDUF IMPARIPENNIS** (Vaillant & Sauvage) 1875
5 cm. Tail lobes rounded. Dark reddish brown to blue-grey; scattered small
blue spots on head, back and upper sides; posterior part of peduncle and tail
pale yellow. A black spot at pectoral base; fins brown or blackish. Entire Indo-
Pacific including Hawaii, but apparently not in Queensland.

**1141. ABUDEFDUF AUREUS** (Cuvier & Valenciennes) 1830
16 cm; D XIII/11–12; A II/13–14; L l 16/9; tr 4/9–10. Bright golden yellow
with scattered blue dots on head. Spiny dorsal dusky, tail very pale yellow.
East Indies, Philippines, S. Japan, Micronesia.

**1142. ABUDEFDUF REX** Snyder 1909
5 cm. Light orange brown on head and back; chin, breast and belly pale lavender or bluish. Narrow irregular blue lines and spots on snout, cheeks and
through eye; a light blue spot on each body scale. A blackish spot at origin of
lateral line. Dorsal orange, other fins pinkish or bluish hyaline. Okinawa.

**1143. ABUDEFDUF DASYGENYS** Fowler 1935
15 cm. Ochreous yellow above, light orange on chin and breast. Scales of
operculum, preoperculum and body below lateral line with a blue basal spot.
Tail forked, yellow, with blue spots at base and with a bluish hyaline inner area;
a black spot at pectoral base. Dorsal greenish yellow, pectorals yellow, ventrals
and anal bluish green. Mozambique and Natal.

**1144. ABUDEFDUF MELANOPUS** (Bleeker) 1856            **Pl. 21**
= **A. XANTHONOTUS** (Bleeker) 1859
Black-footed Sergeant-major
7 cm. East Africa and the Seychelles to the E. Indies, Philippines, Okinawa,
Melanesia and Queensland. Uncommon.

**1145. ABUDEFDUF XANTHURUS** (Bleeker) 1853
20 cm. Brown with 2 vertical black stripes on operculum and dark orange
peduncle, anal fin and tail; ventrals blackish. South-East Africa, E. Indies,
Philippines, Melanesia and Queensland.

**1146. ABUDEFDUF SPAROIDES** (Cuvier & Valenciennes) 1830 **Pl. 21**
**=POMACENTRUS ZANZIBARIENSIS** Von Bonde 1934
15 cm; D XIII/13; A II/12; Sc 30; tr 4/11. East Africa, Seychelles, Aldabra
and Mauritius. Very doubtfully recorded from Fiji. Common in rock pools in
E. Africa.

The following species of *Abudefduf* have also been described from the Indo-Pacific:
*A. bonang* (Bleeker) 1853, Sumatra; *A. bleekeri* Fowler & Bean 1928, E. Indies; *A.
clarkii* Snyder 1911, Japan; *A. notatus* (Day) 1869, Andamans; *A. unimaculatus* C. & V.
1830, E. Indies; *A. azurepunctatus* Fowler & Bean 1928, Philippines; *A. hemicyaneus*
Weber 1913, Kei islands; *A. azysron* (Bleeker) 1877, Amboina; *A. melanocarpus* Fowler
& Bean 1928, Philippines.

Subfamily *Chrominae* Pullers, Humbugs
Small agile fishes of coral reefs and rocky shores found in all warm seas. Very
similar in appearance and habits to the demoiselles and sergeant-majors, they
differ in having compressed teeth. Many species, some of which are well known
aquarium fishes. Species of the genus *Dascyllus* are very deep-bodied with
truncate or emarginate tails; *Chromis* are elongated, with deeply forked tails.

**1147. ACANTHOCHROMIS POLYACANTHUS** (Bleeker) 1855
Spotty-tail
18 cm; D XVII/16; A II/16; L 1 16/2; tr 4–5/12–13. Deep-bodied, tail deeply
forked with pointed lobes. Dark purplish brown or reddish brown; peduncle,
tail, soft dorsal and anal much paler. Body and fins irregularly spotted with
black. Very common in coral in the E. Indies, Philippines, Melanesia and N.
Queensland.

**1148. LEPIDOZYGUS TAPEINOSOMA** (Bleeker) 1856
10 cm; D XII/12–14; A II/14–15; L 1 19/15–16; tr 5/6. Very elongate with
crescentic tail. Eye deeper than wide, a fringe of papillae along hind edge of
eye-socket. Nape slaty, back greenish, silvery on sides and belly; scales with
dusky margins. Dorsal slaty, posterior rays orange; anal similar, tail with
purple wash. East Indies and Philippines.

**1149. LEPIDOZYGUS ANTHIOIDES** Smith 1960
10 cm. Elongated, tail deeply crescentic. Dark greyish violet; chin and breast
vinous red. Dorsal dark red, dark green basally, with 6 oblique narrow purple
lines on anterior part. Anal dark green basally, lavender distally, with 3 dark
green longitudinal lines. Tail dark red with broad orange distal margin. Pectorals
and ventrals vinous red. Deeper coral reefs in the W. Indian Ocean.

**1150. DASCYLLUS ARUANUS** (Linnaeus) 1758     **Pl. 22**
White-tailed Humbug
8 cm; D XII/12–13; A II/12–13; L 1 16–18/7–9; tr 2/9. As figured, but markings
much less distinct in old specimens. Usually in small dense schools associated
with particular coral heads. Very common throughout the entire Indo-Pacific
excluding Hawaii.

**1151. DASCYLLUS MELANURUS** Bleeker 1854     **Pl. 22**
Black-tailed Humbug
7 cm. Scale and fin counts as in 1150. East Indies, Philippines, Micronesia,
Melanesia and Queensland.

**1152. DASCYLLUS TRIMACULATUS** (Rüppell) 1828          **Pl. 22**
White-spot Humbug
12 cm; D XI–XII/15; A II/13–15; L l 17–20/8–9; tr 3/10–11. Size of white
spots differs in different areas. White spots usually lost in old specimens which
become a uniform dark brown, reddish or yellowish on breast and belly. Young
individuals associated with large anemones. Very common throughout the entire
Indo-Pacific excluding Hawaii.

**1153. DASCYLLUS ALBISELLA** Gill 1862
Hawaiian Humbug
12 cm. Fin and scale counts as in 1152. Very similar to 1152, but base of body
scales whitish in adults. Young with very much larger lateral white spot,
nuchal spot small or absent. Common in Hawaii, where it replaces 1152.

**1154. DASCYLLUS RETICULATUS** (Richardson) 1846          **Pl. 22**
Grey Humbug
13 cm; D XII/14–16; A II/13–14; L l 18–19/8–10; tr 3–4/10–11. Old individuals very similar to old specimens of 1152 and 1150, but rear portion of
dorsal and tail contrastingly white. Has been much confused with 1155 and
any record of that species other than from the Red Sea, almost certainly refers to
D. reticulatus. Common in the entire Indo-Pacific excluding the Red Sea and
Hawaii.

**1155. DASCYLLUS MARGINATUS** (Rüppell) 1828          **Pl. 22**
Red Sea Humbug
12 cm; scale and fin counts as in 1154. Confined to the Red Sea and probably
conspecific with 1154, but subspecifically distinct.

**1156. DASCYLLUS CARNEUS** (Fischer) 1885
A mysterious species inadequately described from Mozambique, which may be
a synonym of 1152 or of 1154. A blackish *Dascyllus* with a large pinkish grey
lateral blotch seen by the author in Ceylon may have been this species. The
fish illustrated by Smith (1949) as *D. carneus* is *D. reticulatus*.

**1157. CHROMIS CAERULEUS** (Cuvier & Valenciennes) 1830          **Pl. 22**
Blue Puller
12 cm; D XII–XIII/9–10; A II/9–10; L l 14–17/8–10; tr 1½/7–8. Usually seen
in dense schools of 20–30 individuals stationary about coral heads. Very common
throughout the entire Indo-Pacific excluding Hawaii.

**1158. CHROMIS TERNATENSIS** (Bleeker) 1856
Striped-tail Puller
12 cm. Pearly blue, juveniles with olive back and head, adults more golden.
Spinous dorsal black, outer rays of tail black. East Africa and the Seychelles
to the E. Indies, Philippines, Melanesia and Micronesia.

**1159. CHROMIS OVALIS** (Steindachner) 1900          **Pl. 22**
15 cm; D XIV/11–12; A II/12–13. Young with longitudinal blue lines on head.
Juveniles in tide pools, adults in 10–15 m of water. Hawaii.

**1160. CHROMIS VERATER** Jordan & Metz 1912
23 cm; D XIV/13; A II/13–14. Plain black. Rather deep water, usually in 15 m
or more. Hawaii.

**1161. CHROMIS VANDERBILTI** Fowler 1941

6 cm; D XI–XII/11; A II/10–11. Tail lobes produced. Silvery. Anterior dorsal and anal rays black, posterior dorsal and anal rays abruptly white. Lower rays of tail black. In 5 or more metres of water. Hawaii.

**1162. CHROMIS ANALIS** (Cuvier & Valenciennes) 1830
Brown Puller

15 cm; D XIII/11–12; A II/11–12; L 1 15–16/7–10; tr 2/8. Tail deeply forked, lobes pointed. Brownish yellow, darker above, with a black spot at pectoral base. East Indies, Philippines and Melanesia.

**1163. CHROMIS NITIDUS** (Whitley) 1928
Shining Puller

6 cm. Head yellow, sides silvery. A blackish stripe from snout, through eye to end of anterior dorsal rays. Queensland.

**1164. CHROMIS BITAENIATUS** Fowler & Bean 1928
Banded Puller

5 cm. Bright golden yellow. A wide black band from above eye to end of soft dorsal base and a 2nd wide black band from behind eye to end of middle caudal rays. A black vertical bar on operculum and a black spot at pectoral base. Philippines, Okinawa, E. Indies, Melanesia, Queensland.

**1165. CHROMIS HUMBUG** Whitley 1954
Two-barred Puller

18 mm. Creamy white with 2 broad blackish vertical bands. Known from a single specimen from Green Island, Queensland.

**1166. CHROMIS ATRIPECTORALIS** Welander & Schultz 1951

7 cm. Blue with black pectoral axil and a black margin to the dorsal fin. Central and western tropical Pacific.

**1167. CHROMIS NOTATUS** (Temminck & Schlegel) 1842

5 cm. Silvery; head, dorsal, ventrals, outer anal and tail fins blue-green; pectoral base blackish. South Japan and Ryukyu islands.

**1168. CHROMIS SCOTOCHILOPTERUS** Fowler 1918

15 cm. Olive above, silvery on breast and belly; posterior portion of soft dorsal orange. Tail dusky orange with upper and lower edges blackish. Philippines, E. Indies, Melanesia and Queensland.

**1169. CHROMIS OPERCULARIS** (Günther) 1866                 **Pl. 22**

15 cm. Western Indian Ocean, E. Indies and Philippines.

**1170. CHROMIS NIGRURUS** Smith 1960

8 cm. Slaty blue; an irregular golden yellow patch on operculum continued on body above and behind pectoral base. Scales of operculum with a blue spot; 5 rows of blue spots along scale rows below lateral line. Tail yellow, outer rays black; soft dorsal and anal black with blue posterior rays. Western Indian Ocean.

**1171. CHROMIS ATRIPES** Fowler & Bean 1928

7 cm; D XII/12; A II/12–13; L 1 15/8–9; tr 3/8–9. Pale orange, light olive above. Spinous dorsal dusky olive, soft dorsal yellow-hyaline. Tail dusky orange basally, outer edges blackish at base. Ventrals blackish, pectorals dusky with black spot at base. Philippines and Indonesia.

**1172. CHROMIS AGILIS** Smith 1960
10 cm. Coppery pink, breast and chin violet; pectoral base and anterior margin
of ventrals black. Eye red. East Africa, Seychelles and Amirante islands (Indian
Ocean).

**1173. CHROMIS PEMBAE** Smith 1960
12 cm. Rich coppery brown; eyes orange; pectoral base blackish. Dorsal black
with bright yellow margin. Posterior half of soft dorsal yellow. Anal basally
black, otherwise bright yellow; tail bright yellow. Pemba island (E. Africa).

**1174. CHROMIS DIMIDIATUS** (Klunzinger) 1871                    **Pl. 22**
11 cm; D XII/12–13; A II/12–13; L 1 14–17/8–10; tr 2/9. Common, usually
seen in small widely spaced stationary schools hovering 1 m or so above coral
formations. Red Sea, Indian Ocean, E. Indies, Philippines and Melanesia.
See 1175.

ALLIED SPECIES:
**1175. CHROMIS IOMELAS** Jordan & Seale 1905 Almost identical with 1174, but
scale and fin counts differ. Described from Samoa and seems to replace 1174 in Micronesia and Polynesia.
**1176. C. LEUCURUS** Gilbert 1903 12 cm. There are two forms of this species: a
common all black phase with white tail, and a rarer uniform pinkish brown phase with
black pectoral base. Hawaii and Marianas.

The following species of *Chromis* have also been described from the Indo-Pacific:
*C. amboinensis* (Bleeker) 1873, Amboina; *C. weberi* Fowler & Bean 1928, Java; *C
reticulatus* Fowler & Bean 1928, Philippines; *C cinctus* (Playfair) 1897, Seychelles; *C
axillaris* (Bennett) 1831, Mauritius; *C lineatus* Fowler & Bean 1928, Philippines;
*C desmostigma* Fowler & Bean 1928, Philippines; *C retrofasciatus* Weber 1913, Philippines; *C elerae* Fowler & Bean 1918, Philippines; *C cinerascens* (C. & V.) 1830, Java;
*C azurelineatus* Fowler & Bean 1928, Philippines; *C lepidolepis* Bleeker 1876, Timor;
*C. simulans* Smith 1960, W. Indian Ocean; *C. cupreus* Fowler & Bean 1923, Fiji; *C.
villadolidi* Jordan & Tanaka 1927, Japan.

Subfamily *Cheiloprioninae*
A small group consisting of the single E. Indian and Australian genus *Cheiloprion*. They differ from other Pomacentrids in having greatly thickened lips
curled back over the snout.

**1177. CHEILOPRION LABIATUS** (Day) 1877
Big-lipped Puller
8 cm; D XIII/13; A II/12; L 1 17–18/8–9; tr 2/9. Brown, paler on chin and
breast. Fins black; some blue spots on head and back. Coastal reefs from
Ceylon to the E. Indies, Philippines, Melanesia, Polynesia and Queensland.

Family LABRIDAE
**Wrasses, Rainbow-fishes, Tusk-fishes, Pig-fishes, Hog-fishes**
A large family of marine fishes of moderate size found in all seas, but most
abundant about shallow coral reefs and weedy areas in the tropics. Many species
are brilliantly coloured, some being subject to startling changes of pattern and
colour with advancing age, while others show marked sexual dimorphism. Many
species are highly variable or polymorphic and the systematics of some genera
are very confused. Most species have a dentition which is specially adapted for

crushing molluscs and crustacea, but are partly herbivorous. The lower pharyngeal bones, situated on the floor of the gullet are fused into a triangular plate which bears conical or tuberculate teeth. The front teeth are generally strong and caniniform, while the lateral teeth are more or less fused at the base. Some species have posterior canines, usually at the corner of the mouth, which sometimes stand out at right angles to the jaw; the teeth may be bright green or blue. The palate is toothless. Lips thick and fleshy, often with longitudinal folds. Scales large, cycloid. Lateral line continuous or interrupted below soft dorsal base. Some wrasses construct nests of seaweeds etc. for their eggs and young. Most species are solitary or may be seen in pairs; they are diurnal and may spend the night asleep half buried in sand, or in crevices in rock or coral, or on their side, wrapped in seaweed. The juveniles of some species are found in tidal pools, where their green colour harmonises perfectly with the background. Over 60 genera have been established and almost 500 species are known. The larger forms are food fishes of considerable importance.

### 1178. CIRRHILABRUS SOLORENSIS Bleeker 1853
Thread-finned Tusk-fish
12 cm; D XI–XII/9–10; A III/9; L 1 17/8–10; tr 1½/7. Six canines above, 2 below. Tail rounded; 1st and 2nd rays of ventrals prolonged. Head and back purplish brown, sides creamy; a row of pale blue spots from head to dorsal origin. Scales behind pectorals with broad indigo margin, base of unpaired fins deep indigo. East Indies, Ryukyu, Philippines and Melanesia.

ALLIED SPECIES:
**1179. CIRRHILABRUS CYANOPLEURA** (Bleeker) 10 cm. Back slaty, sides pale buff; 4 horizontal rows of blue spots above pectoral. Dorsal with scarlet submarginal line and white tips; anal scarlet, tail reddish-hyaline, ventrals without prolonged rays. East Indies, Philippines, New Guinea.
**1180. C. JORDANI** Snyder 10 cm. Uniformly reddish with scattered white spots on back. Margin of anal black. Rare, Hawaii.
**1181. C. EXQUISITUS** Smith 8 cm. Olive; top of head to upper lip blue; lips, eyes, chin, breast and anterior sides violet-red. A longitudinal purple stripe and a black spot on peduncle. Dorsal red with blue spots, tail pale violet with red rays, anal violet basally, olive marginally; ventrals violet. Western Indian Ocean.

OTHER SPECIES:
*C. temmincki* Bleeker, Japan and Philippines.

### 1182. CHOERODON SCHOENLEINI (Cuvier & Valenciennes) 1839
Black-spot Tusk-fish
90 cm; D XI–XIII/7–8; A III/9–10; L 1 29; tr 3–4/10. A stocky fish with blunt head profile; tail truncate; 4 anterior canines in each jaw, 1–2 posterior canines in upper jaw. Bright olive above, yellow below; a vertical blue streak on each scale; some irregular bluish or yellow lines on head. Upper lip orange; a yellow line from upper lip to opercular hind margin. A black spot below last dorsal spines, followed by a pale area. Dorsal orange red with blue base and blue margin. East Indies, Philippines, China, Melanesia, Australia, occasionally entering river mouths.

### 1183. CHOERODON ANCHORAGO (Bloch) 1791
Yellow-cheeked Tusk-fish
32 cm; D XIII/7; A III/8–9; L 1 29; tr 2½/8–10. Stocky, head profile blunt, tail truncate. Teeth as in 1182. Dark olive brown with whitish spots, paler

below. Cheeks yellow with red spots. A pale saddle on peduncle and a pale vertical wedge below spinous dorsal. Dorsal with 2 dark longitudinal bands; anal dusky anteriorly, yellow edged with red posteriorly. Tail yellowish. Common from Ceylon and India to Indonesia, the Philippines, Melanesia, Australia and the Palau and Caroline islands.

**1184. CHOERODON ROBUSTUS** (Günther) 1862      **Pl. 27**
30 cm; D XI–XII/8–9; A III/10; L 1 29; tr 3/9. Outer canines turned outwards; lateral teeth fused into a blunt bony ridge. This species and *C. quadrimaculatus* (Günther) 1880 from the Arafura Sea are placed in the genus *Xiphocheilus* Bleeker by some authors. East Africa, Persian Gulf, India and Ceylon; very common in the Seychelles.

ALLIED SPECIES:

**1185. CHOERODON FRENATUS** Ogilby 15 cm. Pink, each scale with a blue spot; 3–4 blue bands across head. Known from deepish water in S. Queensland.
**1186. C. CEPHALOTES** (Castelnau) 35 cm. Light olive, each scale with a vertical blue line widening into spots on peduncle. A diffuse orange blotch on nape and a large dark area below lateral line and behind pectoral. Cheeks with many small red spots. Numerous irregular short dark blue transverse bands across dorsal profile of head, from nape to upper lip. 2–3 short blue lines radiating from the eye and 2–3 more on chin. Dorsal blue with orange margin, tail orange with transverse blue lines, anal yellow with orange margin, ventrals yellow with one or two blue rays. Common on weedy banks in Queensland.
**1187. C. VENUSTUS** (De Vis) 120 cm, but average length 40 cm. Body blue, green or pink, darker above. Numerous round blue spots on body. Chin purple marked with orange. Fins and tail bright yellow marked with blue. Queensland and New South Wales; good eating.
**1188. C. ALBIGENA** (De Vis) 70 cm. Blue; yellow with blue transverse lines above upper lip. Lower lip and chin pink. Dorsal and anal orange yellow with blue spots and lines; tail and paired fins blue. Queensland and Gulf of Carpentaria.
**1189. C. VITTA** Ogilby 22 cm. Pearly with a black band from eye to tail, or a black spot at base of tail. Queensland and Aru islands.
**1190. C. AZURIO** (Jordan & Snyder) 25 cm. Pinkish with blue streaks on body scales, blue lips and blue fin rays. China, Taiwan, Japan.
**1191. C. OLIGACANTHUS** (Bleeker) 21 cm. Green with orange stripes along scale rows. Orange stripes on chin, operculum and about pectoral base. A central yellow spot well behind pectoral, above lateral line. Dorsal and anal olive with orange spots and reticulations. Tail greenish. Anterior edge of ventrals orange. East Indies, Philippines and New Caledonia.

OTHER SPECIES:

*C. margaritiferus* Fowler & Bean, Philippines; *C. zamboangae* (Seale & Bean), Philippines; *C. zosterophorus* (Bleeker), E. Indies and Philippines; *C. melanostigma* Fowler & Bean, Philippines.

**1192. LIENARDELLA FASCIATA** (Günther) 1867      **Pl. 27**
Harlequin Tusk-fish
25 cm; D XII/8; A III/10; L 1 29–30; tr 4/10. Common on the Barrier Reef; also known from Ryukyu.

**1193. LEPIDAPLOIS OXYCEPHALUS** (Bleeker) 1862
Pig-fish
60 cm; D XII/10–11; A III/11; L 1 33–35; tr 6/13. Four anterior canines in each jaw, one posterior canine in upper jaw. Tail slightly emarginate. Dull red with orange-yellow lines along scale rows; a large black spot between 7th and

9th dorsal spines. 4–5 diffuse paler blotches between lateral line and dorsal base. East Indies, Melanesia, Australia, Japan, Hawaii.

### 1194. LEPIDAPLOIS DIANA (Lacépède) 1802
Diana's Wrasse
23 cm; D XII/9–10; A III/10–12; L 1 30–31; tr 4/11. Four anterior canines in each jaw, 1 posterior canine in upper jaw. Lateral teeth fused into a ridge. Bright purplish red, paler below; scales on peduncle and on upper sides with a black spot. Three to four round bluish spots between dorsal and lateral line. Spinous dorsal yellow, soft dorsal red with some black spots; tail red; anal yellow with red rays and 2 large black spots. Ventrals red with a large black central spot. East Africa, Seychelles, India, Ceylon, Indonesia, Philippines, New Guinea.

### 1195. LEPIDAPLOIS MESOTHORAX (Schneider) 1801
20 cm. Bright orange yellow. An oblique black band from pectoral to tip of soft dorsal. Head vinaceous purple. A black spot at pectoral base and a black bar from snout to pectoral base. Anal bright yellow, tail orange yellow. Indonesia, the Phillippines, New Guinea, Queensland, China.

### 1196. LEPIDAPLOIS ANTHIOIDES (Bennett) 1830      Pl. 24
30 cm. East Africa, Seychelles, India, E. Indies, Melanesia.

### 1197. LEPIDAPLOIS AXILLARIS (Bennett) 1831      Pl. 24
Tamarin (Seychelles)
20 cm. South and E. Africa, Seychelles, India, E. Indies.

### 1198. LEPIDAPLOIS PERDITIO (Quoy & Gaimard) 1824
Golden-spot Pig-fish
52 cm; D XII–XIII/10; A III/12; L 1 33; tr 6/12. Head and body bright red, suffused with orange and violet posteriorly. Head and anterior body with numerous yellow spots. A large bright yellow spot from dorsal base below 7th–9th spines to below lateral line, often followed by a large blackish blotch. A 2nd yellow spot on peduncle. Anterior part of dorsal black, remainder scarlet basally, otherwise golden red. Tail red or bright yellow; anal red at base, otherwise golden with blackish margin; paired fins dusky pinkish. East Africa, Mauritius, Ryukyu, Melanesia, Queensland.

### 1199. LEPIDAPLOIS BILUNULATUS (Lacépède) 1802      Pl. 24
A'awa (Hawaii)
60 cm; D XII/9–10; A III/12; L 1 28–30; tr 6/10–12. Two species appear to have been confused under this name: the true *bilunulatus*, misidentified as *L. hirsutus* (Lacépède) 1802, by Smith (1949, 1963), which has a very wide distribution, from S. and E. Africa to the Seychelles, Mauritius, Ceylon, the E. Indies, Philippines, Ryukyu and Melanesia, and a different form which may be confined to Hawaii; if the Hawaiian form is specifically distinct, the oldest name available for it would appear to be: *Lepidaplois albotaeniatus* (Cuvier & Valenciennes) 1839. The differences between the 2 forms are clearly shown on Plate 24. The Hawaiian fish changes considerably with age; individuals exceeding 30 cm are often plain bluish black. See 1200.

### 1200. LEPIDAPLOIS HIRSUTUS (Lacépède) 1802
90 cm; D XII/10; A III/12; L 1 30–33; tr 6/11. Very similar to 1199, but black area extends backwards to ventral aspect of peduncle and to the lower

caudal rays; ventrals black, margin of anal fin black. Philippines, Ryukyu, S. Japan, Fiji and Tuamotu islands. Records from S. and E. Africa and from Mauritius may be based on misidentifications of 1199.

*Lepidaplois hirsutus*

ALLIED SPECIES:

**1201. LEPIDAPLOIS TRILINEATUS** Fowler 23 cm. Red above, golden laterally, silvery pink below. Three narrow blackish lines on upper part of body, two reddish lines on lower part. Natal to the Red Sea.

**1202. L. ALDABRENSIS** Smith 10 cm. Olive with dark purple reticulations. Two black ocelli on dorsal fin, one at pectoral base, one at base of tail and one on anal. A large black blotch on ventrals. Aldabra and Astove islands, in the Indian Ocean.

**1203. L. LUTEOPUNCTATUS** Smith 30 cm. Uniform red, paler below. Dark reddish spots on most body scales; fins red. Western Indian Ocean.

**1204. VERRICULUS SANGUINEUS** Jordan & Everman 1903
19 cm. Similar to members of the genus *Lepidaplois*, but scaly base of dorsal and anal lacking. Red and yellow with a black spot on caudal peduncle. Known from a single specimen taken in deep water at Hilo, Hawaii.

**1205. VERRICULUS OPERCULARIS** (Guichenot) 1847          **Pl. 29**
18 cm. A rare species known from Mauritius, the Comoro islands and from the Kenya coast.

ALLIED SPECIES:

**1206. SEMICOSSYPHUS RETICULATUS** (C. & V.) 80 cm. Adult with a conspicuously humped forehead. Pinkish buff with a dark margin to all scales. Juvenile bright red with a white stripe from eye to middle of caudal base. Tail hyaline with a large round black spot on each lobe; soft dorsal, anal and ventrals black with a white margin. South Japan.

**1207. PSEUDOLABRUS GRACILIS** (Steindachner) 10 cm. A slender pinkish fish with a reddish mid-dorsal stripe and a second reddish stripe from eye to middle of tail base. South Japan.

**1208. PSEUDODAX MOLUCCANUS** (Cuvier & Valenciennes) 1839
                                                                              **Pl. 25**
25 cm; D XI/12; A III/14; L 1 29/2–3; tr 4/10. Superficially similar to the genus *Anampses*, but differs in having large exposed incisor-like anterior teeth. East Africa, Seychelles, Reunion, E. Indies, Philippines and New Guinea.

**1209. CYMOLUTES LECLUSE** (Quoy & Gaimard) 1824
Brown-lined Wrasse
20 cm; D IX/12–13; A III/11–13; L 1 55–60/15–17; tr 4/12. A small-scaled elongate fish with a very rounded blunt head. Posterior canines absent, lateral line interrupted. Variable: green or olive with a blue-edged dark band across shoulders, or with narrow brown transverse lines. Sometimes a round black spot below lateral line. Dorsal pale violet, anal rosy, tail orange with yellowish transverse lines. East Africa to the E. Indies, Philippines, Palau, Fiji, Tonga and Hawaii.

Brown-lined Wrasse

**1210. EPIBULUS INSIDIATOR** (Pallas) 1770                  **Pl. 27**
Telescopefish, Sling-jaw
32 cm; D IX/10; A III/8; L I 15/5–7; tr 2/6–7. Mouth can be protruded into
a long tube. When lying stranded after capture it projects and retracts its
mouth with great speed. Very variable in colour, being yellow, brown, reddish
or greenish, variously marked with pale bands or dark scale margins. Coral
reefs. East Africa, Seychelles, Mauritius, E. Indies, Philippines, Ryukyu,
Melanesia, Australia, New Hebrides, Society and Tuamotu islands.

Mouth of *Epibulus*, extended

**1211. WETMORELLA PHILIPPINA** Fowler & Bean 1928
10 cm; D IX/9; A III/8; L I 15/5–6/2–3; tr 2/6. Preopercular border externally
invisible. Light pinkish with a curved yellow line behind eye and another
across peduncle, continued on soft dorsal and anal. Eye and lips red. An oval
purple spot surrounded by a white ring and by a purple one on anterior anal
rays. A similar spot with incomplete outer ring on anterior dorsal rays. Tail
yellow with blackish spots; ventrals pinkish with large purple spot. East Africa,
Seychelles, E. Indies and Philippines. Rare, included in the synonymy of
*Cheilinus fasciatus* (Bloch) by Herre (1953).

*Wetmorella philippina*

ALLIED SPECIES:
**1212. WETMORELLA OCELLATA** Schultz & Marshall. Similar to 1211, but
lacks the black spots on the tail. Bikini and Rongelap atolls, Marshall islands.
**1213. W. ALBOFASCIATA** Schultz & Marshall 5 cm. Very similar to 1211; known
from a single specimen from Hawaii.

**1214. PSEUDOCHEILINUS HEXATAENIA** (Bleeker) 1857    **Pl. 26**
45 cm; D IX/11–12; A III/9; L I 15–18/4–8; tr 2/6. Four pairs of anterior
canines on upper jaw, one on lower jaw; outer canines of upper jaw flare outwards. Red Sea, E. Africa, Madagascar, Seychelles, E. Indies, Philippines
Tuamotu islands.

ALLIED SPECIES:

**1215. PSEUDOCHEILINUS EVANIDUS** J. & E. 10 cm. Red with numerous narrow yellowish longitudinal lines. Snout and lips bluish. A short horizontal blue stripe from angle of mouth towards preopercular margin and a bright yellow area below it. Preopercular margin purple and a purple spot on operculum, near upper angle. Dorsal red with a longitudinal purple stripe and a yellow stripe through soft dorsal; tail and anal red with blue rays, anal spines prolonged. Rare. Known from widely scattered localities: Seychelles and Hawaii.

**1216. P. OCTOTAENIA** Jenkins 15 cm. Brownish with 8 longitudinal black bands. Hawaii.

**1217. P. TETRATAENIA** Schultz Bluish with four blackish stripes. Hawaii.

**1218. P. MARGARETAE** Smith 10 cm. Wine red with yellow spots on cheeks and 8 dark purple longitudinal stripes on body. Dorsal yellow basally, hyaline with yellow spots distally, with a blue longitudinal line near base and a purple inframarginal line. Tail yellow with faint spots, anal pale yellow with darker spots and two longitudinal red bands. Aldabra island, Indian Ocean.

**1219. PSEUDOCHEILINOPS ATAENIA** Schultz 4 cm. Wine red with narrow sulphur stripes. Fins and tail pink with indigo rays. Eyes scarlet. Celebes, Moluccas, Gilolo.

**1220. LABRICHTHYS CYANOTAENIA** Bleeker 1854
Tube-lip
15 cm; D IX/9; A III/10; L 1 20/5; tr 5/11. Oblong, compressed, head entirely covered by small scales. Mouth very small, lips produced to form a short tube when mouth is closed. Dark brown with yellow lips, faint blue and bronze lines on body, dark blue lines on head and a black spot at pectoral base. Vertical fins with blue margins, tail with a blue transverse curved stripe near base and a pale margin. East Africa, Philippines, Ryukyu, Solomon islands, Samoa and Queensland.

**1221. THALLIURUS CHLORURUS** (Bloch) 1781                 **Pl. 31**
25 cm; D X/9–10; A III/7–9; L 1 15/5–7; tr 2/6–7. One pair of anterior canines on each jaw. Dorsal fin incised between spines in juveniles. Weedy places among coral throughout the Indo-Pacific excluding Hawaii.

**1222. CHEILINUS TRILOBATUS** Lacépède 1802               **Pl. 30**
Triple-tail Maori-wrasse
45 cm; D IX/10; A III/8; L 1 14–15/7; tr 2/6–7. Common in weedy places among coral. A good eating fish. Entire Indo-Pacific excluding Hawaii.

**1223. CHEILINUS FASCIATUS** (Bloch) 1791                  **Pl. 30**
Red-breasted Maori-wrasse
35 cm. As figured, but old specimens much duller and darker. Common through-out the Indo-Pacific excluding Hawaii.

**1224. CHEILINUS DIAGRAMMUS** (Lacépède) 1802             **Pl. 30**
Black-lined Maori-wrasse
48 cm. Common throughout the Indo-Pacific excluding Hawaii.

**1225. CHEILINUS UNDULATUS** Rüppell 1840                 **Pl. 30**
Giant Wrasse
210 cm; D IX/10; A III/8; L 1 14–16/7–11; tr 2/6. Very variable; young specimens more brightly coloured. Large hump on head and thick fleshy lips begin to develop in fishes of 75 cm or so. The largest of all the wrasses, large specimens weighing up to 200 kg. Entire Indo-Pacific excluding Hawaii.

ALLIED SPECIES:

**1226. CHEILINUS OXYCEPHALUS** Bleeker 17 cm. Olive brown, greenish on operculum. Head with small white dots. Four large dark spots along mid-lateral line of body. A black spot sometimes followed by a yellow patch on fore part of dorsal fin. Fins and tail greenish with dusky mottlings and lines. East Indies, Philippines, Melanesia and Queensland to the Society islands.

**1227. C. BIMACULATUS** C. & V. (=**C. CERAMENSIS** Bleeker) 12 cm. Top of head dark green, back grey; chin and lips pale green; cheeks and lower operculum geranium red; red lines radiating from eye; interorbital area spotted with red, spots becoming darker on nape. A diffuse dark band from eye, breaking into blotches on body and ending as a dark shade on the tail. Dorsal green with anterior blue spot, becoming yellow posteriorly, edged with bright red and reticulated with dull red. Tail bright green with red margin, tips and reticulations. Anal and ventrals green reticulated with red. Pectorals pale pink, yellow basally. East Indies, Philippines, Maldives, Seychelles, New Hebrides and Hawaii.

**1228. C. ARENATUS** C. & V. 20 cm. Head red, body violet red, paler on breast. Head speckled with minute red spots, back speckled with white and blackish. A dark diffuse band from eye to middle of tail base. Dorsal olive with a large anterior white-ringed black ocellus. Posterior rays pink. Tail bright yellow with red upper and lower margins and green rays. Anal pink, mottled with yellow, ventrals pink with dark purplish basal blotch. East Africa, Seychelles, Mauritius, E. Indies and Philippines.

**1229. C. CELEBICUS** Bleeker 20 cm. Bottle green with red lines radiating from the eyes and red lines on scales of back, becoming spots on breast and belly and disappearing on middle of sides. A white bar on peduncle. Vertical fins and tail olive speckled and mottled with red. A dark spot surmounted by a yellow one on 1st dorsal membrane. East Indies, Philippines and Solomons.

**1230. C. RHODOCHROUS** Günther 60 cm. Tail rounded. Varies considerably with age. Young specimens reddish with dark bluish lines on head and cheeks. Sometimes a pair of dark horizontal lines behind eye and a white saddle on peduncle. East Indies, Philippines, Ryukyu and Hawaii. Doubtfully recorded from Zanzibar.

OTHER SPECIES:

*C. mentalis* Rüppell (Red Sea, E. Indies, Philippines); *C. oxyrhynchus* Bleeker (E. Indies, Philippines, Ryukyu, Solomons and Australia); *C. unifasciatus* Streets (Philippines and Micronesia); *C. lunulatus* (Forskål) (Red Sea, Seychelles and Mauritius).

## 1231. NOVACULICHTHYS MACROLEPIDOTUS (Bloch) 1791

Pl. 27

23 cm; D IX/12–13; A III/13; L 1 20/4–6; tr 2/9–10. Coral reefs and rock pools. East Africa, Seychelles, E. Indies, Philippines, Ryukyu and Melanesia.

## 1232. NOVACULICHTHYS TAENIOURUS (Lacépède) 1802     Pl. 27
= **N. BIFER** (Lay & Bennett) 1839
Scribbled Wrasse

30 cm; D IX/12–13; A III/12–14; L 1 19–20/5–6; tr 2/10. Changes very considerably with age; *N. bifer* is the dark juvenile with prolonged dorsal spines and was regarded until recently as a distinct species. Old specimens lose the dark lines radiating from the eye. Common in sandy or weedy spots among coral throughout the Indo-Pacific including Queensland and Hawaii. See 1233

## 1233. NOVACULICHTHYS WOODI Jenkins 1900

18 cm. Similar to 1232, but dark lines radiating from eyes always absent, upper pectoral rays and outer ventral rays elongated. A small intense black spot between each pair of dorsal spines. Hawaii only.

**1234. HEMIPTERONOTUS PENTADACTYLUS** (Linnaeus) 1758
Keel-headed Wrasse                                              **Pl. 31**
25 cm; D IX/12; A III/11–12; L 1 20–22/3–6; tr 2/9–10. Sandy areas among
coral. Red Sea and E. Africa to the E. Indies, Philippines, China, Taiwan and
Melanesia. See 1237.

ALLIED SPECIES:
**1235. HEMIPTERONOTUS UMBRILATUS** Jenkins 30 cm. Similar to 1234,
but with a large diffuse black blotch on side, mostly below lateral line. Hawaii.
**1236. H. BALDWINI** J. & E. 22 cm. Spinous dorsal undivided. A small black spot
below dorsal base, above lateral line. Hawaii.
**1237. H. HYPOSPYLUS** Schultz 12 cm. Similar to 1234, but small black lateral
spot placed on scales 7–9, not on 9–11 as 'in 1234. Celebes.
**1238. H. ANEITENSIS** (Günther) 15 cm. Four vertical dark bars on upper sides.
Marshall islands, New Hebrides, Melanesia, E. Indies, Philippines.
**1239. H. CELEBICUS** (Bleeker) 15 cm. Oblong dark mid-lateral patch on caudal
peduncle. Celebes and Philippines.
**1240. H. JACKSONENSIS** (Ramsay) 20 cm. Salmon with oblique fine blue lines
on back and some blue spots at base of ventrals and on lower peduncle. Fins orange.
Lord Howe island, Queensland and New South Wales.

**1241. INIISTIUS PAVO** (Cuvier & Valenciennes) 1839          **Pl. 31**
37 cm. Sandy areas, usually among coral. Entire Indo-Pacific as far as the West
coast of Mexico. *I. pavo*, described from Mauritius, has page priority over *I.
pavoninus* (C. & V.) 1839, which was described from Hawaii. The latter name
is usually included in the synonymy of *I. pavo*, but it is probable that they
are distinct; if so most records from the Indian Ocean would probably apply to
*I. pavo*, while records from the C. Indo-Pacific and the W. and E. Pacific
would probably refer to *I. pavoninus*.

ALLIED SPECIES:
**1242. INIISTIUS NIGER** (Steindachner) 20 cm. Uniform blackish or dark brown.
Hawaii and Philippines.
**1243. XYRICHTHYS NIVEILATUS** J. & E. 25 cm. Two anterior dorsal spines
slightly longer than following spines and only incompletely separated from rest of
dorsal fin. Sandy areas, Hawaii.

**1244. CHEILIO INERMIS** (Forskål) 1775                       **Pl. 23**
Sharp-nosed Rainbowfish, Kupoupou (H), Peche Madame (S)
50 cm; D IX/12–13; A III/12; L 1 45–48; tr 5/13–14. Very variable: yellow,
olive, dark brown or green. Very common in weedy areas among coral throughout
the entire Indo-Pacific including the Red Sea, Hawaii and Australia.

**1245. GOMPHOSUS VARIUS** Lacépède 1802                       **Pl. 27**
=**G. CAERULEUS** Lacépède 1802
=**G. TRICOLOR** Quoy & Gaimard 1824
Bird-wrasse, Perroquet (S), Akilolo, Hinalea i'iwi (H)
30 cm; D VIII/13; A III/10–12; L 1 26–30; tr 3–4/8–10. Only the mature
males (*G. caeruleus*) are blue or green as illustrated. The immature males and
the females (*G. varius* and *G. tricolor*) are various shades of brown with a darker
spot on each body scale and often some red on the snout. A very graceful, active
fish, usually seen on outer reefs where the surf is breaking on the coral. Entire
Indo-Pacific.

**1246. THALASSOMA LUNARE** (Linnaeus) 1758     **Pl. 25**
Moon Wrasse
30 cm; D VIII/13; A III/11; L 1 25–29; tr 3/9–11. Colour variable, but markings of pectoral fin diagnostic. Juveniles with a black spot at base of anterior dorsal rays and a dark patch at base of tail. Indian Ocean, Philippines, Hong Kong, Solomons, New Guinea, New Hebrides and Australia. Replaced in Polynesia by the following closely allied species.

**1247. THALASSOMA LUTESCENS** (Lay & Bennett) 1839
21 cm. Tail lunate. Much confused with 1246 in the literature. ♀ olive with 5 dull red longitudinal bars on head and dull red vertical streaks on each body scale; dorsal and anal olive with dull red broad basal band. Tail yellowish olive with outer rays dull red. ♂ similar, but much of the olive colour replaced by orange yellow with a broad blue-green band from anterior part of dorsal to belly, widening below to include entire ventral surface from ventral fins to base of tail. Polynesia, Hawaii and Queensland.

**1248. THALASSOMA AMBLYCEPHALUS** (Bleeker) 1856 (juvenile)
**=T. MELANOCHIR** (Bleeker) 1857 (adult)
16 cm. Tail lunate. Bright olive green. A blue-edged black stripe from eye to upper angle of operculum and another from angle of mouth to preopercular angle. Body with dark purple vertical streaks on each body scale. Dorsal purple edged with white; tail rusty with reddish brown outer rays; anal pale pink. Ventrals light blue. A blackish spot at upper base of pectoral which is yellow with a large blackish apical spot. Juvenile lacks red markings and has a broad dark stripe from snout through eye to tail base separating the dark olive dorsal surface from the much paler ventral surface. Entire Indo-Pacific.

**1249. THALASSOMA JANSENI** (Bleeker) 1856
Jansen's Wrasse
20 cm; D VIII/13; A III/11; L 1 26–27; tr 2½/9–10. Tail rounded in juveniles, lunate in adults. Yellow with 3–4 wide oblique black transverse bands, 2nd extending to dorsal, 3rd to dorsal and anal. Sometimes bands very wide, masking yellow ground colour. A violet streak from behind operculum to pectoral base. Caudal peduncle greenish yellow, tail dusky with dark purplish outer rays and a black basal spot in juveniles. Pectoral base purplish, fins yellow. East Indies, Philippines, Ryukyu islands, Solomons, New Guinea, New Hebrides, Fiji and Queensland.

**1250. THALASSOMA HEBRAICUM** (Lacépède) 1802     **Pl. 24**
20 cm. Very variable, but oblique pale band on shoulders and facial markings fairly constant. *T. schwanefeldi* (Bleeker) 1853 is probably the juvenile (Smith, 1963). Indian Ocean; especially common in E. Africa and in the Seychelles.

**1251. THALASSOMA DUPERREYI** (Quoy & Gaimard) 1824     **Pl. 25**
Hinalea lauwili, A'ala'ihi (Hawaii)
30 cm. Tail rounded in specimens of up to 10 cm. Adult coloration appears at about 6 cm, juveniles being plain dark above and pale below. One of the commonest wrasses in Hawaii; recorded once from the Philippines.

**1252. THALASSOMA BALLIEUI** (Vaillant & Sauvage) 1875
Hinalea luahine (Hawaii)
60 cm; D VIII/13; A III/11; L 1 27; tr 5/10. Tail truncate with slightly pointed
tips. Uniform slaty grey to brownish yellow with a dark vertical streak on each
body scale; caudal peduncle darker. Old specimens become very dark, almost
black. Hawaii and Johnston island.

**1253. THALASSOMA COMMERSONI** (Cuvier & Valenciennes) 1839
20 cm. Tail lunate. Anterior half of body violet, posterior half olive. Dorsal
violet with yellow base and margin and a black spot between 1st and 3rd spines.
Anal violet with yellow margin. Pectoral black at base and at tip; lobes and base
of tail blackish. Rare. East coast of Africa and Mauritius.

**1254. THALASSOMA QUINQUEVITTATA** (Lay & Bennett) 1839
Red-banded Wrasse
13 cm. Tail emarginate with pointed lobes. Dark green above, paler below. Two
red longitudinal bands from operculum to tail base, connected by numerous
vertical red bars. Two long arched longitudinal black-edged bands on lower
part of head. Dorsal red at base, yellow distally, with a black anterior spot.
Tail pinkish yellow, outer rays red. Pectorals yellow, broadly tipped with black.
Okinawa, E. Indies, Melanesia, Micronesia, Samoa and Polynesia as far north
as Johnston Island and as far east as the Society islands.

**1255. THALASSOMA CUPIDO** (Temminck & Schlegel) 1842
54 cm. Tail truncate. Green above, blue below. Two longitudinal brownish red
stripes from behind head to tail base, the upper crossed by numerous vertical
reddish bars. A dark red stripe from snout to eye, bifurcating behind eye. A
large black spot on opercular angle and pectoral base black. Dorsal green, red
basally, rayed portion with red margin. Tail green with broad blackish base;
anal green with red basal and marginal bands, paired fins light blue. Japan, the
Philippines and Java. The subspecies *T. cupido bipunctatum* Vasiliu 1931 with
a black spot on anal fin, is known from Ceylon.

**1256. THALASSOMA FUSCUM** (Lacépède) 1802                          **Pl. 24**
Green-blocked Wrasse, Marar (S)
30 cm. Very probably the juvenile of 1257. South and E. Africa, Red Sea and
Seychelles to the E. Indies, Melanesia, Micronesia and Hawaii. Probably
recorded from the Philippines under a different name.

**1257. THALASSOMA PURPUREUM** (Forskål) 1775                        **Pl. 24**
45 cm. Probably the adult of 1256. Distribution as above. Usually seen in surge
areas and in the deeper pools; sometimes found asleep among wet weeds at
night, on reefs exposed by the tide. *T. semicaeruleus* (Rüppell) 1835, described
from the Red Sea, is almost certainly a synonym.

**1258. THALASSOMA UMBROSTIGMA** (Rüppell) 1838                      **Pl. 24**
30 cm. Nowhere common, but widely distributed in the entire Indo-Pacific
including the Red Sea and Hawaii, but not Queensland.

**1259. THALASSOMA HARDWICKI** (Bennett) 1830                        **Pl. 25**
Six-barred Wrasse
45 cm. As figured, but variable, some specimens being bright green or blue

all over, with black and red markings. A very common species. The entire Indo-Pacific excluding Hawaii.

**1260. ANAMPSES CAERULEOPUNCTATUS** Rüppell 1828   **Pl. 23**
Spotted Chisel-tooth Wrasse, Tamarin (S)
30 cm; D IX/12; A III/12; L 1 26–29; tr $3\frac{1}{2}$/11. Both jaws with a pair of large anterior chisel-edged incisors. Like other species of the genus it is rare and seldom seen, but wide-ranging. Most of the Indo-Pacific excluding Hawaii and Queensland.

**1261. ANAMPSES PTEROPHTHALMUS** Bleeker 1857
Ocellated Chisel-tooth Wrasse
22 cm. Teeth and fin count as in 1260. L 1 47–50; tr 7/19. Blackish, paler posteriorly, reddish ventrally. Dorsal and anal dark brown with pale spots and lines. A large yellow-ringed black ocellus on hind rays of both fins. Tail blackish brown with narrow white margin. Pectorals yellow. East Indies, Melanesia and Philippines, east to the Carolines.

**1262. ANAMPSES GEOGRAPHICUS** Cuvier & Valenciennes 1839
25 cm. Teeth, fin and scale counts as in 1261. Tail emarginate. Olive, purplish anteriorly, bluish posteriorly. Body scales with vertical blue streaks. Numerous irregular narrow pale lines on head and breast. Dorsal and anal olive, spotted, barred and lined with blue; margins paler. Tail dark blue with red vermiculations and a broad pale margin. The Central and E. Indo-Pacific excluding Hawaii. Also known from Mauritius.

**1263. ANAMPSES DIADEMATUS** Rüppell 1835   **Pl. 23**
25 cm. Teeth and fin counts as in 1261; L 1 29–31; tr 7–8/11. Rare. Entire Indo-Pacific including the Red Sea, but not in Queensland and Hawaii.

**1264. ANAMPSES MELEAGRIDES** Cuvier & Valenciennes 1839
Guinea-fowl Wrasse   **Pl. 23**
25 cm. Teeth and fin counts as in 1261. L 1 27–29; tr 4/9. East Africa, Mauritius, Seychelles, Ceylon, E. Indies, Philippines, Ryukyu islands.

**1265. ANAMPSES TWISTI** Bleeker 1856
18 cm. Teeth, fin and scale counts as above. Blue black, cheeks, chin and breast contrastingly yellow. A red spot on upper angle of operculum. Each body scale with a round blue spot. Dorsal and anal brownish red spotted with blue and with a blue-ringed black ocellus on posterior rays. Tail rounded, brownish red with blue spots and a blue margin interrupted at end of middle rays; paired fins yellow. Rare; E. Africa, Seychelles, E. Indies and Fiji.

**1266. ANAMPSES CUVIERI** Quoy & Gaimard 1824   **Pl. 23**
Opule, Hilu (Hawaii)
38 cm. Very small specimens have no spots on body, but have large black ocelli on posterior dorsal and anal rays. Common in shallow water in Hawaii. See 1267.

ALLIED SPECIES:
**1267. ANAMPSES GODEFFROYI** Günther 37 cm. Similar to 1266, but body scales with light vertical streak, not spot. Known from Hawaii only.
**1268. A. RUBROCAUDATUS** Randall 15 cm. Black with a white spot on each body scale. Tail brilliant scarlet. Hawaii, rare.
**1269. A. CHRYSOCEPHALUS** Randall 18 cm. Head and fore part of body orange with blue lines and spots. Body and tail plain dark brown. Rare, Hawaii.

**1270. A. NEOGUINAICUS** Bleeker. Head and body orange, back blackish brown. Sides of head marked with pearly spots. A vertical pearly streak on each body scale. Dorsal purple with a brown submarginal band and yellow margin. New Guinea.

**1271. HOLOGYMNOSUS SEMIDISCUS** (Lacépède) 1802          **Pl. 29**
50 cm; D IX/12; A III/12; L 1 94–104; tr 6/47–48. As figured, but varies a great deal according to age and sex, some specimens being blue, reddish, orange brown or purplish. East Africa to the E. Indies, Philippines, Ryukyu, Palau, Gilbert, New Hebrides, Fiji and Society islands; also known from New Guinea.

**1272. LABROIDES DIMIDIATUS** (Cuvier & Valenciennes) 1839
Cleaner Wrasse, Blue Streak (Australia), Sea Swallow (S. Africa)          **Pl. 23**
10 cm; D IX/10–11; A III/11; L 1 47–53; tr 4/12–14. Colour and particularly the intensity of the blue varies considerably according to age and mood. In very small individuals the black band is broader and the blue more intense. These fishes live by removing particles of food, parasites and algae from the teeth, mouth, gills and body of larger fishes. Most fishes welcome the attentions of Cleaner Wrasses and it is a common sight to see a large and voracious Rock-cod with its large gape wide open, having its teeth picked by these fishes. Some other quite unrelated fishes, such as the Blenny, *Aspidontus tractus* Fowler, resemble the Cleaner Wrasses so closely, that they are able to approach large fishes with impunity. It has been established that these wrasses are able to change sex: if there is a shortage of males in a local population, some females will change to males, and if there is a shortage of females, the opposite will take place. Tidal pools and coral reefs throughout the entire Indo-Pacific excluding Hawaii, where it is replaced by the following species. See 1419.

**1273. LABROIDES PHTHIROPHAGUS** Randall 1959          **Pl. 23**
12 cm. Identical with 1272 in behaviour and probably no more than a local subspecies thereof. Hawaii.

**1274. LABROIDES BICOLOR** (Fowler) 1928
11 cm. Head and anterior part of body dark steel blue, almost black; posterior part of body, peduncle and tail abruptly straw yellow. Dorsal and anal black with hyaline margin; tail with a black submarginal line and hyaline border. East Africa and the Seychelles to the E. Indies, Philippines and Okinawa.

**1275. CORIS GAIMARDI GAIMARDI** (Quoy & Gaimard) 1824 **Pl. 28**
Gaimard's Rainbowfish, Tomato Wrasse, Lolo (Hawaii)
30 cm; D IX/12; A III/12; L 1 70–80; tr 6–7/30–31. The red and white juvenile pattern persists in fishes of up to 6 cm; fishes between 6 and 10 cm are intermediate. These fishes have a curious wriggling gait and often lie on their sides on the bottom to rest, appearing quite dead for a short while. The young are favourite aquarium subjects and are often seen in shallow rock pools, while the adults may be found in deeper water. Entire C. and E. Indo-Pacific including Hawaii, but not in Queensland. Replaced by the following subspecies in the W. Indian Ocean. See 1276.

**1275a. CORIS GAIMARDI AFRICANA** Smith 1957          **Pl. 28**
30 cm. Adult very different from 1275 in appearance, but identical in structure and habits. Juvenile identical. East Africa, Aldabra, Madagascar, Mauritius, Seychelles.

**1276. CORIS FORMOSA** Bennett 1830 **Pl. 28**
30 cm. Very similar to 1275, but juvenile brick-coloured, not scarlet; adult always with a white caudal margin. Western Indian Ocean including India and Ceylon.

**1277. CORIS FREREI** Günther 1866 **Pl. 29**
=**CORIS HALEI** Day 1888
60 cm. Juvenile unknown. Adult has been much confused with 1276 and 1275. Western Indian Ocean including Ceylon.

**1278. CORIS AYGULA** Lacépède 1802 **Pl. 29**
=**CORIS ANGULATA** Lacépède 1802
100 cm. Juveniles and young adults as figured. Old specimens very dark bottle green, almost black, with profile of head humped, angular. Juveniles common in rock pools, favourite aquarium subjects. The 2 red spots disappear when the fish attains more than 10 cm. Entire Indo-Pacific excluding Hawaii and Queensland.

**1279. CORIS CAUDIMACULA** Quoy & Gaimard 1824 **Pl. 29**
17 cm; D IX/12–13; A III/12–13; L 1 50–53; tr 4/19. A common fish of shallow water and sandy bottoms. Western Indian Ocean and Red Sea. Known from the E. Indies, Philippines, Ryukyu islands and Melanesia as *C. multicolor* (Rüppell) 1835 and *C. variegata* (Rüppell) 1835.

**1280. CORIS FLAVOVITTATA** Bennett 1828 **Pl. 28**
Hilu (Hawaii)
45 cm. Juveniles have sides of body banded with black as well as upper sides. Philippines, Guam and Hawaii, where it is common.

ALLIED SPECIES:
**1281. CORIS LEPOMIS** Jenkins 60 cm. Scales very small. Greenish with yellowish spots and a prominent black spot on upper opercular angle. Hawaii only, common.
**1282. C. VENUSTA** Vaillant & Sauvage 15 cm. Brownish with a red band from edge of operculum to beyond pectoral tip and numerous green spots and lines. Hawaii.
**1283. C. BALLIEUI** Vaillant & Sauvage 35 cm. First dorsal ray prolonged. Light pinkish yellow with irregular green lines on head and dorsal and a green spot on each body scale above lateral line. A dark saddle on nape and another behind pectoral. Tail with interrupted green transverse lines. Lower sides with longitudinal reddish lines. Hawaii, common.
**1284. C. ROSEA** Vaillant & Sauvage 25 cm. First dorsal spine not prolonged, reddish. Possibly conspecific with 1283. Hawaii.
**1285. C. YAMASHIROI** (Schmidt) 12 cm. Violet red, paler below. Top of head greenish with dark lines, operculum violet, pectoral base bright red. Okinawa and S. Japan.
**1286. C. PICTA** (B. & S.) 28 cm. A wide red mid-dorsal stripe from snout to base of tail. A bright chocolate wide mid-lateral stripe from snout through eye to base of tail, with vertical extensions at lower edge; lemon yellow below chocolate stripe. Dorsal fin dark brown at base, with a red longitudinal band; distal half yellow. Tail and other fins orange yellow. Australia and Lord Howe island.

**1287. DUYMAERIA FLAGELLIFERA** (Cuvier & Valenciennes) 1839
**Pl. 31**
20 cm; D IX–X/10–11; A III/9; L 1 22–25; tr 2/7. Male as figured; female brownish olive, variously spotted and mottled. Dorsal and anal fins rounded.

spines less prolonged, dorsal ones black; ventrals reddish with black spots. Shallow water among weeds. South and E. Africa, Seychelles, E. Indies, Philippines, China, Japan, Melanesia.

**1288. PTERAGOGUS OPERCULARIS** Peters 1855
15 cm; D XI/9–10; A III/9–10; L 1 24; tr 2/6. Deep-bodied, mouth large, fins and tail rounded, leading ventral rays very elongated. Brown, variously mottled and spotted with yellowish, reddish and blackish. A very large black spot on operculum. Shallow water among weeds along E. African coast, from Natal to the Red Sea. Also in the Seychelles.

ALLIED SPECIES:
**1289. PTERAGOGUS TAENIOPS** Peters 15 cm. Similar to 1288, but opercular spot lacking and replaced by a white-edged dark line from eye to isthmus. Weedy places from Natal to Zanzibar.

**1290. HEMIGYMNUS FASCIATUS** (Bloch) 1792    **Pl. 31**
Five-banded Wrasse
75 cm; D IX/11; A III/11; L 1 26–29; tr 5/11–14. Lips thick, lower divided into 2 lobes. A pair of large, almost horizontal anterior canines in each jaw. Coral reefs in the Red Sea, Indian Ocean, E. Indies, Philippines, Japan, Melanesia, Carolines and Samoa.

**1291. HEMIGYMNUS MELAPTERUS** (Bloch) 1791
Thick-lipped Wrasse
35 cm. Teeth, fin and scale counts as in 1287, lips becoming very thick with age. Blackish brown posteriorly, paler anteriorly, tail yellow. Juveniles with light silvery grey of head and anterior body separated from posterior black area by an oblique yellow band. Most of Indo-Pacific including Queensland, but not in Hawaii.

**1292. XENOJULIS MARGARITACEUS** (Macleay) 1884
Pearly Rainbowfish
10 cm; D IX/11; A III/11; L 1 28–29; tr 2/7–8. Dorsal membranes excised, tail truncate. Yellowish, darker on top of head. A broad, dark-edged pearly stripe from operculum to tail base. Sides with indistinct dark vertical stripes. A black anterior spot on spinous dorsal and another on posterior soft dorsal. A few black spots on outer caudal rays and sometimes a black ocellus on anal. New Guinea and the Philippines.

**1293. STETHOJULIS AXILLARIS** (Quoy & Gaimard) 1824    **Pl. 31**
Red-spot Rainbowfish
12 cm; D IX/11–12; A III/10–11; L 1 22–28; tr 2½/8–9. Juveniles with one or more small black ocelli on caudal peduncle. Coral reefs and rock pools throughout the entire Indo-Pacific including the Red Sea, Queensland and Hawaii.

**1294. STETHOJULIS KALOSOMA** (Bleeker) 1852    **Pl. 31**
12 cm. Very common in weedy tidal pools throughout the Indo-Pacific excluding Hawaii.

**1295. STETHOJULIS PHEKADOPLEURA** (Bleeker) 1849
12 cm. Similar to 1294, but brown. Lower sides with up to 4 short rows of dark

spots along scale rows. Weedy tidal pools in the E. Indies, Philippines, Japan, Melanesia and Queensland.

**1296. STETHOJULIS STRIGIVENTER** (Bennett) 1832          **Pl. 31**
Silver-streaked Rainbowfish
15 cm. Shallow coastal waters and rock pools. Entire Indo-Pacific excluding Hawaii. See 1297.

**1297. STETHOJULIS RENARDI** (Bleeker) 1851
12 cm. Very similar to 1296, but scales of thorax much enlarged. Treated as the adult male of 1296 by Smith (1963). Most of Indo-Pacific, but exact distribution impossible to ascertain owing to confusion with 1296. Not in Hawaii.

**1298. STETHOJULIS ALBIVITTATA** (Bonnaterre) 1788          **Pl. 31**
15 cm. Apparently recorded from the entire Indo-Pacific, including the Red Sea, Queensland and Hawaii.

ALLIED SPECIES:
**1299. STETHOJULIS CASTURI** (Bleeker) 12 cm. Lower flanks bluish white. A large red crescent surrounding pectoral base. Queensland and S. Polynesia.
**1300. S. TRILINEATA** (B. & S.) 15 cm. Olive, paler below, with 4 blue longitudinal lines: 1st along dorsal profile; 2nd from snout through eye to upper part of tail base; 3rd from upper lip below eye to pectoral base; 4th from corner of mouth to lower part of tail base. India, E. Indies, Philippines and Melanesia; also recorded from the Red Sea and Madagascar. See 1301.
**1301. S. INTERRUPTA** (Bleeker) 12 cm. Very similar to 1300, but upper blue line drops from back to upper part of peduncle, 2nd line curves downwards and ends on opercular upper angle; 3rd is interrupted by a wide gap behind eye and 4th is interrupted behind pectoral base. South and E. Africa to the E. Indies, Philippines, China and Melanesia.

**1302. PSEUDOJULOIDES CERASINUS** Snyder 1904
10 cm. Slaty blue, reddish when young, with a dark stripe edged below by a mid-lateral blue line which is interrupted at operculum, then passes through eye to snout. A dark marginal crescent on tail. Rare; deepish waters in Hawaii.

**1303. MACROPHARYNGODON MELEAGRIS**
(Cuvier & Valenciennes) 1839
Reticulated Wrasse
15 cm; D IX/11; A III/11–12; L 1 27–29; Tr 2½/9. Dorsal of even width, tail rounded. Two pairs of anterior canines in each jaw; outer canine of upper jaw hooked outwards and backwards; upper jaw with a posterior canine. Scales of thorax smaller than scales of body. Lateral line bent sharply at 20th–22nd scale. Body brownish, each scale with a light blue, brown edged spot. Head pinkish-violet with dark-edged orange bands and spots extending on to breast. Dorsal and anal violet with a darker submarginal line and a series of brown-edged light spots; a black spot between 1st and 3rd dorsal spines. Tail pale brownish violet with irregular, interrupted transverse brown bands. Coral reefs in Indonesia, the Philippines, New Guinea, the Solomons, Marshall Caroline and Ryukyu islands. See 1305.

**1304. MACROPHARYNGODON PARDALIS** (Kner) 1867          **Pl. 26**
12 cm. Black spots and blotches very variable and irregular. Rather rare Philippines, Marshall islands, Fiji and Samoa.

## 1305. MACROPHARYNGODON GEOFFROYI
(Quoy & Gaimard) 1824
15 cm. Similar to 1303, but apparently lacks black spot on dorsal fin. Not uncommon in Hawaii at about 10 m. Also known from Indonesia, the Philippines and Samoa, but often confused with 1303.

ALLIED SPECIES:

**1306. MACROPHARYNGODON VARIAVALVUS** Smith 8 cm. Bright green with a blue spot on each body scale. Three purplish violet saddles; breast pinkish with purple blotches, head marked with irregular purple lines. Dorsal green with a red margin on spinous part, continued as a submarginal band on rayed portion which is edged with blue; 3 blue spots between each pair of spines and rays. Tail reddish with green rays. Anal red with blue spots and a blue margin. Ventrals purple with pinkish spots. Western Indian Ocean. Rare.

**1307. M. BIPARTITUS** Smith 8 cm. Green, breast and belly purple-red. Six longitudinal purple-red stripes from snout and chin to middle of sides; rear part of body marked with irregular purple red spots and blotches. Dorsal and anal purple-red, spotted, lined and edged with green. Tail hyaline with green rays and a broad, irregular purple-red margin. Rare, W. Indian Ocean.

**1308. M. NEGROSENSIS** Herre. A little known species from the Philippines.

## 1309. HALICHOERES CENTRIQUADRUS (Lacépède) 1802      Pl. 25
30 cm; D IX/10–11; A III/11; L 1 25–26; tr 2½–3/9. Very variable, but always with a prominent yellow saddle followed by a blackish mark; the yellow spot on peduncle is also very conspicuous, particularly when seen from above. The white form seems the commonest in the Indian Ocean; the blue and green forms are more often seen in the Pacific. Very common on coral throughout the entire Indo-Pacific, but not in Hawaii.

## 1310. HALICHOERES TRIMACULATUS (Griffith) 1834      Pl. 26
15 cm; D IX/11; A III/11; L 1 25–28; tr 2½/9. Usually seen in sandy areas. East Indies, Philippines, China, Japan, Queensland, Palau, Fiji, Samoa and Tuamotu islands and Melanesia.

## 1311. HALICHOERES SCAPULARIS (Bennett) 1831      Pl. 26
18 cm; D IX/11–12; A III/11; L 1 25–29; tr 2–3/8–9. As figured, but paler, with a more prominent dark lateral band when young. Very common in sandy areas throughout the entire Indo-Pacific excluding Hawaii.

## 1312. HALICHOERES NEBULOSUS (Cuvier & Valenciennes) 1839
Clouded Wrasse                                    Pl. 26
13 cm; D IX/11; A III/10–11; L 1 25–29; tr 1½–2/9–10. Very variable; usually in weedy areas from E. Africa and the Seychelles to the E. Indies, Philippines, Melanesia, Queensland, Fiji and Samoa.

## 1313. HALICHOERES HOEVENI (Bleeker) 1851      Pl. 26
Three-eyed Wrasse
14 cm; D IX/11–13; A III/11–13; L 1 26–28; tr 2/9. Ocelli larger and more clearly marked in young individuals. Uncommon. Coral reefs in the E. Indies, Philippines, Palau, Solomon, New Hebrides, Fiji, Samoa and Society islands.

**1314. HALICHOERES NOTOPSIS** (Cuvier & Valenciennes) 1839
Two-eyed Wrasse                                                    **Pl. 26**
12 cm; D IX/12–13; A III/12; L 1 27–29; tr 2½–3½/9–10. As figured, but young
darker, with 3 white spots along back. Widespread, but nowhere common.
East Africa and the Seychelles to Ceylon, the E. Indies, Philippines, Guam,
Palau and the Society islands.

ALLIED SPECIES:

**1315. HALICHOERES MELANURUS** (Bleeker) 11 cm. Dusky red; six greenish
saddles on back. Body with many blue-green longitudinal stripes. Head marked with
irregular blue-edged green bands. Dorsal and anal red with green base and margin. A
black spot in pectoral axil. Tail yellow with 4 brownish transverse lines. East Indies,
Philippines, Micronesia, Melanesia and Samoa.

**1316. H. LEPARENSIS** (Bleeker) 8 cm. Body greenish, chin and breast yellow.
Scale centres silvery; 4–6 dark green vertical bands on upper sides. A red band from
snout to eye, dividing into 5 branches on upper operculum. Body with a series of pinkish
lines along scale rows. Dorsal and anal yellowish green with purplish reticulations
enclosing pale spots. A small white-ringed black spot between 1st and 2nd dorsal spines
and a much larger such ocellus between 1st and 3rd dorsal rays. Tail yellowish green
with a small ocellus at base of upper rays. Andamans, Indonesia, Philippines, Palau,
Guam and New Caledonia.

**1317. H. MARGARITACEUS** (C. & V.) 10 cm. Pale olive, darker above. Most
scales with silvery centres and dark edges forming an irregular criss-cross pattern.
Blue-edged dark streaks radiating from eye and red-edged brown spots behind eye;
A pink stripe with dark edges below eye. Dorsal with oblique reddish bars, a small
black ocellus between first two spines and a larger one on anterior rays. Anal yellowish
with oblique red bars, tail yellow with narrow vertical brown bars. Indian Ocean,
C. Indo-Pacific, Queensland and Samoa.

**1318. H. ARGUS** (B. & S.) 11 cm. Dark green; body scales with a red spot with blue
or black centre forming longitudinal rows which are interrupted near back by 4–5
patches of light scales; head with irregular red stripes and spots. Dorsal and anal with
several rows of dark-ringed red spots. Tail yellow with red ocelli or reticulations. East
Indies, Philippines, Indo-China, Fiji and Melanesia.

**1319. H. CHLOROPTERUS** (Bloch) 18 cm. Green with broad violet or blue bands
on head and anterior part of body, broken into blue-edged green ocelli behind and
above pectoral. A blackish-blue bar across pectoral base. Dorsal green with median
longitudinal purple band; anal purple with median longitudinal green band. Tail
greenish yellow with transverse rows of purple spots. East Indies, Philippines and
Melanesia.

**1320. H. GYMNOCEPHALUS** (B. & S.) 16 cm. Brownish above, paler below. A
large blackish blotch on sides, behind pectoral; scales above and behind blotch with
black centres, forming horizontal rows. A dark bar across pectoral base. Head with
irregular, broken reddish bands; fins hyaline. East Indies, Philippines, Palau, New
Hebrides, Solomons and New Guinea.

*Halichoeres melanurus*          *H. leparensis*          *H. argus*

**1321. H. KAWARIN** (Bleeker) 10 cm. Green; a diffuse, very broad dark cross-band below middle of dorsal; some bold purple markings on face and snout and 4–5 purple-red lines along scale rows from operculum to dark cross-band; most body scales with a red-purple centre; an irregular dark blotch on peduncle. Dorsal greenish with oblique red cross-bands not reaching margin and a large black spot on anterior rays. Tail pinkish with irregular transverse rows of red spots. Anal red at base, outer third pink, with a broken longitudinal green median band. South and E. Africa, Seychelles to E. Indies, Andamans, Philippines, Samoa, Gilbert and Society islands.

**1322. H. MARGINATUS** Rüppell 13 cm. Bright red with numerous parallel green lines from snout to tail base; base of pectoral black. Dorsal and anal purple with numerous green spots and vermiculations. Tail purplish with a dark-edged green curved transverse band at base and a green margin. Red Sea, E. Africa, Seychelles to E. Indies, Philippines, Melanesia, Samoa, Marquesas and Society islands.

**1323. H. BIMACULATUS** Rüppell 20 cm. Tail truncate with pointed tips. Back and middle of sides green; head below mouth and eye blue; lower posterior sides and peduncle pale blue. Irregular purple and violet lines on head and cheeks. A yellow spot at upper angle of operculum. A black blotch on lateral line below 8th dorsal spine and a purple band from black spot to operculum. A narrow purple line from operculum along pectoral base to belly, well behind ventrals. An irregular broad red stripe from below black lateral spot to base of tail with some scattered red spots below and separating dorsal green from ventral light blue. Dorsal red with some green basal spots and a submarginal yellow line edged with light blue. Anal yellow with a red margin and a blue basal band enclosing red spots between the rays. Tail red with some dark blue spots and a dark blue transverse line. Western Indian Ocean.

**1324. H. KALLOCHROMA** (Bleeker) 12 cm. Marked with irregular longitudinal alternating pale and darker rose-violet bands; fins and tail similarly marked; pectoral axil black, sometimes a black spot on upper tail base. East Indies, Philippines, Marshalls, Fiji, Samoa and Society islands.

**1325. H. MINIATUS** (C. & V.) 8 cm. Greenish above, belly purplish, breast and chin yellow. A pink stripe from corner of mouth, below eye to opercular margin. Brown stripes on head, brown spots on back and posterior sides. A diffuse black blotch behind eye. Unpaired fins and tail with black spots on rays. East Indies, Philippines, China, Queensland, New Hebrides, Fiji and Madagascar.

**1326. H. BINOTOPSIS** (Bleeker) 9 cm. Back brown reticulated with dark violet and with 4 darker cross-bands. Head with undulating violet-red stripes. A red-edged black spot at top of tail base. Dorsal with numerous red spots and a red-ringed black spot between first two spines and another on first rays. Anal with yellow ocelli; tail orange. A violet stripe across pectoral base. East Indies, Philippines, Palau, New Hebrides, Fiji and Banks islands.

**1327. H. JAVANICUS** (Bleeker) 11 cm. Brownish red, silvery on belly. A vertical blue band behind eye and several oblique red stripes on head. A black spot at pectoral base. Dorsal reddish with 2–3 rows of round yellow spots. Tail reddish with irregular yellow spots, anal red. East Indies, Philippines, Hong Kong, Ceylon, Zanzibar.

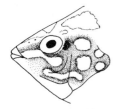

*H. gymnocephalus*

*H. marginatus*

**1328. H. HYRTLI** (Bleeker) 11 cm. Back olive, belly white; a mid-dorsal dark brown band and a dark brown band, interrupted by a red opercular spot, from snout, through eye to middle of tail base, followed by a black spot. Broad dark blue vertical bands alternating with narrow green stripes behind eye. A dark spot at pectoral base. Unpaired fins and tail with dark reticulations. Persian Gulf to Ceylon, E. Indies, Philippines and China.

**1329. H. LEUCURUS** (Walbaum) 12 cm. Green above, yellow below, each scale with a red basal spot; head with orange spots and bands. Pectoral base black. Dorsal and anal green with oblique reddish cross-bars and scarlet margins; tail bright green with 4 narrow red transverse lines and a pale reddish margin, broadest at outer angles. Andamans, E. Indies, Philippines, Indo-China, Solomons and New Guinea.

**1330. H. BICOLOR** (Schneider) Two very distinct dark longitudinal bands on upper sides and a large white-ringed black spot between 6th and 9th dorsal spines; tail pale. East Indies, Malaya and the Philippines.

**1331. H. MELANOCHIR** Fowler & Bean 12 cm. Purplish; dorsal and anterior body scales with a black basal spot. Head narrowly striped with reddish. Dorsal purplish with 4 scarlet longitudinal bands anteriorly, 3 posteriorly; anal similar. Tail dull red, darker at margins, rays olive yellow. Ventrals orange, black anteriorly; pectorals light green, with very dark purple base. Philippines.

**1332. H. DESMOGENYS** Fowler & Bean 11 cm. Green with 5 blackish narrow dorsal saddles. Lower sides of head and flanks with purplish brown stripes; dorsal brownish red with 3 rows of rounded blue spots and a blue margin posteriorly. Anal reddish brown with two irregular longitudinal green bands and a blue margin. Tail red-brown with numerous interrupted transverse blue bands. Ventrals green, pectorals pale yellowish with black spot at base. Philippines.

**1333. H. PAPILIONACEUS** (C. & V.) 10 cm. Dusky green above, cheeks apple green, breast and belly yellowish green. Head with numerous irregular wine red stripes narrowly edged with black. Upper part of body with 5–7 dark vertical blotches, the anterior pair connected by two horizontal bands behind operculum, the lower band reappearing on peduncle. Dorsal with a black spot between 4th and 6th spines. Tail pale with 2–3 narrow transverse lines and a broad dark margin. East Indies, Philippines, New Guinea and Solomon islands.

**1334. H. NIGRESCENS** (Schneider) 16 cm. Green above, pale yellowish below. Chin and lower part of head pink. Head marked with purplish pink irregular sinuous bands and spots; many of body scales with purplish centres forming irregular interrupted bands and diffuse dark saddles on upper sides. Dorsal purplish with a black spot between 5th and 6th spines and with 2 rows of yellow spots. Anal purplish with yellow spots near base. Tail purplish with small irregular yellow spots, outer angles broadly yellowish. East Africa, E. Indies, Philippines, China, Taiwan, Japan, Queensland.

**1335. H. POECILOPTERUS** (Schlegel) 25 cm. Male brown dorsally, golden on upper sides, bright green mid-laterally and paler below; red and brown spots and bars on body scales forming several indistinct dark lines along scale rows; head marked with green-edged bright red bands and spots. Female similar, but ground colour pale pinkish white with a dark brown mid-dorsal band and a crenulate mid-lateral dark stripe from snout through eye to middle of tail base. Most body scales with darker basal spots forming faint longitudinal bands. Philippines, Taiwan, China and Japan.

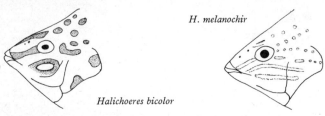

*H. melanochir*

*Halichoeres bicolor*

**1336. H. TENUISPINIS** (Günther) 16 cm. Body and top of head emerald green; lower part of head sulphur yellow, breast and belly bluish white, becoming blue on peduncle. Numerous orange spots on upper part of head and sides; a blue-edged purplish stripe from snout to eye, breaking into four broken bars behind eye. Dorsal yellowish green with three irregular red longitudinal bands. Tail pink. Anal similar to dorsal, but paler, pectorals yellow at base. Philippines, China, Korea and Japan.

**1337. H. HARTZFELDI** (Bleeker) 18 cm. Olive green above, yellow below, head green. Scales of upper back with red posterior half. Numerous red lines and spots on head. A bright yellow spot at pectoral base. A mid-lateral salmon stripe from operculum to tail base and some vertical salmon streaks below it. Dorsal red with green spots at base, a broad median yellow band edged with pale purplish and a pale margin. Anal similar, with pink margin. Tail green, yellowish distally, with reddish tips and two red transverse lines. Pectoral axil blackish. East Indies and Philippines.

**1338. H. PODOSTIGMA** (Bleeker) 16 cm. Dark olive shading to bluish below. Purplish pink lines and spots on body and head; a large bright orange patch above pectoral base, base itself with a black ocellus. Dorsal and anal reddish with blue-rimmed olive spots and bands. East Indies and Philippines.

**1339. H. ORNATISSIMUS** (Garrett) 18 cm. Brick red above, pale blue below; scales on sides with green spots, head green with reddish lines. Always a small black spot behind eye and generally a black anterior spot on dorsal, often followed by a larger one on anterior rays and sometimes by a third spot on posterior rays. Hawaii only, usually in 7–8 m of water where it is not uncommon.

**1340. H. HORTULANUS** (Lacépède) 17 cm. Whitish with 3 yellow patches on back; pectoral base yellow; some orange spots on sides above pectoral and before dorsal origin. Scales of sides with two blackish spots, sometimes connected; eye orange. Head marked with purple-edged pink streaks. Dorsal, anal, tail and ventrals golden yellow; pectorals with a dark spot. East Indies, Ryukyu, Guam, Marshall islands and New Guinea.

The following rare and little known species of *Halichoeres* have also been described from the Indo-Pacific: *H. cyanopleura* (Bleeker), E. Indies and Philippines; *H. leucostigma* Fowler & Bean, Philippines; *H. timorensis* (Bleeker), Indonesia; *H. prosopeion* (Bleeker), E. Indies, Philippines and Ryukyu islands; *H. biocellatus* Schultz, Marshall islands; *H. dianthus* Smith, Mozambique; *H. lapillus* Smith, Mozambique; *H. richmondi* Fowler & Bean, Philippines and E. Indies; *H. reichei* (Bleeker), Philippines and Indonesia; *H. solorensis* (Bleeker) E. Indies, Philippines and east to the Marquesas; *H. vrolicki* (Bleeker), E. Indies and Philippines.

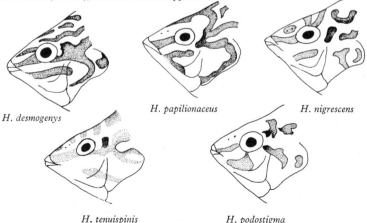

H. desmogenys        H. papilionaceus        H. nigrescens

H. tenuispinis        H. podostigma

Family SCARIDAE **Parrotfishes, Uhu (Hawaii), Kakatoi (Seychelles)**
Medium to large very colourful reef fishes of all warm seas. Parrotfishes feed
on vegetable matter and invertebrates and their teeth are fused into a parrot-
like beak which is well adapted to crushing coral and molluscs. Some species
have posterior canines. The scales are very large and there are 2 to 4 rows on the
cheeks below the eyes; opercular scales large. The lateral line is interrupted
below the hind end of the dorsal base. Scale and fin counts are very similar in
most species, which have been separated on the basis of colour and pattern.
However, recent studies suggest that most brown and red forms are females or
young males, whereas the blue and green individuals are old males. As a result
there has been a great deal of confusion and the synonymy is voluminous. In
this work we follow a recent revision by Schultz.

Parrotfishes are related to the wrasses and are similar in behaviour; at night
they usually go to sleep in a loose cocoon of mucus, sand and weeds in a hole in
the coral. Small brown or red individuals are usually seen in small schools, but
the large blue or green males are generally solitary. They swim rather slowly,
with a slow, deliberate flapping of the pectorals. Most parrotfishes are valued
food fishes, but some are considered poisonous in some areas at certain times of
the year.

There are two subfamilies: the *Scarinae*, with completely fused teeth and the
*Sparisomatinae* with incompletely fused teeth.

Subfamily *Sparisomatinae*
**1341. LEPTOSCARUS VAIGIENSIS** (Quoy & Gaimard) 1824　　**Pl. 31**
=**SCARICHTHYS CAERULEOPUNCTATUS** Bleeker 1862
Blue-speckled Parrotfish
35 cm; D IX/10–11; A III/8–9; L 1 18–21/4–6; tr 1½/6–7. *Vaigiensis* is the ♀;
the ♂ (figured), with canines and blue spots, long regarded as a distinct species,
was called *caeruleopunctatus*. Very common, usually in quite large schools in
shallow water where the bottom is sandy and there is much sea weed. An important food fish. Entire Indo-Pacific excluding Hawaii; one of the few species
which has been able to establish itself in the Mediterranean thanks to the Suez
Canal.

**1342. CALOTOMUS SPINIDENS** (Quoy & Gaimard) 1824　　**Pl. 32**
=**C. SANDWICHENSIS** Gosline & Brock 1960
Half-toothed Parrotfish
30 cm; D IX/10; A III/9; L 1 18–20/4–5; tr 1½/6–7. Adult may be as figured,
dark green with pinkish red spots and markings, or brown, but may always be
recognised by the narrow white caudal margin. Juveniles brownish, mottled
and speckled with darker and paler brown, often with a black anterior spot
on dorsal, pink stripes radiating from eye, but lacking white caudal margin.
Common in weedy places throughout the entire Indo-Pacific including Hawaii

**1343. CALOTOMUS JAPONICUS** (Cuvier & Valenciennes) 1839
16 cm. Tail rounded. Olive brown above, reddish or greenish below; males
mottled with blue, females with reddish. Five rows of whitish spots on head
and upper sides. Precise distribution difficult to ascertain, as it is often confused
with the juvenile of 1342, but it is probably almost as widely distributed,
though not as common.

**1344. SCARIDEA ZONARCHA** Jenkins 1903
25 cm. Dorsal spines stronger and sharper than in most other parrotfishes.
Tail rounded. Colour variable, but generally greyish, speckled and spotted with
white, yellow and blackish; 3 orange brown bands alternating with white marks
on the chin. Known from Hawaii only.

Subfamily *Scarinae* Typical Parrotfishes

**1345. SCAROPS RUBROVIOLACEUS** (Bleeker) 1849     ♀ **Pl. 34,**
**=CALLYODON AFRICANUS** Smith 1955                     ♂ **Pl. 35**
Palukaluka (Hawaii)
75 cm; D IX/10; A III/9; L 1 18–20/5–7; tr 1½/6–7. *Africanus* is the adult
male, *rubroviolaceus* the female. The young are reddish brown. A common and
important food fish; entire Indo-Pacific including Hawaii.

**1346. BOLBOMETOPON MURICATUS** (Cuvier & Valenciennes) 1839
Double-headed Parrotfish, Filambase (Seychelles)
120 cm, 75 kg; D IX/9–10; A III/9; L 1 17–19/10–11; tr 1½/5–7. Old individuals
develop a large rounded cushion on forehead. Juveniles dull brown with some
white spots, becoming greenish brown and finally uniform green. Flesh pale
green. Often in large schools, usually in deep water. East Africa and Seychelles
to E. Indies, Thailand, Philippines, Samoa, Palau, Caroline and Solomon
Islands and New Guinea.

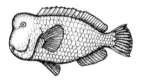

Double-headed Parrotfish

**1347. BOLBOMETOPON BICOLOR** (Rüppell) 1828          **Pl. 33** (♀)
**=SCARUS PULCHELLUS** Rüppell 1835 (♀)
**=CETOSCARUS BICOLOR** Smith 1956
**=CETOSCARUS PULCHELLUS** Smith 1956
120 cm; D IX/9–10; A III/9; L 1 16–19/5–7; tr 1½/7. Adult female as figured.
The male (*bicolor*) attains 50 cm; it is very dark reddish brown above and pur-
plish below, with 2 black spots on most body scales and blackish brown fins.
Juvenile pinkish white with a broad black-edged vertical orange band on head,
orange tail and an orange-edged black spot on spinous dorsal. Half grown
individuals are pale grey with orange head, black fins and tail. Entire Indo-
Pacific excluding Hawaii.

**1348. YPSISCARUS OVIFRONS** (Temminck & Schlegel) 1846
**=CALLYODON VIRIDIFUCATUS** Smith 1956
25 cm. Teeth white. Green; chin, breast and anterior belly orange to red. Base
of tail blue; upper body scales with a red vertical streak; eye orange, an irregular
vertical red stripe in front of eye, merging with red colour of chin. Dorsal and
anal red with green base and blue margin. Tail green with a red or violet band
inside upper and lower margins. Paired fins blue or green with an anterior red
submarginal stripe. East Africa and Seychelles to C. Indo-Pacific.

**1349. YPSISCARUS OEDEMA** (Snyder) 1909
43 cm. Teeth white. Uniform deep chocolate brown, eye yellow, fins blackish.
Adults develop a swollen crest on top of the head. Ryukyu, Okinawa and
Philippines.

**1350. SCARUS HARID** Forskål 1775                              **Pl. 35**
Long-nosed Parrotfish
75 cm; D IX/10; A III/9–10; L 1 17–18/9; tr 1½/7. Colour variable, but can
always be recognised by its slender shape and long, pointed snout. Female
of W. Indian Ocean subspecies (*vexillus* (Smith) 1959) as figured; male bright
pink, head and snout dark red on top; 2 short green horizontal stripes behind
eye. Dorsal and anal red with a longitudinal series of green spots. Outer rays of
tail very much prolonged, dark purplish; basal half of tail red with a vertical
series of dark spots, distal half green. The subspecies from the E. Indies,
Philippines, Japan and the Pacific (*longiceps* C. & V. 1839) is green above and
yellowish orange below, the scales edged with purplish pink. The head is
purplish grey above and yellowish orange below with pink and orange streaks
radiating from the eye. Dorsal and anal with blue spots and margins. Tail with
red outer rays. The typical subspecies *harid* is confined to the Red Sea.

**1351. SCARUS GIBBUS** Rüppell 1828                            **Pl. 35**
**=S. MICRORHINOS** Bleeker 1854
**=S. STRONGYLOCEPHALUS** Bleeker 1854
2 m. Teeth pale bluish in old specimens; old males have strongly produced
outer caudal rays and vertical red streaks on body scales and red bands on
unpaired fins. Specimens of 2 m are exceptional, the average large male being
60 cm in length. Most of the Indo-Pacific and Red Sea, but not in Hawaii nor
in Queensland.

**1352. SCARUS FLAVIPECTORALIS** Schultz 1958
30 cm. Teeth yellowish pink, 1–3 posterior canines in upper jaw. Body scales
yellow, edged with red on anterior half of body, with green on posterior part;
top of head dark red, cheeks whitish, breast blue. A broad yellow-edged green
stripe from snout through eye to upper angle of operculum. Dorsal yellow with
a pink basal band, a large green spot between each pair of spines and rays and a
blue-green margin. Anal red with blue margin. Tail yellow, purple and blue at
base, outer rays green. Paired fins yellow. East Indies and Melanesia.

**1353. SCARUS DUBIUS** Bennett 1828
38 cm. Teeth pink; 1–2 canines in upper jaw. Purplish or reddish brown, often
with pale longitudinal streaks on belly. Dorsal, anal and tail brown; anal with a
narrow blue edge. Pectorals yellowish with a dark basal spot. Peduncle and tail
yellowish. Mauritius, E. Indies, Philippines, Melanesia, China, Queensland,
the Caroline, Hawaiian, Society and Marquesas islands.

**1354. SCARUS LUNULA** (Snyder) 1908                           **Pl. 35**
55 cm. Teeth white. Humped profile of head characteristic. Widespread, but
uncommon; known from such scattered localities as E. Africa, the Seychelles,
Okinawa and the Marshall islands.

**1355. SCARUS FORMOSUS** Cuvier & Valenciennes 1839           **Pl. 32**
34 cm. Teeth white. One to two posterior canines in upper jaw. East Indies,
Philippines, Melanesia, Samoa, Marshall islands and Hawaii.

**1356. SCARUS PERSPICILLATUS** Steindachner 1879      **Pl. 34**
Uhu (Hawaii)
60 cm. Mature males and females strikingly different, as shown in plate 34.
Second row of scales on cheek incomplete. Confined to Hawaii, where it is the
commonest parrotfish.

**1357. SCARUS VENOSUS** Cuvier & Valenciennes 1839
38 cm. Tail truncate, teeth white. Head blue-grey, body olive with 4–5 indistinct darker cross-bands; body scales edged with purplish pink. Some
indistinct violet red markings on cheek, chin and across snout. Dorsal bright
olive green with a violet red basal band, a violet red submarginal line and a
blue margin. Tail, anal and paired fins greyish violet. East Africa and the
Seychelles to the E. Indies and Marshall islands.

**1358. SCARUS TAENIURUS** Cuvier & Valenciennes 1839      **Pl. 33**
=**S. BATAVIENSIS** Bleeker 1857
=**PSEUDOSCARUS OKTODON** Bleeker 1861
=**XANOTHON FOWLERI** Smith 1956
=**XANOTHON CARIFANUS** Smith 1956
60 cm; D IX/10; A III/9; L 1 17–18/7–10; tr 1½/6–7. A most variable fish,
as can be seen from the synonymy; the red pectoral fin with narrow blue or
green superior margin appears to be the only reasonably constant character,
as it is present even in the uniform brown phase (*oktodon*). The form figured on
plate 33 is *fowleri*, as determined by the late Prof. Smith. Known from the
entire Indo-Pacific, including Hawaii.

**1359. SCARUS FORSTERI** Cuvier & Valenciennes 1839      **Pl. 32**
=**S. JENKINSI** Jordan & Everman 1903
=**XANOTHON BATAVIENSIS** Smith (not Bleeker) 1956
60 cm. Another very variable species; in the green phase the scale margins may
be yellow or red as well as the unpaired fins. Known from most of the Indo-
Pacific, including Hawaii, but apparently not in Queensland.

**1360. SCARUS ENNEACANTHUS** Lacépède 1802      **Pl. 33**
=**S. CAPITANEUS** C. & V. 1839
37 cm. Variable, some specimens being plain green with dark blue fins; the
blue pectoral is probably a reasonably stable character for the green phase.
Indian Ocean.

**1361. SCARUS RHODUROPTERUS** (Bleeker) 1861      **Pl. 32**
30 cm. Apparently no green phase is known for this species. East Africa and the
Seychelles to the E. Indies and Philippines.

**1362. SCARUS SORDIDUS** Forskål 1775      **Pl. 33**
=**S. PURPUREUS** C. & V. 1839
=**XANOTHON BIPALLIDUS** Smith 1956
95 cm; D IX/9–10; A III/9–10; L 1 17–18/3–7; tr 1½/6–7. Canines small or
absent. Teeth white, becoming green in old males. Green form variable, with
red, purple or dark blue spots on body scales; green unspotted area on caudal
peduncle fairly constant. The much smaller brown individuals may have red
teeth and be uniform reddish brown with darker scale margins, or may have 2
longitudinal series of white spots on the body and a highly contrasting pale
caudal peduncle with a large round black spot. Known from most of the Indo-
Pacific including Hawaii; apparently not recorded from Queensland.

**1363. SCARUS TROSCHELI** Bleeker 1853
=**CALLYODON BLEEKERI** Weber & De Beaufort 1940
32 cm. Teeth green; 1–2 posterior canines in upper jaw. Green with a purplish
red bar on each body scale; a large yellow area on cheek bordered above and
below by irregular narrow greenish yellow lines. Dorsal green with 2 longitudinal red bands. Anal green basally, blue distally with a median longitudinal
red band. Tail green with a mauve or purplish bar along each lobe. Lips may be
red. East Indies, Philippines, Ponape, Carolines, New Ireland, New Guinea
and Solomon islands.

**1364. SCARUS CAPISTRATOIDES** Bleeker 1849      **Pl. 33**
=**S. CYANOTAENIA** Bleeker 1854
42 cm. Teeth pinkish in old individuals. Canines prominent. East Africa and
the Seychelles to the E. Indies and Queensland.

**1365. SCARUS DIMIDIATUS** Bleeker 1859
30 cm. Teeth white. Head and anterior part of body pale blue, contrasting
strongly with dark green hind part. A square purple blotch on top of head;
a curved green band from corner of mouth to pectoral base. Dorsal pale blue
with a brown-edged green longitudinal band; anal blue-green with a narrow
dusky pink basal band; tail blue-green; pectoral green with some purplish
pink near the middle. East Indies, Philippines, New Guinea, Palau, Solomon,
Tonga and Samoan islands.

**1366. SCARUS GLOBICEPS** Cuvier & Valenciennes 1839
=**PSEUDOSCARUS PSILONOTUS** Kner 1868
50 cm. Adult with prominent rounded head. Green; chin, throat and breast blue.
Eye red; numerous dark violet vermiculations on upper head. Area between
spinous dorsal base and pectoral base closely dotted with dark violet; scales of
hind part of body and peduncle with a large dark violet basal spot. Two to three
violet horizontal bands on lower sides. Dorsal red with a blue margin and some
posterior green spots; tail green with dark violet outer rays; anal dark violet
with a green margin; pectoral green with a broad dark violet stripe along upper
margin. East Africa, Seychelles, E. Indies, Marshall islands, Queensland and
Tahiti.

**1367. SCARUS CHLORODON** Jenyns 1842
Synonymy voluminous. 38 cm. Teeth green. Dark green, scale centres paler;
lower parts of head and body pinkish orange. Green lines radiate from eye;
edge of upper lip green; a green U across chin and another behind mouth.
Dorsal brown, irregularly marked and edged with green; anal green with a
median orange band. Tail green with dark outer rays and an orange hind margin.
There is also a bright dark red form with bluish white spots and margins to
body scales, brownish violet tail with faint milky spots, slaty pectorals, red
anal, dorsal and ventrals (*improvisus* Smith 1956). East Africa and the Seychelles
to the E. Indies, Philippines, Carolines, Melanesia, Samoa and Ellice islands.

**1368. SCARUS RUBROFASCIATUS** (Smith) 1955
45 cm. Teeth red. Head and anterior half of body blackish brown; posterior
half bright red with 2 blackish cross-bands and a round black spot on caudal
peduncle. Tail red, unpaired fins red more or less mottled with black, paired
fins blackish. Red Sea and E. Africa to the E. Indies.

**1369. SCARUS CAUDOFASCIATUS** (Günther) 1862
33 cm. Teeth white. Olive green above, salmon below, with 3–4 dark saddles
on back; some green markings around lips and on lower cheeks. Tail yellowish
green; dorsal olive with slaty margin; anal pale blue with reddish median bar;
ventrals washed with salmon, pectorals yellow. There is also a bright red form
with 4–5 dark purplish vertical bands,. red fins and a black spot at base of
pectoral. Mauritius and Zanzibar to the E. Indies, Philippines, Caroline, Marshall, Solomon and Samoan islands.

**1370. SCARUS LEPIDUS** Jenyns 1842
40 cm. One form is very dark bottle green with red teeth, eyes, tail, anal and
ventral fins; another form is olive brown above, salmon below, with an elongate
longitudinal blue patch from gill opening to pectoral fin tip; lower lip, chin and
throat salmon; fins pink to dusky orange. East Africa to Seychelles, E. Indies,
Philippines and Solomon islands.

**1371. SCARUS FASCIATUS** Cuvier & Valenciennes 1839
50 cm. Teeth white. Male orange with green vermiculations on head and snout
and broad grass-green margins to scales of back and upper sides. Caudal peduncle
orange posteriorly with darker spots at base of scales. Dorsal fin orange with
green spots, bands and margin; tail orange with green outer rays and 2 vertical
series of green spots; anal orange with a green margin and some green spots
along base. Pectorals green with orange base and anterior rays. Ventrals yellow
with blue-green anterior margin. The female is green on back, posterior sides
and peduncle, blue on top of head, flanks surrounding pectoral base, breast and
belly. Snout, chin and cheeks orange with green vermiculations. Dorsal orange
with violet base, narrow blue margin and a pale green spot between each pair
of spines and rays. Tail orange with blue outer rays and green longitudinal
streaks becoming blue at hind margin. Anal violet with blue margin and green
basal spots, pectorals yellow with blue tip and red anterior rays, ventrals hyaline.
India, E. Indies, Philippines, Melanesia, Polynesia and Queensland.

**1372. SCARUS FRENATUS** Lacépède 1802
**=S. SEXVITTATUS** Rüppell 1835
30 cm. Green, red or brown with up to 6 more or less distinct dark longitudinal
stripes from operculum to base of tail. Teeth reddish, eyes, tail and fins red,
dorsal and anal with a narrow blue margin. Red Sea, E. Africa and the Seychelles to the E. Indies, Philippines, Solomon islands and Samoa; also in
Mauritius.

**1373. SCARUS JANTHOCHIR** Bleeker 1853
**=PSEUDOSCARUS FALCIPINNIS** Playfair 1867
52 cm. Profile of head strongly concave above eye, convex from above eye to
dorsal origin. Tips of tail greatly prolonged in old examples. Teeth green.
Head above eye, body above pectoral base and caudal peduncle dark blackish
green. Snout, chin, throat and breast bright green; a red line round lips and an
irregular mid-ventral stripe from chin to anal origin. Eye red. Dorsal blue with
red streaks not reaching the margin between each pair of spines and rays. Tail
green with red outer rays; anal green with a submarginal red stripe. Ventrals
green with red anterior rays. East Africa and Persian Gulf to the E. Indies,
Philippines and Caroline islands.

**1374. SCARUS GHOBBAN** Forskål 1775                    **Pls. 32 & 34**
100 cm; D IX/10; A III/9; L 1 17–18/5–7. Extremely variable, synonymy
highly involved. Some specimens have 3–4 irregular blue cross-bands on body,
others are predominantly blue, olive or pink; the form figured on plate 32 was
described as a separate species (*Callyodon apridentatus* Smith 1956). A very
common, important food fish. Occurs throughout the Indo-Pacific, from the
Red Sea to the Mexican coast, but apparently not in Hawaii. In Queensland
it is known as *Callyodon pyrrhostethus* Marshall.

**1375. SCARUS SCABER** Cuvier & Valenciennes 1839
23 cm. Teeth white; snout strongly convex in profile. Yellowish, top of head
dusky, snout dark red. Four to five indistinct blackish saddles on back; fins
and tail vinous red. South and E. Africa to the Seychelles, E. Indies, Philippines,
Japan, Palau, Solomon, Samoan and Ellice islands.

**1376. SCARUS OVICEPS** Cuvier & Valenciennes 1839
**=S. PECTORALIS** C. & V. 1839
45 cm. Teeth white, no posterior canines. Dusky olive above, pale pink below.
Two to three narrow yellowish oblique bands directed downward and forward;
fins greyish, yellow distally. Juveniles with a black stripe from snout through
eye to upper angle of operculum. The blue form has a pink chin and throat,
purple edged anterior body scales, vertical red bars on posterior body scales,
blue tail with purple outer rays, red dorsal with blue margin, blue anal with
narrow purple basal band and green pectorals with purple median stripe. Red
Sea and E. Africa to the E. Indies, Philippines, New Guinea, Solomon, Caroline,
New Hebrides, Gilbert, Samoa, Society and Tuamotu islands.

**1377. SCARUS NIGER** Forskål 1775                      **Pl. 35**
40 cm. Adult as figured. Younger individuals may have lighter green, red-
edged body scales and red breast and head, red fins and red base to tail; green
markings around lips, on snout and on top of head characteristic. Red Sea, E.
Africa and Seychelles to E. Indies and Melanesia.

**1378. SCARUS CYANOGNATHOS** Bleeker 1849              **Pl. 34**
52 cm. Synonymy involved. Variable and may be much greener than specimen
figured. East Africa and the Seychelles to the E. Indies, Philippines and Solomon
islands.

**1379. SCARUS MADAGASCARIENSIS** (Steindachner) 1887
23 cm. Ground colour deep, rich dark red; a longitudinal green stripe above
eye and one below eye meeting a further green stripe above upper lip and a
blue one across chin; lower lip blue. Numerous dark longitudinal lines alternating with pinkish lines from operculum and pectoral base to base of tail; fins
and tail bright dark red with narrow blue or green margins. Rare. Red Sea,
E. Africa, Madagascar, Seychelles to the E. Indies.

**1380. SCARUS MUS** (Smith) 1959
22 cm. Deep green, body scales edged with dark purple; teeth white, upper
lip red and 2 dark red stripes across chin. Cheeks and area behind eye purple;
a green stripe across snout, continued below eye to angle of operculum. Dorsal
and anal purple with blue-green margins; tail green with a purple basal area
and purple and blue outer rays. Pectorals blue with purple base and a broad
purple stripe along anterior margin. Ventrals purple with narrow blue anterior
margin. Indian Ocean and E. Indies.

**1381. SCARUS BLOCHI** Cuvier & Valenciennes 1839
30 cm. Teeth yellowish white. Green with red-edged scales above, red to pink
below; peduncle green. Top of head reddish brown, lower parts orange with
wavy blue or green lines behind eye; snout green. Dorsal orange with blue
margin. Tail yellowish green, blue at base, outer rays blue; anal brownish red
with blue margin. Pectoral blue with broad red stripe below blue anterior ray.
Mauritius and India to the E. Indies, Philippines, Ryukyu, Carolines, Melanesia,
Society and Tuamotu islands.

**1382. SCARUS AERUGINOSUS** Cuvier & Valenciennes 1839
35 cm. Teeth white or pink, canines absent. Red brown with 2–4 narrow yellowish longitudinal stripes on breast reaching anal origin. Peduncle sometimes
paler than body. Fins and tail red, dorsal and anal with dark margins. Red Sea,
E. Africa and the Seychelles to the E. Indies and Melanesia.

The following species are also known from the Indo-Pacific: *Scarus javanicus* Bleeker
1854, E. Indies and Philippines; *S. lavia* Jordan & Everman 1903, Hawaii; *S. bowersi*
(Snyder) 1909, E. Indies, Philippines and Ryukyu islands; *S. jonesi* (Streets) 1960,
Palmyra and Marshall islands; *S. fehlmanni* Schultz 1969, Red Sea; *S. marshalli*
Schultz 1958, Indian Ocean to C. Indo-Pacific.

Family CIRRHITIDAE **Hawkfishes, Curlyfins, Handfishes**
Small to moderate-sized carnivorous fishes similar to the Scorpaenids, but
lacking the bony stay across the cheek. Usually seen resting on coral branches
or heads, ready to dart after any suitable prey that may come within range;
after a short dash, whether successful or not, they return to their customary
perch. Solitary and sedentary. Elongated to oblong and somewhat compressed.
Scales moderate. Lateral line continuous, almost straight. Cheeks and operculum
scaly. A single dorsal fin. Tail rounded or slightly emarginate, seldom forked.
Lower 5–8 pectoral rays unbranched, thickened, projecting beyond upper
rays. Mouth moderate, terminal, protrusible. A fringe present behind anterior
nostril. A small Indo-Pacific family found in warm, shallow, rocky waters.

**1383. CIRRHITUS PINNULATUS** (Bloch & Schneider) 1801
22 cm; D X/11; A III/6; sc 39–40; tr 4–5/9. Scales cycloid. Head blunt, profile
of snout steep. Lips thick, teeth villiform. A tuft of cirri on posterior rim of
anterior nostrils. Tip of dorsal spines with a tuft of cirri. Posterior margin of
preoperculum finely serrated. Tail truncate, slightly convex. Whitish tinged
with olive overlaid with brown blotches and some black spots. Tip of chin with a
dark brown spot and a distinct blackish spot behind eye. Three to four irregular
dark vertical bars below dorsal base, most distinct in young individuals. Fins
with dark spots on membranes, tail with dark spots on rays. Two yellowish
brown streaks under eye. Pectorals dull orange. Marshall, Phoenix and Society
islands. The species recorded by Smith from the Indian Ocean under this
name is probably the very similar *C. spilotoceps* Schultz.
ALLIED SPECIES:
**1384. CIRRHITUS ALTERNATUS** Gill 25 cm. Whitish marbled with irregular
brownish cross-bars overlaid by round dark-edged white spots. No black spots. Hawaii
and Johnston island.
**1385. C. ALBOPUNCTATUS** Schultz Brownish markings indistinct, mottled;
head and body marked with numerous rows of very small white spots. Tonga islands.
**1386. C. NIGROPUNCTATUS** Schultz Head and body dorsally and anteriorly
with numerous scattered black specks. Mauritius.

**1387. C. OXYRHYNCHUS** (Bleeker) 8 cm. Pinkish white; 10–12 rather wavy pinkish brown vertical bands on head and body, the 4 middle ones invading base of dorsal. Tail and fins rose, unspotted. Fiji and the E. Indies.

**1388. CIRRHITICHTHYS OXYCEPHALUS** (Bleeker) 1885        **Pl. 6**
8 cm; D X/12–13; A III/6–7; L 1 40; tr 3/10–11. As figured, but intensity of markings variable. Reunion, Buru, Amboina and Fiji.

**1389. CIRRHITICHTHYS APRINUS** (Cuvier & Valenciennes) 1829
10 cm; D X/12; A III/6; L 1 39–41; tr 4/9–11. Both jaws with short anterior canines. First dorsal ray prolonged into a free filament. Pinkish brown with rows of large brown blotches often fusing into irregular cross-bands in old individuals. Dorsal and anal marbled with brown and often with a dark border. Tail usually spotted, often dark-bordered. Red Sea and E. Africa to the E. Indies, Philippines, Ryukyu islands, Melanesia, Marshall and Society islands.

ALLIED SPECIES:
**1390. CIRRHITICHTHYS AUREUS** (T. & S.) 8 cm. Golden brown with darker spots on head and faint mottling on body. Fins and tail unspotted. South Japan.

**1391. GYMNOCIRRHITES ARCATUS** (Cuvier & Valenciennes)
**Pl. 6**
15 cm; D X/11; A III/6; L 1 45–48; tr 5½/11–12. Variable, sometimes paler and more reddish than figured, but pattern unmistakable. Mauritius, East Indies, New Britain, New Guinea, Marshall islands, Hawaii and Tahiti.

**1392. PARACIRRHITES FORSTERI** (Bloch & Schneider) 1801 **Pl. 6**
25 cm; D X/11; A III/6; L 1 45–49; tr 5/10–12. East Africa to the East Indies, Philippines, Melanesia, Ryukyu, Marshalls, Marquesas, Fiji, Samoa and Hawaii.

ALLIED SPECIES:
**1393. PARACIRRHITES HEMISTICTUS** (Günther) 20 cm. Similar to 1392, but differs in having no solid dark lateral band; upper sides densely spotted with blackish; two irregular rows of spots below pale mid-lateral stripe, head unspotted. Marshall to Society islands.

**1394. P. CINCTUS** Günther 12 cm. Pinkish or reddish with 5 slightly oblique transverse bars; fins and tail generally unspotted. Hawaii.

**1395. CIRRHITOIDEA BIMACULA** Jenkins 8 cm. Snout pointed, dorsal cirri well developed. A round black spot on upper angle of operculum and another below base of last dorsal rays. Scattered localities throughout the Indo-Pacific: E. Africa, Seychelles, Marshall islands and Hawaii, where it is common.

**1396. C. UNIMACULA** Kamohara Similar to 1395, but scales smaller, opercular spot lacking, dorsal spot present. South Japan.

**1397. C. SEXFASCIATA** Schultz 8 cm. Light brown with six darker brown vertical bands: 1st below eye, 2nd below first 2 dorsal spines to behind pectoral base; 3 more bands below dorsal base and one on caudal peduncle. Fins and tail uniform brown. Marshall islands.

**1398. CYPRINOCIRRHITES POLYACTIS** (Bleeker) 12 cm. Uniform yellowish or orange; tail emarginate with prolonged outer rays; 1st dorsal ray produced into a long isolated filament. Rare; known from the E. Indies, Queensland and Madagascar.

OTHER INDO-PACIFIC SPECIES:
*Cyprinocirrhites ui* Tanaka; *Amblycirrhitus indicus* Fowler; *Cirrhitus fasciatus* Bennett.

Family CHEILODACTYLIDAE **Morwongs**
Very closely related to the Cirrhitidae and included in that family by some
authors, but differ in having a bony projection above the eye and a profile which
is much elevated at the dorsal origin. Tail forked, pectorals with extended lower
rays used as feelers, anterior dorsal rays often elevated; generally white with
black transverse or oblique bands. Few species, mostly from the cooler waters of
Australia and the Cape and from Japan. Some species venture into rather deep
waters.

**1399. CHEILODACTYLUS VITTATUS** Garrett 1864                    **Pl. 8**
30 cm; D XV/29. Not uncommon in Hawaii, usually at about 30 m.

Family OPISTOGNATHIDAE **Smilers, Jaw-fishes**
A small family of curious bottom-dwelling fishes which occur in all warm waters.
Generally found in flat sandy or coral rubble areas, where some species dig a
burrow with their jaws, while others use old sea-worm holes. Some species live
in association with a prawn. Jaw-fishes are solitary, never stray far from their
burrows and spend much of their time in a vertical position, ready to pounce
on any small fish, or to retreat into their hole, tail first, if alarmed. Most jaw-
fishes are rare, very little is known about them and many species are known
from a few specimens only. Oblong and somewhat compressed. Head large.
Scales rather small, cycloid. Lateral line high on body, incomplete, usually
terminating about middle of dorsal base. A single continuous dorsal fin, the
rays longer than the spines. Two anal spines. Pectorals and tail broadly rounded.
Mouth large, horizontal, terminal and protrusible.

**1400. OPISTOGNATHUS PAPUENSIS** Bleeker 1868
=**GNATHYPOPS MACULATA** Ogilby 1920
45 cm; D XII/16; A II/15; L 1 110–120; tr 7–8/38–46. Eyes face downwards.
Lateral line ends below 10th dorsal ray. Greenish brown above, pale below.
Spotted with blue or black all over, spots on head smaller than on upper body.
A large blackish spot hidden by pectorals. Dorsal and pectoral spotted, other
fins unmarked. West New Guinea, Aru islands, Torres Straits, Queensland.

ALLIED SPECIES:
**1401. OPISTOGNATHUS MUSCATENSIS** Boulenger 45 cm. Whitish, mot-
tled with pale blue and olive green. Dorsal with 3 large blue-edged black spots. Persian
Gulf, Red Sea and E. Africa as far south as Natal.
**1402. O. NIGROMARGINATUS** Rüppell 20 cm. Brownish yellow marbled with
brown. Dorsal with a pale-edged oblong black spot on 4th–8th spines. A diffuse dark
spot on centre of tail fin. Tropical Indian Ocean.

**1403. MEROGYMNUS EXIMIUS** Ogilby 1908
38 cm; D XI/13; A I/12; scales very small, covering only part of sides and
belly. Golden brown above; sides with 2 series of large round or oval golden
spots separated by broad blue bands; belly and end of tail violet mottled with
greenish gold; head lavender with violet spots and bars. Operculum with an
irregular vertical deep-blue band. Dorsal olive with a pale blue basal band and a
purple margin; anal blue with 2 series of golden spots. Tail blue with purple or
olive rays. Ventrals bluish black; pectorals yellowish brown with 1–2 vertical
blue bars at the base. Queensland only.

*Merogymnus eximius*

Family PARAPERCIDAE
**Grubfish, Weevers (Australia), Smelts (S. Africa)**
A small family of small to moderate bottom dwelling carnivorous fishes of the
Indo-Pacific and Red Sea. Goby-like, elongate and cylindrical with small scales
extending onto head, cheeks and operculum. Lateral line complete, straight.
Soft dorsal higher than spinous dorsal, sometimes separated by a deep notch.
Anal without spines, or with one weak spine. Eyes large, near superior profile.
Mouth terminal, slightly oblique, protractile. Should be handled with care as
they can inflict painful wounds with the dorsal and opercular spines. Usually
found in weedy places, some species at considerable depth.

**1404. PARAPERCIS XANTHOZONA** (Bleeker) 1849
20 cm; D V/18–21; A I/17–18; L l 58; tr 5–6/14–18. Tail slightly rounded.
Brownish red above, pale below. Nine dark saddle-like cross-bars interrupted
by a pale mid-lateral band which is continued as a whitish blotch on tail. Head
mottled. Dorsal with a black basal blotch between 1st and 3rd spines. Fins and
tail pale with dark spots. Reported from Zanzibar, the E. Indies and New
Guinea.

**1405. PARAPERCIS CYLINDRICA** (Bloch) 1792
**=PERCIS HEXOPHTHALMA** C. & V. 1829 (♀, with spots, not lines on
head)
30 cm; D V/19–22; A I/16–18; L l 66–71; tr 8/16. Tail truncate. Pale reddish
brown above, creamy below. A series of short oblique stripes on back, formed
by dark-edged scales. Sides with 3 longitudinal rows of 7–8 dark elongate
spots, sometimes faintly connected by dark cross-bands; 3 or more such
posterior spots developed into white-edged ocelli. Head with dark spots;
dorsal and anal yellow with dark spots, tail with a large central blackish blotch.
Red Sea and most of the Indo-Pacific, but not in Hawaii.

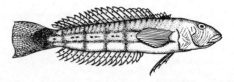

*Parapercis cylindrica*

ALLIED SPECIES:
**1406. PARAPERCIS TETRACANTHA** (Lacépède) 25 cm. Tail truncate. Grey
with 3 longitudinal series of pale yellow spots and a dark ocellus on shoulder. Fins pale,
dorsal with 3 rows of dark spots, tail with transverse rows of dark spots and a dark
superior basal blotch. East Indies, Philippines, Melanesia, Fiji, Samoa and Society
islands.
**1407. P. CLATHRATA** Ogilby 12 cm.' Nine black spots in a straight line below
lateral line, some dark mottling on back, a distinct black ocellus above upper angle of
operculum and a large dark blotch on lower operculum, behind corner of mouth.
East Indies, Philippines, Palau islands, Guam, Fiji, Samoa and Society islands.
**1408. P. NEBULOSUS** (Q. & G.) 30 cm. Tail truncate with prolonged outer rays.
Red, contrastingly creamy below, with blue lines between eye and upper lip and an
irregular longitudinal series of mid-lateral blue spots. Dorsal pale yellow, spinous
portion blackish. Tail red with transverse series of small blue and black spots; anal

creamy with red margin and oblique pale blue lines. Pectorals yellow, ventrals white tipped with red. The fish figured by Smith (1949) under this name is whitish with 7 mid-lateral dark blotches, blackish head and ventrals and pale fins with small dark spots. South and E. Africa, Seychelles, E. Indies and Queensland.

**1409. P. CEPHALOPUNCTATUS** (Seale) 12 cm. Orange brown above, creamy below; 9 brownish bars on sides, a dark brown blotch below pectoral base and two dark brown, orange-edged spots on sides. A central dark blotch followed by a pale blotch. Tips of dorsal and anal blue, paired fins orange. Guam and Marshall islands.

**1410. P. PULCHELLA** (Day) 12 cm. Pink, brownish above, with 8–9 white cross-bars. Some black marks at base of tail; base of spinous dorsal black; a median series of small black spots below eye. Tropical Indian Ocean.

**1411. P. SCHAUINSLANDI** (Steindachner) 18 cm. Sc 60; a deep notch between spinous and soft dorsal. A series of prominent dark spots along dorsal; tail lunate. Common in 30 m or more in Hawaii.

The following species, mostly from deep waters, have also been described from the Indo-Pacific: *Parapercis multifasciatus* (Doderlein), Japan; *P. sexfasciatus* (T. & S.), Japan; *P. elongata* Fourmanoir, Vietnam; *P. dorsenebulosa* Martin & Montalban, Philippines; *P. montillae* Martin & Montalban, Philippines; *Pteropsaron incisum* Gilbert, Hawaii; *Neopercis roseoviridis* Gilbert, Hawaii; *N. tessellata* Herre, Philippines.

## Family TRICHONOTIDAE Sand-eels, Hairfins

A family of a few small, little-known fishes from the tropical Indo-Pacific. Generally found in sandy areas where they burrow head first to spend the daytime buried in the sand. Small and very elongate and slender. Scales small, absent on head, cheeks and operculum. Lateral line complete and uninterrupted. Dorsal very long, continuous in the females; first 2 rays greatly elongated into long filaments in the males of some species. Anal very long with a single weak anterior spine. Mouth large, horizontal, protrusible. The following species will serve to describe the family:

## 1412. TRICHONOTUS SETIGER Bloch & Schneider 1801 Fig., p. 25

20 cm; D VI–VII/40–43; A I/36; L 1 60; tr 4/4½. Lower jaw projecting; teeth pointed, lower ones hooked. Anterior dorsal rays produced into free filaments in males. Ventrals elongate, tail oval. Brown with a black spot on each scale of lateral line. Rows of small black-edged ocelli on dorsal, posterior part of anal and basal half of tail. Coastal and brackish waters from the Andaman islands to the E. Indies, Philippines, Melanesia and Australia.

## Family CHAMPSODONTIDAE Sabre-gills

Small carnivorous fishes found in deep water throughout the Indo-Pacific. Usually they move in large schools over sandy bottoms, rising to the surface at night. Elongate and compressed, with minute granular scales. Two lateral lines, both with transverse branches. Preoperculum ends in a long sharp spine. Short spinous dorsal fin separated from soft dorsal, which has one anterior spine. Tail forked. Eyes near top of head, each with a superior tentacle. Mouth very large, oblique. Gill opening very wide.

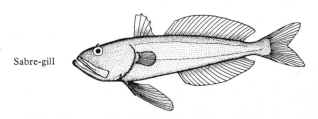

Sabre-gill

## Family URANOSCOPIDAE Star-gazers, Pufferfish

A family of some 8 genera and 25 species of bottom-dwelling carnivorous fishes known from rather deep water in all warm seas. Star-gazers have very large heads, large, almost vertical mouths and are able to inflate the belly, rather like tobies (Lagocephalidae). They lie buried in the sand or mud of the bottom with eyes and mouth exposed and they attract their prey by causing a filament in the lower jaw to wriggle, rather like a worm. Some species are capable of inflicting a severe electric shock.

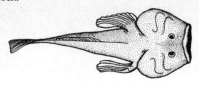

Star-gazer

## Suborder **Blennioidei** (=Blenniina)

Small to moderate sedentary fishes of all warm littoral waters. Most species occur in tide pools or crevices in rock or coral, but a few have adapted to brackish and even fresh water. Several families are included in this suborder.

## Family XENOCEPHALIDAE Armoured Blennies

Head very large and body small. Vent in hind half of body. Head truncated and protected by armoured plates and spines. A single dorsal fin, pectorals present. A single imperfectly known species described from New Ireland (*Xenocephalus armatus* Kaup, 1858).

## Family XIPHASIIDAE Hair-tailed Blennies

Rather large, extremely elongated, compressed eel-like blennies, widely distributed in the Indo-Pacific. Several species have been described, but they may be growth stages and colour variants of a single species (*Xiphasia setifer* Swainson 1839). Naked, lateral line on upper half of sides, not reaching end of body. Dorsal fin extremely long, continuous, originating on head, in front of eyes, consisting of over 100 rays; anal similar, confluent with tail and dorsal. Middle rays of tail produced into long filaments. Pectorals rounded, with lower rays thickened; ventrals consisting of 3 rays. Gill openings consisting of small lateral apertures. Mouth small and terminal. Up to 65 cm. Coral reefs, often in deep water; India, E. Indies, Philippines, Melanesia and Japan.

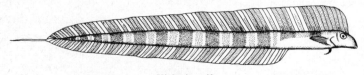

*Xiphasia setifer*

Family BLENNIIDAE (including SALARIIDAE) **Blennies, Naked Blennies**
A large family of small agile, carnivorous fishes found in shallow water among
coral and rock formations in all warm seas. Many species live in tidal pools,
sheltering in shells or under stones, while others take cover among weeds.
Some are able to hop out of the water and to crawl over mud and rocks in
search of food. Most species have drab colours which harmonise with their
environment, but some are brilliantly coloured. In many species the sexes are
differently coloured, but in some genera the males have modified anal spines
and develop a crest on top of the head. Some blennies are armed with strong
sharp canines with which they transfix their prey, or inflict a painful bite if
carelessly handled. The eggs are usually laid in the empty shell of a mollusc
and guarded until they hatch. Blennies are oblong and compressed and lack
scales. Lateral line complete, or much reduced; a single dorsal fin, often notched
between spines and rays, sometimes partially confluent with tail and anal.
Pectorals present. Anal armed with 2 anterior spines. Ventrals jugular, attached
well before pectorals, consisting of a small spine and 2–4 rays. Head smooth or
decorated with simple, branched, or fringed tentacles (cirri), usually at the
nostrils, above the eyes and on the nape.

Blennies are similar to the gobies in appearance and habits, but may be
recognised by the anterior position of the ventral fins. A large family with some
150–200 Indo-Pacific species, many of them little-known, similar and confusing
even to the specialist. Careful, prolonged collecting is certain to yield new species
in almost any suitable locality. Only the commonest, better known and more
interesting species can be discussed in a work of this nature.

Subfamily *Blenniinae*
Unlike the following subfamily, p. 221, the true blennies have normal fixed teeth.

**1413. PETROSCIRTES MITRATUS** Rüppell 1828
Helmeted Blenny
8 cm; D XI/14–15; A II/14–15; P 14–15; V I/3. Gill openings above pectoral
base. Supraorbital cirrus branched, nasal cirrus simple; fringed cirri on nape,
along preopercular margin and on chin. Anterior dorsal spines elevated, forming
a crest, which is higher in the males. Pale greenish yellow mottled with greenish
brown and spotted with orange; 4–5 rather indistinct irregular dark cross-bars
on body extending to dorsal fin. Some dark lines and spots on the head. Eye
golden. Dorsal and tail with numerous pale milky bluish spots, anal with dark
dots on the rays. Paired fins unspotted. Usually in shallow rock pools; very shy
and adept at hiding, but hops out of the water to feed; common. Red Sea and
entire Indo-Pacific excluding Hawaii.

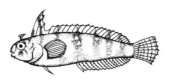

Helmeted Blenny

ALLIED SPECIES:

**1414. PETROSCIRTES ANOLIUS** (C. & V.) 75 mm. Chestnut brown to olive green; anterior part of body with indistinct blackish cross-bars; posterior body with 3 indistinct longitudinal dark bands and some blackish spots. Head with one or two vertical pearly streaks and a dusky spot on cheek. Dorsal olive with 3–4 anterior oblique dark bars; anal orange brown with three rows of blue spots on rays. Tail orange, pectorals olive with dark basal spot, ventrals sky-blue. Lives in bivalve shells; Queensland and New South Wales.

**1415. P. AURATUS** Seale 6 cm. No cirri, no lateral line; lower canines very large. Bright lemon yellow including all fins except median portion of tail, which is hyaline. Fiji.

**1416. P. ATRODORSALIS** Günther 7 cm. Cirri and lateral line lacking; lower canines very large. Head and anterior body light blue becoming pale pinkish yellow posteriorly. A black line through eye to nape and continued on anterior part of dorsal; remainder of dorsal yellow; tail hyaline, elongated outer rays yellow. Japan, Marshall islands, Samoa and Fiji.

**1417. P. LINEOLATUS** Kner 6 cm. No cirri; lower canines larger than upper. Light brown; a mid-dorsal black band from upper lip to interorbital and a parallel black band from corner of mouth to each eye; two round black spots behind eye and 3 irregular black bands from cheek to cheek across chin and throat; some black speckling below eye; a dark spot at pectoral base. Tail rounded, light brown; dorsal with numerous oblique violet lines; anal similarly marked, but with a blackish margin. East Indies, Melanesia, Polynesia and Fiji.

### 1418. ASPIDONTUS GORRORENSIS (Herre) 1936

5 cm; D 40; A 24; P 14. Cirri absent. Lower canines larger than upper. Brown with a blue stripe from eye to base of tail; 10 blue vertical bands deflected backwards below median stripe. Dorsal with blue submarginal band and blue margin. Anal dark brown distally. Tail and pectorals hyaline. Melanesia.

### 1419. ASPIDONTUS TRACTUS Fowler 1903                    Pl. 36

12 cm. A remarkable mimic of the Cleaner Wrasse (*Labroides dimidiatus*); see 1272. Western Indian Ocean. See also 1420.

ALLIED SPECIES:

**1420. ASPIDONTUS TAENIATUS** Q. & G. 13 cm. Very similar to 1419, possibly a senior synonym  East Indies, Philippines, Guam, Caroline islands, New Guinea, Solomons, Fiji, Samoa, Tahiti and Tuamotu islands.

**1421. A. FLUCTUANS** (Weber) 8 cm. Pale greyish lavender, head pinkish; a blue edged reddish stripe from eye to above pectoral base, whence it is continued to base of tail as a series of 9 black rectangles. Dorsal and anal bright green with narrow brown margins. Tail pinkish hyaline. East Africa and the Seychelles to the E. Indies.

**1422. A. WAMIZIENSIS** Smith 8 cm. Very similar to 1421, but bright lavender, head orange brown, eye red, a bright green crescent below eye and a solid black stripe from eye to base of tail. Coast of Mozambique.

### 1423. BLENNECHIS FILAMENTOSUS Cuvier & Valenciennes 1836

12 cm; D 36–38; A 25–28. Anterior dorsal rays much elevated, forming a crest; tail truncate. Greenish yellow, chin, throat, cheeks and breast yellow; a dark stripe from snout through eye to upper angle of operculum; body with 7–9 vertical green bands extending on dorsal and deflected backwards on anal; interspaces with an irregular green spot on upper back. Dorsal and anal with marginal hyaline spots between green bands. Tail green with a complete hyaline margin. Iris consisting of alternating white and green wedges. South and E. Africa and the Seychelles to the E. Indies.

**1424. RUNULA RHINORHYNCHOS** (Bleeker) 1852      **Pl. 36**
8 cm; D XI/33–35; A II/31–33; P 12; V I/3. Lateral line obsolete. No superior canines, but lower jaw armed with a pair of long curved posterior canines. Usually in shallow water among weeds. South and E. Africa, Seychelles to E. Indies, Philippines, New Guinea, New Hebrides and Palau islands.

ALLIED SPECIES:

**1425. RUNULA TAPEINOSOMA** (Bleeker) 10 cm. White with a broad dark blue median band separated into rectangular segments. Chin, breast and tail bright orange; pectorals yellow. Dorsal and anal olive, dorsal with a blue basal band. South and E. Africa and Seychelles to E. Indies, Melanesia and Queensland. Often nibbles at the legs of swimmers.
**1426. R. AMBLYRHYNCHUS** (Bleeker) 5 cm. Tail emarginate. Brownish above, paler below; numerous narrow dark vertical bands on upper sides. Dorsal pale, with 7–9 blackish vertical bands and a narrow blackish margin; anal with 5 such bands; tail and pectorals hyaline. East Indies, Philippines and Melanesia.
**1427. R. EWAENSIS** Brock 12 cm. Brick red with longitudinal blue stripes; probably lives in tubular burrows, since it has been found in pipes hauled to the surface. Rather deep water, Hawaii only.
**1428. R. GOSLINEI** Strasburg 5 cm. Upper half brown, lower half abruptly white. A narrow white longitudinal band through brown dorsal area. Ranges from 1–2 m of water to considerable depths; often nibbles at the legs of swimmers. Hawaii.

**1429. OMOBRANCHUS ELONGATUS** (Bleeker) 1855
6 cm; D XII–XIV/18–20; A II/20–23; P 13–14; V I/2. Gill opening a vertical slit above pectoral base. Tail truncate, tips sometimes produced. Cirri absent. Light green; a blackish dorsal stripe from upper lip to nape and one from lower lip to eye; eye blue; a brownish red patch on cheek, bisected by 2 oblique blue lines and a blue edged reddish brown ocellus at upper angle of operculum; upper sides spotted with dusky from dorsal origin to base of 4–5 anterior dorsal rays. Seven to nine blue cross-lines alternating with dusky ones on body; the anterior ones vertical, but not reaching dorsal base, the posterior ones complete, but sharply angled forward, the last one not angled, very oblique and continued on upper tail base. Soft dorsal higher than spinous part, green with an oval dark blue spot between 9th and 12th rays, and numerous very oblique narrow dark blue lines. Anal buff, dark green distally with 7–8 dark basal spots, 7–8 narrow oblique white lines and the tips of the rays white. Paired fins and tail pale, unspotted. Shallow coastal waters and tidal pools from E. Africa and the Seychelles to the E. Indies, Melanesia, Polynesia, N. Australia, Fiji and Hawaii.

ALLIED SPECIES:

**1430. OMOBRANCHUS KALLOSOMA** (Bleeker) 9 cm. Head smooth, soft dorsal higher than spinous part, tail truncate with tips produced. Brownish yellow to light olive with 9–12 dark cross-bars, the anterior ones oblique, then becoming increasingly angled forward. Several green spots on chin and throat and along back. Dorsal dusky pink with an oval black spot between 9th and 12th rays. In shallow water among stones. South and E. Africa to the E. Indies and Philippines.
**1431. O. STRIATUS** (Jatzow & Lenz) 10 cm. Males with prominent crest on head. Dorsal of even height, tail rounded. Pale yellowish olive with numerous dark vertical bands; a blackish spot at upper angle of operculum; fins pale, unmarked. Usually found under stones in shallow water, sometimes in estuaries; E. Africa and Natal.
**1432. O. MEKRANENSIS** (Regan) 5 cm. Tail rounded. Green with 4 dark blue vertical stripes below eye and a pale-edged blue ocellus behind eye. Body with irregular vertical pale blue lines and spots and numerous small black spots. Fins and tail bright yellow, unmarked. Red Sea and E. Africa.

**1433. DASSON VARIABILIS** (Cantor) 1849
Sabre-toothed Blenny
12 cm; D XI/17–21; A II/17–22; P 13–15; V I/3–4. Dorsal of uniform height,
tail truncate. Lower canines very large and sharp. Cirri above nostril, eye and
nape, simple; several cirri on chin. Lateral line normal anteriorly, reduced to
isolated pores from 11th dorsal spine to tail base. Greenish yellow with a broad
mid-lateral dark band from eye to base of tail where it widens, often constricted
at regular intervals to form a series of connected spots. Dorsal and anal with
oblique rows of dark spots; dorsal with a dark basal band. Bites if handled
without due care; found in weedy areas. South and E. Africa to the Seychelles,
India, Ceylon, the E. Indies, Philippines, Melanesia and Queensland.

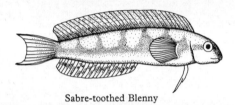

Sabre-toothed Blenny

**1434. MEIACANTHUS GRAMMISTES** (Cuvier & Valenciennes) 1836
Black-banded Blenny
8 cm; D 29–30; A 17–19; P 14; V I/3. Males with a pair of cirri on chin, 2
pairs on nape and several between the eyes and on sides of head. Lateral line
reduced to a few pores above pectoral. Dorsal of even width. Creamy with 2
longitudinal black stripes in the male and 3 in the female, continued on tail.
Dorsal and anal with black submarginal lines. Shallow coastal waters and rock
pools in the E. Indies, Philippines, Yap, Melanesia and Queensland.

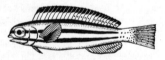

Black-banded Blenny

ALLIED SPECIES:
**1435. MEIACANTHUS MOSSAMBICUS** Smith 7 cm. Uniform dark brown;
tail emarginate, with prolonged outer rays, bright yellow. Mozambique, among coral. A
fish which was this species, or an extremely similar undescribed one, was seen by the
author near Rabaul, New Britain.

**1436 LAIPHOGNATHUS MULTIMACULATUS** Smith 1955      Pl. 36
25 mm. Nasal and supraorbital cirri present. East Africa, rare.

**1437. ENCHELYURUS BRUNNEOLUS** Jenkins 1903
25 mm. No cirri on neck and above eye; jet black or very dark brown all over.
Common among dead coral in Hawaii.

Subfamily *Salariinae* Skippers, Rockhoppers
Teeth weak and movable, implanted in the lips, not in the jaws; otherwise
similar to the *Blenniinae*.

### 1438. CIRRIPECTES VARIOLOSUS (Cuvier & Valenciennes) 1836
8 cm; D XII/14–15; A II/15–16; P 15; V I/4. Nasal cirrus with 3–6 filaments,
supraorbital cirrus with 3–5 filaments and a fringe of simple cirri across nape,
interrupted in the middle. Lateral line poorly developed posteriorly. Anterior
dorsal rays prolonged, tail truncate. Dark brown, cheeks with red spots. Upper
edge of tail yellowish. Spinous dorsal and pectorals tipped with red. Entire
Indo-Pacific including the Red Sea, Queensland and Hawaii.

ALLIED SPECIES:
**1439. CIRRIPECTES SEBAE** (C. & V.) 10 cm. A continuous fringe of simple
cirri across nape. Sometimes a low fleshy ridge on head. Tan to dark brown; young with
a dark mid-lateral line which breaks into blotches with age and eventually develops
into a pattern of 5–12 dark vertical bands. Cheeks, operculum and throat covered with
pale round spots enclosed by dark reticulations. Fins and tail pale, unmarked. East
Indies, Melanesia and Marshall islands, usually in shallow water where wave action is
strong.
**1440. C. OBSCURUS** Borodin 18 cm. Male dusky rose, female golden brown, both
with tiny white dots, a dark spot behind eye and plain blackish spinous dorsal. Common
in shallow water above rocky bottoms in Hawaii.
**1441. C. LINEOPUNCTATUS** Strasburg 8 cm. Cirrus above eye unbranched;
body with rows of small yellow or white spots. Rocky areas where the surf is strong;
Hawaii and Johnston island. Common.
**1442. C. QUAGGA** (Fowler & Ball) 7 cm. Tan to dark brown with 8–15 dark vertical
bars; often speckled with small black and white dots. A dark bar below centre of eye
and another behind it meeting its fellow on throat. Fins unmarked. Wake and Marshall
islands, in areas of strong surf action.
**1443. C. FUSCOGUTTATUS** Strasburg & Schultz 10 cm. Dark brown covered
all over with fairly large blackish spots; eye crimson, upper edge of tail orange. Samoa
and Marshall islands.
**1444. C. PERUSTUS** Smith 8 cm. Red, front of head black; some blackish mottling
on hind body; spinous dorsal and pectorals yellow; soft dorsal and anal red; tail red
shading to black posteriorly, with a hyaline margin. East Africa.

### 1445. ENTOMACRODUS STRIATUS Quoy & Gaimard 1824
10 cm; D XII–XIII/15–16; A 16–17. Tail truncate. Pale brownish yellow with
numerous black spots on body, dorsal and tail. Operculum and pectoral base
with minute red dots. An oblique blue stripe behind eye; a wide blackish
band from below level of eye through middle of upper lip, continued longitudinally under the chin; a comma-shaped blackish stripe from below centre of
eye to corner of mouth and 2 oblique blackish stripes from mouth to median
chin stripe. Paired fins and anal hyaline, unmarked. South and E. Africa to the
Seychelles, Mauritius, Madagascar, the E. Indies, Philippines, Micronesia and
Polynesia as far as Tahiti.

ALLIED SPECIES:
**1446. ENTOMACRODUS DECUSSATUS** (Bleeker) 13 cm. Nuchal cirrus
simple. Supraorbital cirri large, branched. Grey, light tan or olive; body and head with
numerous dark blotches arranged to form 6 very irregular double vertical bars. A dusky
bar below eye and a dark bar on pectoral base. Dorsal, anal, tail and pectorals barred
with dark brown. East Indies, Philippines, Marshall islands, New Hebrides and Samoa.

**1447. E. MARMORATUS** (Bennett) 12 cm. Supraorbital cirrus with numerous branches and a pair of tentacles on each side of neck. Body with numerous interrupted dark bars arranged like rough chevrons. Dorsal with numerous oblique dark bars; tail with 3 transverse bars and pectorals with one. Hawaii only, principally in the surf zone of rocky coasts.

## 1448. ALTICUS SALIENS (Forster) 1788
Jumping Blenny
8 cm; D XIV/21–23; A II/24–27; P 15; V I/4. Males with a high triangular crest on head; nasal cirrus small and simple; supraorbital cirrus branched, nuchal cirrus absent. A deep notch between spinous and soft dorsal. Tail rounded. Lateral line consisting of a few anterior pores. Dark brown or blackish with faint black cross-bands; fins dark, dorsal with a row of pale spots. Female paler, with some dark spots on head and anterior body. Rock pools; Madagascar, Mauritius, India, Andamans, E. Indies, Philippines, Melanesia, Palau islands, Fiji, Samoa, Queensland and the Red Sea.

## 1449. LOPHALTICUS KIRKI (Günther) 1868                    Pl. 36
8 cm. Male as illustrated; female without the rounded posterior part of crest. Very common in tidal rock pools in the W. Indian Ocean.

## 1450. SALARIAS FASCIATUS (Bloch) 1786                    Pl. 36
Banded Blenny
10 cm; D XII/18–20; A II/19–21; P 14; V I/2. Crest absent in both sexes; all cirri branched; lateral line ending above vent. Dorsal continuous. Very common in tidal rock pools throughout the entire Indo-Pacific excluding Hawaii.

ALLIED SPECIES:
**1451. SALARIAS SINUOSUS** Snyder 7 cm. Crest lacking in both sexes; nasal cirrus bifid, supraorbital cirrus simple. Dorsal notched, anterior anal rays much prolonged in males. Brownish with 5–6 double lines enclosing dark midlateral blotches which are also surrounded by blue dots; snout and operculum dark blackish green; 2 brown spots behind eye and numerous dark spots on head and anterior back. Dorsal with oblique reddish lines, anal very dark with a series of round white spots along base. Pectoral rays dark with white spots; tail slightly emarginate with indications of dark spots. Shallow weedy pools. East Africa, Aldabra, Seychelles, E. Indies, Philippines, Ryukyu, Okinawa, Melanesia, Queensland, Tonga, Samoa and Fiji.
**1452. S. GUTTATUS** C. & V. 7 cm. Male with low fleshy ridge on head; nasal cirrus simple, supraorbital cirrus bifid, nuchal cirrus spatulate. Tail slightly rounded. Dorsal and anal as in 1451. Brownish with faint vertical bands. Head and anterior body with pale spots and vermiculations. A large blue spot on each side of throat. Spinous dorsal and tail with rows of black dots. Indonesia, Philippines, Melanesia, Queensland, Samoa and Fiji.
**1453. S. FUSCUS** Rüppell 10 cm. No nuchal cirri. Last dorsal and anal rays much prolonged; body and fins very dark, nearly black; tail and pectorals yellowish. South and E. Africa, E. Indies and Queensland.

## 1454. ISTIBLENNIUS PERIOPHTHALMUS
(Cuvier & Valenciennes) 1836
False Mudskipper
15 cm; D XIII/19–20; A II/20–22; P 14; V I/3. Males with low fleshy ridge on head. Nasal cirrus palmate, supraorbital and nuchal cirri simple. Dorsal deeply notched, tail rounded. Lateral line ends below spinous dorsal. Olive grey, paler

below. Eight to nine irregular brown transverse bands bifurcated near abdomen; 2 longitudinal rows of pale blue spots enclosed by black rings. Sides of head and upper parts of body with small black spots. Dorsal mottled; spinous part with large red-brown spots in some males. Margin of anal blackish. Shallow tidal pools; jumps and skips with considerable ease. Most of the Indo-Pacific and Red Sea, but apparently not in Hawaii and Queensland.

**1455. ISTIBLENNIUS ANDAMANENSIS** (Day) 1859              **Pl. 36**
10 cm. A very agile small fish of shallow tidal pools; Indian Ocean; especially common on the E. African coast.

ALLIED SPECIES:
**1456. ISTIBLENNIUS EDENTULUS** (B. & S.) 16 cm. Males with well developed crest. Nasal cirrus with 3–5 filaments, other cirri simple. Dorsal deeply notched, tail rounded; lateral line complete. Reddish with 6 double wavy dark cross-bands. Posterior body spotted in females. Dorsal and anal with longitudinal bands in males, with longitudinal rows of spots in females. Tail and pectorals unmarked. Red Sea and entire Indo-Pacific, but not in Hawaii.
**1457. I. ZEBRA** Vaillant & Sauvage 15 cm. Very similar to 1456 from which it differs in lacking cirri on the side of the neck. Hawaii only, where it is very common in tidal pools.
**1458. I. GIBBIFRONS** (Q. & G.) 12 cm. Similar to 1456 and 1457; head and anterior back with many small bluish spots, especially in the males; body with the usual dark paired bands and scattered bluish spots; dorsal with reddish vermiculations, tail and anal unmarked. Common in most of the Indo-Pacific including Hawaii, but not in Queensland.

**1459. HALMABLENNIUS LINEATUS** (Cuvier & Valenciennes) 1836
Black-lined Blenny
16 cm; D XIII–XIV/21–25; A 23–25; P 14; V I/3. Males with very large crest. Nuchal cirrus absent, other cirri branched. Dorsal deeply notched, tail rounded. Brown mottled with olive and reddish; males with dark spots on crest and with 6 pairs of black spots along dorsal base; both sexes with 6 narrow irregular dark cross-lines. Dorsals with oblique lines in males, unmarked in females. Entire Indo-Pacific excluding Hawaii.

ALLIED SPECIES:
**1460. HALMABLENNIUS MELEAGRIS** (C. & V.) 13 cm. Males crested. Brownish with 7 indistinct dark vertical bands; head and sides with irregular rows of small silvery ocelli. Dorsal fin marked with alternate dark and pale oblique bands. Anal with 2 or more longitudinal rows of pale spots. Tail with pale streaks and spots in males, unmarked in females. South and E. Africa to the E. Indies, Melanesia and Queensland.
**1461. H. STRIATOMACULATUS** (Kner) 10 cm. Male with a long low crest; supraorbital cirrus longer in males. Brownish olive with numerous irregular dark transverse lines coalescing into large dark blotches, especially in males; pale interspaces very narrow. Spinous dorsal with 3 longitudinal dark lines, soft dorsal with several oblique dark lines; dorsal and anal with dark margin in males, not females. Western Indian Ocean.

**1462. EXALLIAS BREVIS** (Kner) 1868
Pao'o kauila, O'opu pao'o (Hawaii)
15 cm. Males with anal spines embedded in fleshy pads. A pair of short cirri on each side of chin. Males pinkish to orange with head, body and fins covered

by numerous clusters of small red or brown spots. Females orange brown, duller, spotted with brown. Most of Indo-Pacific including Hawaii, but not in Queensland.

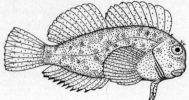

*Exallias brevis*

**1463. ECSENIUS MANDIBULARIS** McCulloch 1923
6 cm; D XII/12; A II/17; P 13; V 2. Male crested, with very high, rounded dorsals and some caudal rays slightly prolonged; anal spines modified into fleshy lobes. Female without crest, dorsals lower, anal spines normal. Light brown with 2 longitudinal rows of evenly spaced dark spots. Fins unmarked. Queensland only.

ALLIED SPECIES:
**1464. ECSENIUS HAWAIIENSIS** Chapman & Schultz 12 cm. Known only from 14 specimens taken from the fouling on the bottom of a barge which had been towed from Guam to Honolulu.

**1465. ANTENNABLENNIUS VELIFER** Smith 1959
8 cm. A long, simple, pendulous tentacle behind each nostril; profile of head vertical, nuchal cirri long, supraorbital cirri absent. Male crested. Dorsal continuous, 2nd–4th spines longer than subsequent spines, rays longer than last spines, notch shallow. Tail rounded. Pale slaty with dark irregular blotches on sides continued on dorsal and numerous black and white dots, especially on head and spinous dorsal. Chin and nasal tentacle orange; distal part of soft dorsal with numerous horizontal red lines. East Africa.

Family CLINIDAE **Scaled Blennies**
Small fishes which are closely related to the true blennies, but differ in having most of the body covered by fairly large scales. The typical subfamily (*Clininae*) is strongly represented in the cooler waters of the southern hemisphere, especially in S. Africa and Australia, with very few species reaching the tropics. The small subfamily *Tripterygiinae* is mainly tropical.

Subfamily *Tripterygiinae*
A group of some 50 species of small fishes known from coral reefs and rocky areas in the Indo-Pacific, tropical Atlantic and Mediterranean. They differ from the *Clininae* in having 3 distinct dorsal fins.

**1466. TRIPTERYGION HEMIMELAS** Kner & Steindachner 1866
=**T. ATRICEPS** Jenkins 1903
3 cm; D III; XII–XIII; 9–10; A I/17–20; L 1 16–19/16–19. Two lateral lines. A small cirrus above nostril and one above eye. Bright red, males with black

*Tripterygion hemimelas*

head. Usually found among dead coral or in crevices in rocks where surf action is strong. Samoa, Hawaii, Ryukyu, Mariana and Marshall islands.

ALLIED SPECIES:

**1467. TRIPTERYGION MINUTUM** Günther 2 cm. Males pale brownish above, dark brown on belly, breast and pectoral base as well as lower sides of head. Philippines, Marshalls, New Hebrides and Samoa.

**1468. HELCOGRAMMA OBTUSIROSTRE** (Kluzinger) 5cm. Pale pinkish brown, variously spotted and mottled with dark purplish brown; males with purple upper lip, blue lower lip followed by a broad slightly ascending bright green stripe ending opposite base of ventrals; lower sides of head blue; a large bright green area at pectoral base enclosing 1 or 2 black spots. Female similar, but lacking all blue and green markings; fins of female with dark brown spots. East coast of Africa.

## Family CONGROGADIDAE **Eel-blennies**

Small very elongate blennies with scaled bodies, dorsal and anal fins confluent with tail, small pectorals and ventrals which are vestigial or absent. They differ from the true eels in their dentition. A few Indo-Pacific species usually found in shallow muddy waters.

## 1469. CONGROGADUS SUBDUCENS (Richardson) 1843
Mud Blenny

50 cm; D 71–74; A 60; P 9–10; Sc 120. Olive sprinkled with rusty blotches, those on chin, throat and belly alternating with bluish white blotches; dorsal and anal light olive with several rows of bright red spots. A large white-ringed blue-black ocellus on the operculum; pectorals pinkish. East Indies, New Guinea, Queensland, N. and W. Australia.

Mud Blenny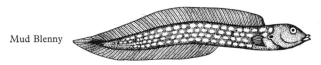

## Family NOTOGRAPTIDAE **Bearded Snake-blennies**

Very similar to the eel-blennies, but differ in the presence of ventral fins reduced to a single ray and in having a small chin barbel. A few species from New Guinea and tropical Australia.

## 1470. NOTOGRAPTUS GUTTATUS Günther 1867
Spotted Snake-blenny

12 cm; D LXII–LXVIII/2; A XXXVII–XLI/2; P 19; V I; Sc 200; tr 31. Mouth large and horizontal; chin barbel as long as eye. Pale brown above, white below. Upper parts closely dotted with brown, especially anteriorly; spots on head larger and ocellated; dorsal with rather indistinct brown spots. Coastal and estuarine waters. New Guinea and Queensland.

Spotted Snake-blenny

## Suborder **Ophidioidei**

Very small to moderate-sized eel-like fishes of all seas. Related to the blennies, but differ in lacking all fin spines and in having the ventrals, when present, reduced to one or two filaments.

### Family BROTULIDAE **Blindfish, Eel-pouts**
Small to moderate fishes found in deep water in most seas. Elongate and compressed; dorsal and anal usually confluent with tail which tapers to a point. Snout and chin armed with barbels in some species; others blind or almost blind.

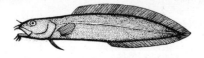

*Brotula multibarbata*

### Family CARAPIDAE **Pearl-fishes, Messmate-fishes**
Small slender fishes of coral reefs which live in association with star-fishes, sea-cucumbers, or oysters. They shelter in the intestine or mantle of the host, which they enter tail first, generally with the head and forward-placed vent remaining exposed, but they leave the host to seek food. Some species shelter in crevices or bury themselves in the sand of the bottom. The larvae have a long fringed filament on the neck and swim with the head down. The eggs are embedded in a mass of slime. Very elongate; tail tapering to a sharp point. Lateral line present; dorsal and anal long, confluent with tail. Vent on throat, just ahead of anal origin. Ventrals absent. Pectorals present or absent. Mouth fairly large, not protractile, with small teeth.

### 1471. **JORDANICUS GRACILIS** (Bleeker) 1856
Lipless Messmate-fish
23 cm. Lower jaw lipless, hidden under skin. Vent below pectoral base. Translucent yellowish or mauve to violet with brown and black spots and mottling. Associated with starfish and sea-cucumbers. Known from scattered localities throughout the Indo-Pacific including S. Africa and Hawaii.

Lipless Messmate-fish

OTHER SPECIES:
**1472. ONUXODON MARGARITIFERAE** (Rendahl) 10 cm. Lower lip well developed; a pair of anterior canines in both jaws. Vent slightly behind pectoral base. Translucent pink with tip of tail black. Generally associated with pearl oysters and related bivalves, occasionally with sea-cucumbers. Indian Ocean, E. Indies, Melanesia, Hawaii.
**1473. O. PARVIBRACHIUM** (Fowler) 8 cm. Armed with huge teeth; rather deep and laterally compressed, tapering sharply at tail. Seychelles to the E. Indies.
**1474. SNYDERIDIA CANINA** Gilbert 30 cm. Anal fin commencing behind dorsal. Teeth very large. Known from a single specimen taken in deep water off Hawaii.

**1475. CARAPUS HOMEI** (Richardson) 20 cm. Vent anterior to pectoral base. Canines absent. Translucent bluish or reddish with dark cross bars and some silvery spots on sides. Associated with sea-cucumbers. Entire Indo-Pacific including Hawaii and Queensland.

**1476. C. PARVIPINNIS** (Kaup) 30 cm. Body cylindrical; canines absent; head broad. Reddish brown, translucent, with small dark specks. Central Indo-Pacific.

**1477. C. HOULTI** (Ogilby) 28 cm. Greyish brown with darker dots. Associated with sea-cucumbers. Queensland only.

## Suborder **Callionymoidei**

Family CALLIONYMIDAE **Dragonets, Mandarin-fishes**

Small fishes which live on the bottom in the coastal waters of all warm seas; some occur in tidal pools and on shallow coral reefs, others in deeper waters. The shallow water forms spend much of the day buried in the sand for concealment. Superficially similar to the Platycephalidae, they differ in having a small terminal mouth, greatly restricted gill openings and a characteristic preopercular spine. The sexes differ considerably in some species.

Body elongate, almost cylindrical, without scales; head depressed, teeth small and feeble. Gill opening a rounded pore on each side. Two dorsal fins, spines weak; fins generally elongate, more so in the males. Fertilisation internal, eggs pelagic. Most species are small and fragile, making identification difficult; methodical collecting will no doubt yield many new species.

Head of Dragonet

## 1478. ELEUTHEROCHIR OPERCULARIS

(Cuvier & Valenciennes) 1837
Flap-gilled Dragonet

8 cm; D̦ IV/9; A 9; P 21–24. Operculum ending in a flap of skin which extends over pectoral base. Preopercular spine ending in a hooked barb and with 3–6 barbs along its upper margin. Tail truncate. Brown or grey, throat and belly white, nape and back with black specks. Spinous dorsal and ventrals black; soft dorsal with black spots. India, E. Indies, Philippines and Melanesia.

## 1479. CALLIONYMUS SAGITTA Pallas 1770

11 cm; D IV; 9; A9; P 17–19. Operculum without free edge. Ventrals connected to pectoral base by a broad membrane. Preopercular spine curved with a basal barb and 4–5 barbs along inner margin. Tail rounded with incised membranes. Brown above with dark specks and milky white spots and blotches, lighter below; a row of dark brown spots along sides. Spinous dorsal all black in females, with white base in males. Soft dorsal and tail spotted; anal spotted or uniform. Bourbon, India, Ceylon, E. Indies, Philippines and Melanesia.

### 1480. CALLIONYMUS FILAMENTOSUS
Cuvier & Valenciennes 1837
Threadfin Dragonet
16 cm; D IV; 9; A 9; P 18. Eyes very close together. Preopercular spine straight, basal barb present. Tail pointed with 2 middle rays prolonged in males. First dorsal spine a long free filament in the males. Reddish brown above, paler below. Upper parts with pale, dark-ringed spots. First dorsal with white-ringed black ocelli. Soft dorsal with oblique series of dark dots on rays and dark margin. A dark blotch before pectoral base. East Indies, Philippines and Melanesia.

### 1481. CALLIONYMUS MARMORATUS Peters 1855
15 cm; D IV; 8–9; A 7–8. Two barbs on preopercular spine. Dark greyish green mottled and spotted with light grey and dark blue; paler below. Males with a bright red curved band across throat, ending at pectoral bases; eyes red in males, yellow in females. Spinous dorsal much longer in males, blackish with blue vermiculations. Soft dorsal reddish brown with dark specks; tail similar, rounded, very broad, especially in males. Pectorals red, ventrals blackish with red margin; anal reddish brown with dark spots in females, blackish with blue spots in males. East Africa, South to Delagoa Bay.

*Callionymus marmoratus*

ALLIED SPECIES:

**1482. CALLIONYMUS DECORATUS** Gilbert 27 cm. Males with black lines on throat and very long tail. Common in shallow water in Hawaii.

**1483. C. CAERULEONOTATUS** Gilbert 10 cm. Differs from 1482 in having a narrower head, upturned tip to preopercular spine and a few enlarged teeth in lower jaw. Known from a few specimens dredged from deep water in Hawaii.

**1484. C. CALLISTE** Jordan & Fowler 10 cm. First dorsal higher than 2nd; anal much higher posteriorly. Cheek with two and operculum with one vertically elongate black streak. East Indies, Philippines, Japan, Queensland.

**1485. C. WILBURI** Herre Preopercular spine with 2 sharp hooks at inner margin. Spinous dorsal with only 3 spines. East Indies and Philippines.

**1486. C. COOKII** Günther 6 cm. Preopercular spine with 6 barbs along upper margin; all fins very elongate, 1st dorsal spine much prolonged. Pale blue grey, white below, variously spotted and mottled with darker grey, brown and white. Polynesia and Fiji.

**1487. DIPLOGRAMMUS GORAMENSIS** (Bleeker) 6 cm. Very similar to 1486 and possibly conspecific. Snout more pointed, tail more elongate, anal black with white tipped rays in male. East Indies, Philippines and Marshall islands.

**1488. SYNCHIROPUS SPLENDIDUS** (Herre) 1927      **Pl. 36**
Mandarin-fish
10 cm; D IV; 9; A 8; P 29; V I/5. As illustrated. A most brilliant little known fish. Shallow water in the Philippines, E. Indies, Melanesia and Queensland.

**1489. SYNCHIROPUS PICTURATUS** (Peters) 1876      **Pl. 36**
10 cm. A rare fish known from the Philippines and Melanesia.

**1490. SYNCHIROPUS CALAUROPOMUS** (Richardson) 1848
30 cm; D IV; 8; A 7; P 19–20. Preopercular spine curved, bifid, without basal barbs. Tail round in females, but middle rays produced and membranes incised in males. Brown above and white below; sides with yellow lines in males and pink spots in females. First dorsal with purple blotches in males, completely purplish in females; soft dorsal and anal yellow with large brown spots; tail yellow, with ocellated spots in the males. East Indies, Japan, Philippines and Melanesia.

ALLIED SPECIES:
**1491. SYNCHIROPUS LINEOLATUS** (C. & V.) 10 cm. Tail rounded; 1st dorsal greatly elevated in the males. Mouth and lower part of head scarlet; 5–6 greyish saddles on back. Spinous dorsal with white spots, some dark-ringed in males; 3–4 oblique brown bands on ventrals and tail. Anal red with dark margin and 2–3 rows of blue spots. India, Ceylon, E. Indies and Melanesia.
**1492. S. OCELLATUS** (Pallas) 10 cm. Body with dark brown and white bars; spinous dorsal with 3–4 distinct ocellated black spots. East Indies and Philippines.
**1493. POGONEMUS POGOGNATHUS** Gosline 35 mm. Preopercular spine short. A conspicuous fringe of tentacles projecting from edge of lower lip. Taken only once, but in large numbers, in shallow water off Kauai, Hawaii.

**1494. DACTYLOPUS DACTYLOPUS** (Cuvier & Valenciennes) 1837
Fingered Dragonet
20 cm; D IV; 8; A 7; P 18. Preopercular process conical, without basal barbs. The ventral spine and 1st ventral ray detached from rest of fin. First 3 dorsal rays very much prolonged and filamentous in the male; tail rounded, very large; all fins elongate. Dark golden brown with large irregular dark blotches and numerous blue and black specks. Spinous dorsal smoky with blue spots and orange margin; soft dorsal yellow with elongate blue-edged black spots. Tail yellow with numerous blue lines, lower membranes black with blue streaks; anal bluish grey with blackish spots; pectorals hyaline, ventrals smoky, mottled with gold and blue. East Indies and Philippines to Queensland and W. Australia.

Fingered Dragonet

Family DRACONETTIDAE
A small family of deep water fishes which are very closely related to the Callionymidae, but differ in having the preopercular spine replaced by 2 enlarged spines at the edge of the operculum.

## Suborder **Siganoidei**

Family SIGANIDAE
**Spinefeet, Rabbitfish, Tafi (Swahili), Cordonniers (S), Dengkis (Malay)**
Moderate-sized herbivorous fishes of the Indo-Pacific. They are usually found in small schools in weedy areas in shallow water, where they may be seen nibbling at the vegetation with their heads pointing downward. The fin spines are very sharp and can inflict painful wounds if the fish are handled without due care.

Oval and compressed. Body slimy, covered by small thin, embedded scales which are scarcely visible. Lateral line single and complete. A single continuous dorsal fin preceded by a single buried procumbent spine. Anal fin with 7 spines. Ventrals behind pectorals, consisting of 2 spines separated by 3 rays. Good eating and among the more important inshore economic fishes in the tropics. About 25 species are known from all over the tropical Indo-Pacific, but none in Hawaii.

**1495. LO VULPINUS** (Schlegel & Müller) 1844                    **Pl. 37**
Fox-face, Fox-fish
23 cm; D VIII/10; A VII/9. Differs from other members of the family in its tubular snout. Young individual as figured; the black spot may be absent, elongated, or there may be more than one; old specimens much duller and darker, sometimes with posterior part of body contrastingly paler than anterior. A favourite aquarium fish. East Indies, Philippines, Palau, Caroline, Marshall, Solomon islands and Queensland. *Lo unimaculatus* Everman & Seale 1907 is probably a juvenile.

**1496. SIGANUS ROSTRATUS** (Cuvier & Valenciennes) 1835
Rabbit-faced Spinefoot
35 cm; D XIII/10; A VII/9; L 1 170–200; tr 18–19/88–95. Anterior nostril with long flap. Last dorsal spine shorter than 1st; soft dorsal and anal low and rather rounded; tail deeply forked. Body covered by small pale spots enclosed by fine brown reticulations; some dark spots scattered on sides. Most of the Indo-Pacific including the Red Sea and Queensland.

**1497. SIGANUS SPINUS** (Linnaeus) 1758                          **Pl. 37**
35 cm; fin count as above, scales a little larger. As figured, but pattern very variable. Indonesia, Philippines, Ryukyu, Melanesia, Fiji, Samoa and Queensland.

**1498. SIGANUS ORAMIN** (Bloch & Schneider) 1801                **Pl. 37**
Pearl-spotted Spinefoot
27 cm; L 1 180–200; tr 20–23/97–104. Pearly spots disappear shortly after death; usually blackish when seen in the market. Very common throughout the entire Indo-Pacific, but not in Queensland.

**1499. SIGANUS CORALLINUS** (Cuvier & Valenciennes)    **Pl. 37**
Orange Spinefoot
27 cm; L 1 160–175; tr 20/100. Anterior nostril without flap. Blue spots disappear shortly after death. Most of the Indo-Pacific including Queensland;
common in the Seychelles.

**1500. SIGANUS JAVUS** (Linnaeus) 1766    **Pl. 37**
Streaky Spinefoot
32 cm; L 1 200; tr 30–35/120–130. Anterior nostril without flap. Ceylon, India,
East Indies, Philippines, Melanesia and Queensland.

**1501. SIGANUS VIRGATUS** (Cuvier & Valenciennes) 1835    **Pl. 37**
26 cm. Variable; dark bands less contrasted in old specimens, blue lines less
distinct. East Indies, Philippines and Melanesia.

**1502. SIGANUS LINEATUS** (Cuvier & Valenciennes) 1835    **Pl. 37**
Mi-Mi (Townsville), Gold-lined Spinefoot
38 cm. Markings variable in colour and intensity, but large golden spot below
soft dorsal generally present. Philippines, Okinawa, Ryukyu, Solomon islands,
New Guinea and Queensland, where it is especially common. Possibly a
synonym of *S. guttatus* (Bloch) 1787.

**1503. SIGANUS STELLATUS** (Forskål) 1775    **Pl. 37**
Rabbitfish, Slimy, Spiny, Tafi (Swahili)
32 cm. Indian Ocean; especially common in shallow weedy areas in E. Africa
and the Seychelles. See 1514.

**1504. SIGANUS FUSCESCENS** (Houttuyn) 1782
35 cm; L 1 270; tr 25–30/120. Soft dorsal and anal low and rounded; tail
slightly forked. Uniform dusky brown, sometimes with faint dark spots on sides.
Tail dusky brown with indistinct vertical bands. Japan, China, the Philippines,
Guam, the Carolines and New Guinea.

ALLIED SPECIES:
**1505. SIGANUS TETRAZONUS** (Bleeker) 12 cm. Tail slightly emarginate.
Yellowish with 4 double undulating transverse brown bands on upper sides. Fins
yellowish with dark blotches. East Indies, Philippines and New Guinea.
**1506. S. DOLIATUS** (C. & V.) 25 cm. Soft dorsal and anal elevated and pointed;
tail emarginate. Brownish above, pale grey below. Head and front part of body with
pale wavy bands edged by narrow black lines, some transversely across snout; similar
blue lines across cheek and vertically on upper sides, becoming horizontal on lower
sides and peduncle. Pectoral base and throat striped yellow and grey. First dorsal olive
to orange, soft dorsal and tail yellow, anal orange. East Indies, Philippines, Palau
islands, Carolines, New Guinea, Queensland, New Hebrides, Fiji and the Society
islands.
**1507. S. PUELLUS** (Schlegel) 30 cm. Soft dorsal and anal elevated and pointed;
tail forked. Yellow to orange, olive above. A broad dark band from origin of dorsal,
through eye to chin, broken into round spots above eye. Numerous narrow blue lines
on body: vertical above pectoral, horizontal on back and sides, coalescing to form a
network on belly. Fins yellow, unmarked. East Indies, Philippines, Palau, Gilbert
and Solomon islands, New Guinea.
**1508. S. VERMICULATUS** (C. & V.) 38 cm. Soft dorsal and anal elevated and
angular; tail emarginate. A convoluted network of irregular blue lines almost as wide as
brown interspaces, covering entire body and head. Blue lines less numerous and more
horizontal in juveniles. Dorsal and anal clouded with brown, tail spotted, pectorals

yellowish. Marine, but often in brackish waters, sometimes entering rivers. Mauritius, E. Indies, Philippines, Melanesia, Queensland, Marshall to Society islands.

**1509. S. CHRYSOSPILOS** (Bleeker) 38 cm. Soft dorsal and anal elevated, dorsal very pointed; tail deeply forked. Body and head covered by evenly spaced golden hexagonal spots which vary in size but are smaller than pupil, separated by a fine network of blue lines; a large blackish spot on shoulder, ringed with white in juveniles. Fins brownish, tail and soft dorsal spotted like the body. Pectorals yellow. Cocos islands, E. Indies, Philippines, Melanesia, Fiji and Samoa.

**1510. S. CONCATENATUS** (C. & V.) 38 cm. Tail emarginate. Light bluish, covered with evenly spaced orange spots smaller than pupil. Tail pale blue, tips darker. A large orange spot at base of soft dorsal. Similar to 1502, but body more elongate. India, E. Indies, Philippines, Okinawa, Ryukyu.

**1511. S. CANALICULATUS** (Mungo Park) 25 cm. Rather elongate, tail slightly emarginate. Brown with numerous small pale dots and a dark blotch on shoulder. Seychelles, India, E. Indies, Melanesia, Queensland, China, Japan.

**1512. S. RIVULATUS** (Forskål) 30 cm. Whitish with very irregular blackish vermiculations and yellow fins. Red Sea, E. and S. Africa, Seychelles and probably India; eastern limits of range uncertain owing to confusion with other species.

**1513. S. SUTOR** (C. & V.) 37 cm. Dull violet with scattered small distinct orange dots; tail violet; pectorals dusky orange, other fins reddish grey. Bourbon, Seychelles, India, E. Indies, Philippines.

**1514. S. PUNCTATISSIMUS** Fowler 28 cm. Very similar to 1503, but spots much smaller. East Indies and Philippines.

## Suborder **Acanthuroidei**

Small to moderate herbivorous fishes, generally associated with coral reefs. Mostly compressed, with minute shagreen-like scales, a single complete lateral line and a continuous dorsal fin. Anal with 2–3 spines; pectorals present, ventrals under or slightly behind pectorals. Mouth small, terminal, teeth small.

### Family ZANCLIDAE **Moorish Idol**
The family consists of a single wide-spread Indo-Pacific species. Small and orbicular, with minute ctenoid scales, strongly arched lateral line, tubular snout and small teeth. Superficially similar to the Chaetodontidae and formerly placed near that family by some authors. However, the structure of the larva affords good evidence of the close affinity of the Zanclidae with the Siganidae and the Acanthuridae.

### 1515. ZANCLUS CANESCENS (Linnaeus) 1758                              Pl. 40
= CHAETODON CORNUTUS Linnaeus 1758 (juvenile)
Moorish Idol

23 cm; D VI–VII/39–42; A III/31–37. A single series of long setiform teeth. Juveniles (*cornutus*) with a sharp preorbital spine at corner of mouth; adults with a pointed horn on each side of interorbital. Usually seen in small schools nibbling among coral branches in shallow water. A favourite aquarium subject. This species is regarded as an object of considerable reverence by some Moslem populations. Entire Indo-Pacific and East to the Pacific coast of Mexico.

Family ACANTHURIDAE
## Surgeon-fishes, Lance-fishes, Tangs, Unicorn-fishes, Chirurgiens (S), Licornes (S), Cornes (Mauritius)

Compressed, elevated to oval fishes which generally occur in small schools and feed by scraping algal growth off rocks and coral, usually in shallow water. Typical surgeon-fishes are armed with a sharp retractile bony scalpel on each side of the caudal peduncle, with which they can inflict painful wounds if carelessly handled. Unicorn-fishes have 2–3 sharp fixed bony plates on each side of the peduncle and some species have a horn-like process above the snout, which is especially well developed in old males. The larger species are of some economic value. All warm seas, some 60 species in the Indo-Pacific.

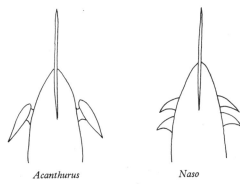

*Acanthurus*                    *Naso*

Caudal spines of Acanthuridae

### 1516. ZEBRASOMA VELIFERUM (Bloch) 1795                    Pl. 38
Sailfin-tang
40 cm; D IV/28–33; A III/22–26. Very variable; juveniles strongly marked, usually with yellow tail and a black mark surrounding the scalpel; old specimens almost black, with faint yellowish lines on body and fins and yellow spots on head. Small specimens are good aquarium subjects. Entire Indo-Pacific.

### 1517. ZEBRASOMA SCOPAS (Cuvier) 1829                    Pl. 38
Brown Sailfin-tang
22 cm; D V/23–25; A III/19–21. Some specimens darker than figured, some orange brown, but whitish scalpel always conspicuous. Much confused with 1518 and treated by some authors as a form of it. The 2 species have a different range however, with very little overlap. East Africa and the Seychelles to the E. Indies, Philippines, Melanesia, Queensland, Fiji and Samoa, Marshall islands and Marianas.

### 1518. ZEBRASOMA FLAVESCENS (Bennett) 1828                    Pl. 38
Yellow Sailfin-tang; Lau'i-pala (Hawaii)
20 cm. Very common in shallow water in the Hawaiian islands and possibly confined to that area; yellow specimens recorded from the Marshall islands may be pale variants of 1517; brown specimens are not known from Hawaii.

**1519. ZEBRASOMA XANTHURUM** (Blyth) 1852
Yellow-tailed Sailfin-tang
20 cm. Purplish blue with bright yellow tail and pectorals. Numerous small purple spots on head, throat and breast. Red Sea, E. Africa, Arabia, Persian Gulf, India and Ceylon.

**1520. CTENOCHAETUS STRIGOSUS** (Bennett) 1828      **Pl. 40**
Hawaiian Hair-toothed Tang; Kole (Hawaii)
18 cm. Much confused with 1521, but probably confined to the Hawaiian islands, where it is a common surgeon-fish and indeed one of the commonest inshore fishes. Teeth slender, movable.

**1521. CTENOCHAETUS STRIATUS** (Quoy & Gaimard) 1824
28 cm; D VIII/28–30; A III/25–27. Very similar to 1520, but lacks the yellow ring surrounding the eye. Common throughout most of the Indo-Pacific, from S. and E. Africa to Queensland and Polynesia, but not in Hawaii.

**1522. CTENOCHAETUS HAWAIIENSIS** Randall 1955
25 cm. Differs from 1520 and from 1521 in having the tail truncate, not lunate. Eye without yellow ring. Common in deeper water around the main island of Hawaii.

**1523. CTENOCHAETUS CYANOGUTTATUS** Randall 1955
15 cm. Tail truncate, tips not produced. Blackish with numerous blue dots on head and body. Seychelles to the C. Indo-Pacific; the precise limits of its range are uncertain because of confusion with 1521.

**1524. PARACANTHURUS HEPATUS** (Linnaeus) 1766     **Pl. 38**
=**ACANTHURUS THEUTHIS** Lacépède 1802
Wedge-tailed Blue Tang; Flag-tail Surgeon-fish
25 cm; D IX/19–20; A III/18–20. A single retractile caudal spine. Adults and old specimens tend to lose much of their brilliance becoming dull pale violet grey, but usually retaining some blue on the head. Coral reefs throughout the entire Indo-Pacific excluding Hawaii, but nowhere common.

**1525. ACANTHURUS TRIOSTEGUS** (Linnaeus) 1758     **Pl. 40**
Convict Surgeon-fish
25 cm; D IX/22–24; A III/19–22. The commonest inshore surgeon-fish, generally in very shallow water and in tidal rock pools; occasionally seen in quite large schools. Entire Indo-Pacific excluding Hawaii, where it is replaced by the following species. Has also been recorded from the Gulf of California.

**1526. ACANTHURUS SANDVICENSIS** Streets 1877
Convict Tang, Manini
22 cm. Extremely similar to 1525 and regarded as a subspecies of it by some authors; it differs in having a longer black mark at the pectoral base and a slightly higher fin ray count. Behaves like 1525 and is very common in Hawaii and Johnston island.

**1527. ACANTHURUS GUTTATUS** Bloch & Schneider 1801    **Pl. 39**
Spotted Surgeon-fish
30 cm; D IX/27–30; A III/23–26. Usually seen in small schools in inshore turbulent waters. Mauritius to the E. Indies, Philippines, Melanesia, Gilbert, Society and Hawaiian islands.

**528. ACANTHURUS LEUCOPAREIUS** (Jenkins) 1902          **Pl. 39**
Head-band Surgeon-fish; Maikoiko (Hawaii)
20 cm; D IX/25–27; A III/23–25. Shallow water on reefs, usually in rather
large schools. Philippines, Marcus island, Easter island, Samoa and Tubuai;
very common in Hawaii.

**529. ACANTHURUS NIGROFUSCUS** (Forskål) 1775
17 cm; D IX/24–27 (usually 25); A III/22–24. Lavender brown with small
orange dots on head; fins brown: tail with narrow posterior white margin, dorsal
with narrow black margin, anal with narrow blue margin. A black spot at
posterior dorsal axil and a smaller one at posterior anal axil. East Africa, Red
Sea, Seychelles, Mauritius, India, Philippines, E. Indies, Melanesia, Ryukyu,
Japan and Hawaii where it is very common.

**530. ACANTHURUS NIGRORIS** Cuvier & Valenciennes 1835
Maiko (Hawaii)
25 cm. Very similar to 1529, but lacks white posterior margin to the tail. Dark
brown with narrow irregular longitudinal blue lines; unpaired fins brownish
yellow with longitudinal blue bands; usually a vertical white band at base of
tail. Probably confined to Hawaii, where it is very common; records from other
parts of the Pacific and from the Seychelles probably refer to 1531 and perhaps
to other species as well.

**531. ACANTHURUS ELONGATUS** (Lacépède) 1803
15 cm; IX/24–25; A III/22–24. Dark grey with numerous close-set blue specks.
Six faint wavy yellow lines from snout to eye; a narrow white posterior caudal
margin; dark spots at posterior dorsal and anal axils purple edged with orange.
Marshall islands, Guam, Truk and Samoa.

**532. ACANTHURUS FULIGINOSUS** Lesson 1830          **Pl. 39**
=**A. XANTHOPTERUS** C. & V. 1835
Ring-tail Surgeon-fish; Pualu (Hawaii)
50 cm; D IX/25–27; A III/23–25. The largest species of the genus and probably
the most widespread. Entire Indo-Pacific as far as the Pacific coast of Mexico.
Synonymy involved and much confused with other species.

**533. ACANTHURUS MATA** (Cuvier) 1829          **Pl. 39**
Pualu (Hawaii)
40 cm; D IX/25–26; A III/24. Blue colour of fins only apparent in certain
lights; in the water, especially at some depth it appears blackish with a whitish
ring at the base of the tail. India, Hawaii, where it is common, and Marshall
islands. Exact range uncertain owing to confusion with other species, but most
probably very widespread.

**534. ACANTHURUS DUSSUMIERI** Cuvier & Valenciennes 1835
Palani (Hawaii)                                          **Pl. 39**
40 cm; D IX/25–27; A III/24–26. Caudal spine especially sharp and long;
should be handled with care. Common throughout most of the Indo-Pacific,
from S. Africa to the Philippines, Japan and Queensland, but absent from
Oceania except Hawaii, where it is very common.

**1535. ACANTHURUS THOMPSONI** (Fowler) 1923
20 cm. Dark olive drab with a dark brown spot at pectoral base; tail lunate; dorsal and anal with submarginal yellowish bands and narrow blue margins. Hawaii and Wake Island, in rather deep water; records from E. Africa and the Seychelles, doubtful.

**1536. ACANTHURUS PHILIPPINUS** Herre 1927
22 cm. Tail deeply lunate with prolonged tips. Dark chocolate brown with light yellow tail. East Indies, Philippines, and Marshall islands.

**1537. ACANTHURUS BLEEKERI** Günther 1861
37 cm. Elongate, caudal peduncle slender, tail emarginate with outer rays prolonged, caudal spine short. Very dark slaty, almost black with numerous pale bluish narrow longitudinal lines on head and body. Eye enclosed by an oblong yellowish horizontal band which ends at opercular margin. Caudal spine white, surrounded by black. Red Sea, E. Africa and Seychelles to the E. Indies, Philippines, Micronesia and Polynesia as far as the Tuamotu islands.

**1538. ACANTHURUS MACULICEPS** (Ahl) 1924
35 cm. Tail lunate. Brown with numerous pale longitudinal lines on body and pale spots on head; base of tail paler; a black bar on shoulder. Pectorals tipped with yellow. East Indies, Philippines and Melanesia.

**1539. ACANTHURUS OLIVACEUS** Bloch & Schneider 1801    **Pl. 39**
32 cm; D IX/26–28; A III/25–26. Variable, some specimens with very little orange. *A. chrysosoma* Bleeker 1857, described from the E. Indies, is probably the yellow juvenile form. East Indies, Philippines, Melanesia, Queensland, Taiwan, Micronesia and Polynesia as far as Hawaii, Tahiti and Fiji. Very common over shady bottoms in Hawaii, where it is known as Na'ena'e.

**1540. ACANTHURUS TENNENTI** Günther 1861
30 cm. Similar to 1539, but orange stripe replaced by 2 thick black stripes at the shoulder, one on top of the other. Possibly a western subspecies or a synonym of 1539. East Africa, Seychelles, Mauritius.

**1541. ACANTHURUS NIGRICANS** (Linnaeus) 1758    **Pl. 39**
=**CHAETODON GAHM** Forskål 1775
Black-barred Surgeon-fish
34 cm. Caudal spine rather long. Uncommon and usually in rather deep water where there is little or no wave action. Entire Indo-Pacific including the Red Sea and Queensland, but not in Hawaii.

**1542. ACANTHURUS BARIENE** Lesson 1830
Black-spot Surgeon
42 cm. Tail deeply lunate. Brown with numerous fine bluish longitudinal lines. A blue-edged round black spot at shoulder. Caudal base abruptly pale. New Guinea, Philippines, Celebes and Moluccas.

**1543. ACANTHURUS PYROFERUS** Kittlitz 1834    **Pl. 39**
Orange-gilled Surgeon-fish
25 cm; D VIII/27–28; A III/24–26. Rare and generally solitary. East Indies Philippines, Melanesia, Caroline islands, Fiji and Samoa, Polynesia as far as Tahiti. Has been confused in the literature with the completely different

*A. leucosternon* (Bennett); *A. celebicus* Bleeker 1852 is probably a synonym; Bleeker's figure is very similar to *pyroferus*, but has an orange tail margin instead of a yellow one.

**1544. ACANTHURUS ALIALA** Lesson 1830                  **Pl. 38**
=**A. GLAUCOPAREIUS** C. & V. 1835
White-cheeked Surgeon-fish
27 cm. Extent of white mark on cheek variable. East Indies, Philippines, Melanesia, Micronesia, Polynesia including Hawaii and Tahiti, west coast of Mexico and C. America; records from the Red Sea and Mauritius require confirmation.

**1545. ACANTHURUS ACHILLES** Shaw 1803                  **Pl. 38**
Achilles Tang, Paku'iku'i (Hawaii)
25 cm; D IX/29–33. Usually in rather turbulent waters of exposed reef areas. China, Philippines, Micronesia, Polynesia and Hawaii.

**1546. ACANTHURUS LEUCOSTERNON** (Bennett) 1832        **Pl. 38**
Blue Surgeon-fish
23 cm. One of the loveliest of coral fishes and a favourite aquarium subject. Generally solitary or in pairs, sedentary in shallow water; always hides in the same hole or crevice when alarmed. East Africa, Seychelles, India and Ceylon; certain to occur in Madagascar and Mauritius.

**1547. ACANTHURUS LINEATUS** (Linnaeus) 1758           **Pl. 38**
Blue-lined Surgeon-fish
28 cm; D IX/27–30; A III/25–28. A very active and agile fish of turbulent waters, often seen in very large numbers where the waves are breaking on the coral. Most of the Indo-Pacific excluding Hawaii and Queensland. Very common in E. Africa and at the Seychelles.

The following have also been described from the Indo-Pacific; several are most probably synonyms of foregoing species.
*Acanthurus mindorensis* Herre 1927, Philippines; *A. marginatus* C. & V. 1835, Carolines; *A. sohal* (Forskål) 1775, Arabia; *A. flavoguttatus* Kittlitz 1834, Carolines; *A. undulatus* C. & V. 1835, Indian Ocean; *A. grammoptilus* Richardson 1842, Queensland; *A. aterrimus* Günther 1871, Samoa; *A. nubilus* Fowler & Bean 1929, Indonesia; *A. melanosternon* Smith 1955, W. Indian Ocean.

**1548. CALLICANTHUS LITURATUS** (Bloch & Schneider) 1801
Green Unicorn                                        **Pl. 40**
50 cm; D VI/28–30; A II/28–30. Two sharp fixed longitudinal keels on peduncle. Young individuals with basal half of dorsal and anal black. Generally seen in small schools around coral heads in shallow water. Entire Indo-Pacific including the Red Sea, Queensland and Hawaii.

**1549. CYPHOMYCTER VLAMINGI** (Cuvier & Valenciennes) 1835
                                                    **Pl. 40**
75 cm; D VI/26–27; A II/26–27. Two fixed caudal keels. East Africa and the Seychelles to the E. Indies, Philippines, Melanesia, Marshall islands, New Hebrides and Tuamotu islands.

**1550. CYPHOMYCTER TUBEROSUS** (Lacépède) 1802          **Pl. 40**
Humpnose Unicorn
60 cm; D V/27–29; A II/26–27. Two fixed caudal keels. Domed hump on head
grows to a large size with age. East Africa, Seychelles and Mauritius to the E.
Indies, Philippines, Melanesia, Queensland, Ryukyu, Caroline, Gilbert and
Tonga islands.

**1551. NASO UNICORNIS** (Forskål) 1775
Long-snouted Unicorn; Kala (Hawaii)
60 cm; D V–VI/27–31; A II/26–30. Two fixed caudal keels. A horizontal horn
above snout, especially long in old males. Tail truncate with greatly prolonged
outer rays in old specimens. Grey brown, yellowish below. Lips blue, a blue
bar at pectoral base, caudal keels hooked, grey, each surrounded by a blue spot.
Dorsal and anal yellowish with blue lines and spots. Entire Indo-Pacific.

**1552. NASO BREVIROSTRIS** (Cuvier & Valenciennes) 1835          **Pl. 40**
Short-snouted Unicorn
43 cm; D V–VI/27–29; A II/28–30. Caudal keels sharp, hooked. The horn is
long and well developed in old males, shorter in the females. Often found in
very large schools around reefs. Very common in the entire Indo-Pacific excluding Queensland.

**1553. NASO RIGOLETTO** Smith 1952          **Pl. 40**
60 cm. Two sharp hooked caudal keels. Females hornless. Indian Ocean,
solitary.

**1554. NASO ANNULATUS** (Quoy & Gaimard) 1824
Ring-tailed Unicorn
45 cm; D V/26–28; A II/27–29. Female hornless, male with short blunt horn.
Tail emarginate; 2 fixed caudal keels. Slaty grey, darker above. Dorsal and
anal with a black submarginal line and white margins. Caudal peduncle with
an encircling white ring. Tail pale with a black submarginal line and white
border. Entire Indo-Pacific except Hawaii, where its presence needs confirmation.

**1555. NASO HEXACANTHUS** (Bleeker) 1855
50 cm. Tail emarginate, or slightly lunate. Two fixed caudal spines. Forehead
smooth, hornless in both sexes. Dark olive grey to light purplish blue; tail
dark blue shading to green posteriorly. Dorsal and anal brownish yellow with
light blue longitudinal lines. Usually in deeper water, in large schools. East
Indies, Philippines to Guam and Hawaii, where it is very common.

**1556. NASO BRACHYCENTRON** (Cuvier & Valenciennes) 1835
51 cm; D V/28–29. Horn very long and slender; no white ring on peduncle.
Grey. Very closely allied to 1551, but with very strong dorsal spines only half as
long as in that species. East Indies, Philippines and Melanesia.

ALLIED SPECIES:
**1557. NASO GENIMARGINATUS** Herre 1927 45 cm. Hornless in both sexes;
two fixed caudal spines. Dusky brown; Operculum bordered all round by a deep
brown band. Tongue blue black. Philippines only, rare.
**1558. N. LOPEZI** Herre 1927 35 cm. Hornless in both sexes. Elongate and slender;
tail slightly lunate. Two fixed caudal keels. Eye large; head, body, anal, dorsal and
caudal fins spotted. Philippines only, rare.

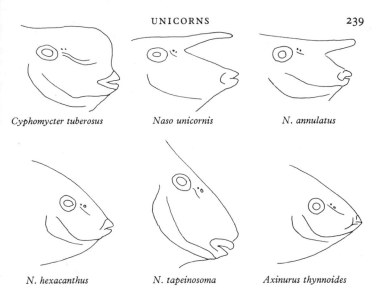

Cyphomycter tuberosus     Naso unicornis     N. annulatus

N. hexacanthus     N. tapeinosoma     Axinurus thynnoides

**559. N. VOMER** (Klunzinger) 1871. Very similar to 1558, but confined to the Red Sea.

**560. N. TAPEINOSOMA** (Bleeker) 1854 48 cm. Old males with slightly humped snout. Two fixed keels on each side of peduncle. Uniform brown, dorsal and anal with 3 longitudinal blackish bands and narrow white edges. Tail brown with posterior white margin. East Indies and Philippines.

**561. AXINURUS THYNNOIDES** (C. & V.) 1835 30 cm. Slender, without horns or protuberances; a single fixed keel on each side of caudal peduncle. East Africa and the Seychelles to the E. Indies, Philippines and New Guinea.

**562. PRIONURUS MICROLEPIDOTUS** Lacépède 1804 24 cm. Without horns or hump. Pale grey; 3 very sharp fixed keels on each side of caudal peduncle, each surrounded by a large black spot. Japan and Ryukyu islands.

## Suborder **Gobioidei**

A very large group of small sluggish carnivorous fishes known from all seas. Many are found in brackish water, some occur in fresh water only and a few are equally at home in fresh and salt water.

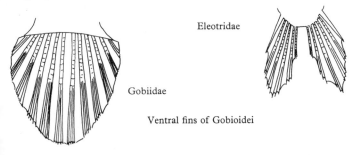

Eleotridae

Gobiidae

Ventral fins of Gobioidei

Family PERIOPHTHALMIDAE **Mud-hoppers, Mud-skippers**
A small family of amphibious fishes which inhabit muddy foreshores and
mangrove swamps in Africa and in the Indo-Pacific. They seek their food by
wriggling and skipping over rocks and mud and may even climb up mangrove
stems. When alarmed they jump and skip into cover with remarkable speed and
agility. Very active and quarrelsome little fishes which are able to spend much
time out of water thanks to their capacity for storing oxygenated water in the
gill chambers and keeping their gills moist. They are also able to breathe
through peripheral blood vessels in the skin and tail, and may often be seen sitting
up in the open with their tail in the water and occasionally rolling in the water
to moisten the skin. Their revolving, protruding eyes with a movable lower lid
are also an adaptation to an amphibious existence.

Very elongate with scales on back, cheeks and operculum. First dorsal elevated, 2nd dorsal low and short based. Pectorals with a muscular base used as a
limb for locomotion. Ventrals very close together, completely united to each
other in some species.

**1563. PERIOPHTHALMODON SCHLOSSERI** (Pallas) 1769
26 cm; D III–V; I/12–13; A I/11–12; P 16–20; Sc 50–60; tr 14. Tail rounded;
ventrals completely united, basal membrane well developed. Blackish with a
few pale blue ventral spots. First dorsal dark with pale margin, 2nd dorsal with a
median longitudinal dark band. Paired fins yellowish. Mud flats in India, the E.
Indies, Philippines, Melanesia, Queensland and Fiji.

**1564. PERIOPHTHALMODON BARBARUS** (Linnaeus) 1766
27 cm; D IV–VII; I/12; A I/11–12; P 16; Sc 50–51; tr 14. Similar to 1559, but
scales larger, 1st dorsal margin conspicuously white. India, Andamans, Thailand,
E. Indies, Philippines, China, N.-W. Australia, Queensland, Fiji and Polynesia

**1565. PERIOPHTHALMUS VULGARIS** Eggert 1935
10 cm; D X–XVII; I/10–12; A I/10–11; P 13; Sc 75–85; tr 17. Ventrals separated, basal membrane absent. Tail rounded. Dark brown above, paler below,
with dark oblique bands on back. Dorsal fins brown at base, blackish mesially,
with a longitudinal row of white spots and a white margin. Anal and ventrals
white, pectorals and tail spotted. Mud flats and mangrove swamps. East Indies
and Melanesia.

**1566. PERIOPHTHALMUS KOELREUTERI** Bloch & Schneider 1801
15 cm; D IX–XV; I/11; A I/10–11; Sc 70–90; tr 17. Ventrals united at base
only by a deeply emarginated basal membrane. Tail truncate. Blackish with
irregular darker markings and some light spots; operculum with light spots.
Dorsals with white margins, dark median band and white basal spots. Anal
white, other fins spotted. East Africa to the Seychelles, E. Indies, Micronesia,
Melanesia, Polynesia and Queensland. Also known from W. Africa. See 1567.

**1567. PERIOPHTHALMUS CANTONENSIS** (Osbeck) 1765
14 cm; D XI–XIII; I/11–12; A I/8–10; Sc 76–78; tr 23–24. Tail rounded,
ventrals united at base. Colour and markings as for 1566. Distribution as for
1566, but described from Canton and known from China, Taiwan, Japan and
Korea as well.

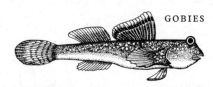

*Periophthalmus cantonensis*

## 1568. PERIOPHTHALMUS SOBRINUS Eggert 1935
15 cm; similar to other species, but 1st dorsal long-based, extremely elevated. East Africa and Seychelles to the E. Indies.

## 1569. SCARTELAOS VIRIDIS (Hamilton-Buchanan) 1822
Blue Mud-hopper; Bearded Goby
13 cm; D V; I/25–26; A I/23–26. Scales rudimentary. A row of short barbels on lower surface of head. Third spine of 1st dorsal extremely elongated. Tail very pointed. Slaty blue above, paler below. Some small black spots on head, pectoral base, back and dorsal fins. Sides marked with short transverse bands. Tail banded above, white below, tipped with black. Mud flats from India to the E. Indies, Philippines, China, Melanesia and Australia.

## Family GOBIIDAE Gobies
Mostly small fishes, some being among the smallest known vertebrates (*Pandaka* sp., from the Philippines). The marine species are usually solitary, sedentary, bottom dwelling fishes found in tidal pools, around coral reefs, among weeds and in estuarine waters. Most species are drab and harmonise with their surroundings, but some of those living among coral are very colourful. They lay elongated eggs in clusters attached to shells, sticks, stones and other submerged objects, and care for the eggs until hatching.

Oval to elongate; mouth large. Scales absent or present, on body only. Two dorsal fins, dorsal spines very weak; anal with a single weak spine; tail free. Ventral fins united along inner margin, sometimes connected to the belly by a membrane to form a sucking disc. Lateral line absent. This is the largest family of marine fishes and many of the species are very similar, confusing and poorly known. Intensive collecting is certain to yield many new discoveries. Only the commoner, more widespread and better known representatives can be discussed in a work of this nature.

## 1570. PARAGOBIODON ECHINOCEPHALA (Rüppell) 1828
Warty-headed Goby
38 mm; D VI; I/9–10; A I/8–9; P 18–22; Sc 22–27; tr 9–11. Oval and compressed; head obtuse, covered by numerous papillae. Head orange to orange-red; body usually darker, often black; fins generally darker than body. Coral pools. Red Sea and E. Africa, Seychelles and Madagascar to the E. Indies, China, Philippines, Melanesia, Queensland, Samoa and the Tuamotu islands.

## 1571. GOBIODON CITRINUS (Rüppell) 1835                    Pl. 41
Yellow Coral-goby
55 mm; D VI; I/10–11; A I/10. Scales absent, skin granular. Variable: green, yellow, to orange. Usually seen in small groups perched in the branches of a coral head. Red Sea, E. Africa and the Seychelles to the E. Indies, Melanesia and Fiji.

## 1572. GOBIODON RIVULATUS (Rüppell) 1828                    Pl. 41
50 mm. Structurally as above. Very variable: yellow, green, or brown. Habits as above. Entire Indo-Pacific excluding Hawaii.

### 1573. GOBIODON HISTRIO (Cuvier & Valenciennes) 1837
Blue-spotted Coral-goby
72 mm. Orange, darker above. Head with vertical blue bands separated by
dark bars. Body with broken longitudinal blue lines. Two vertical blue lines
on pectoral base. Fins yellow or orange. East Indies, Melanesia and Polynesia.

### 1574. GOBIODON QUINQUESTRIGATUS
(Cuvier & Valenciennes) 1837
Five-streaked Coral-goby
5 cm. Brownish to deep red. Fins red or blackish. Head and front of body with
5 slightly oblique, almost vertical narrow blue stripes. East Indies, Philippines,
Melanesia, New Hebrides, Fiji, Tonga, Tahiti and Queensland.

### 1575. STENOGOBIUS GENIVITTATUS (Cuvier & Valenciennes) 1837
16 cm; D VI; I/10–11; A I/10–11; Sc 50–55; tr 12–14. Greenish with 8–12 dark
cross-bands; scales of upper sides with a vertical dark line. A broad dark band
obliquely across cheek from eye. Dorsals with irregular lines and spots. Tail
reddish violet, pectorals yellow. Anal red in males, blue in females. Shallow
coastal waters, often in brackish areas. East Indies, Philippines, Melanesia,
Micronesia and Polynesia to Hawaii and the Society islands.

### 1576. OXYURICHTHYS PAPUENSIS (Cuvier & Valenciennes) 1837
**Pl. 41**
17 cm; Sc 75–80; tr 20. Nape with a low longitudinal median crest. East Africa
and Seychelles to the E. Indies, Philippines, Melanesia and Australia.

### 1577. CALLOGOBIUS SCLATERI (Steindachner) 1880
Fringe-head goby
5 cm; Sc 30; tr 11. Head and anterior body with raised fleshy flaps and papillae.
Tail oblong. Light brown with darker mottlings and 2 dark vertical bars, one
below each dorsal fin. Coral reefs. East Indies and Melanesia.

### 1578. CRYPTOCENTRUS CRYPTOCENTRUS
Cuvier & Valenciennes 1837                                             **Pl. 41**
8 cm. Scales minute. Usually in rock pools, often living in a burrow in association with a prawn. Common in E. Africa, recorded from several widely scattered
Indo-Pacific localities, as far as Japan.

### 1579. STIGMATOGOBIUS JAVANICUS (Bleeker) 1856
6 cm. Upper jaw prominent. Body with 2–3 alternating longitudinal rows of
5 blotches; a dark oblique stripe below 1st dorsal. A dark spot between 3rd and
5th dorsal spines. East Indies, Philippines and Melanesia.

### 1580. ZONOGOBIUS SEMIDOLIATUS (Cuvier & Valenciennes 1837
**Pl. 41**
35 mm. Generally found in weedy rock pools. Andamans, E. Indies, Philippines,
Melanesia, Micronesia and Polynesia as far as Tahiti.

### 1581. AMBLYGOBIUS ALBIMACULATUS (Rüppell) 1828
White-spotted goby
12 cm; D VI; I/13–15; A I/14; Sc 50–55; tr 18–19. Back and upper sides greenish, head reddish, yellowish white below. Five to six dark vertical bands on
body. A row of violet-ringed yellow ocelli on upper part of head and neck.
Cheeks and operculum with blue ocelli and several oblique dark lines on head

and anterior body. Dorsals orange to red, other fins yellow; some black spots on 1st dorsal and one on upper part of tail base. Shallow coastal waters throughout most of the Indo-Pacific including the Red Sea and Queensland, but not in Hawaii.

**1582. AMBLYGOBIUS BYNOENSIS** (Richardson) 1844
10 cm. Olive with 2 midlateral longitudinal dark bands, upper one from snout through eye, lower one from pectoral base, ending in a black diamond-shaped spot at base of tail. A dozen dark cross-bands not reaching belly. Some red spots on head and 2 oblique red stripes on lower head. Dorsals with brown margin, broad yellow submarginal band and red vermiculations. Other fins yellowish green, anal with a dark margin. Andaman islands to the E. Indies, Philippines, Melanesia and Australia.

**1583. AWAOUS OCELLARIS** (Broussonet) 1782
26 cm. Elongate, cylindrical anteriorly, compressed posteriorly. Lips thick, upper jaw prominent. Buffish brown with numerous variable darker blotches and spots on upper sides and head. A blackish blotch at base of tail and an ocellated black spot on 1st dorsal. Two dark lines below eye and a black bar at pectoral base. Second dorsal and tail with dark spots. Estuarine waters from Arabia, Reunion, Mauritius and Madagascar to India, E. Indies, Philippines, China, Taiwan, Melanesia, Micronesia and Polynesia.

**1584. BATHYGOBIUS FUSCUS** (Rüppell) 1828      **Pl. 41**
12 cm; D VI; I/9–10; A I/8–9; Sc 38–40; tr 11–13. Variable and given to rapid colour changes, but always harmonising perfectly with the bottom of shallow tidal pools where it likes to rest motionless for long periods. Entire Indo-Pacific including the Red Sea and Hawaii.

**1585. ACENTROGOBIUS CAUERENSIS** (Bleeker) 1853      **Pl. 41**
7 cm. Colours variable, but dark vertical line through eye always present. Shallow tidal pools from E. Africa and the Seychelles to the E. Indies, Philippines and S. China.

**1586. ACENTROGOBIUS REICHEI** (Bleeker) 1853      **Pl. 41**
7 cm. Variable. Shallow rock pools from E. Africa and the Seychelles to the E. Indies.

**1587. ACENTROGOBIUS ORNATUS** (Rüppell) 1828
10 cm; D VI; I/10–11; A I/8–9; Sc 28; tr 8–9. Green to olive above, paler below; 3 purple transverse streaks and some yellow spots on head; top of head and body with irregular rows of violet spots; 2 inferior longitudinal rows of larger violet spots. Dorsals red to yellow with violet spots and streaks and oblique yellow lines. Tail orange with dark spots. Ventrals orange with violet tips; anal orange with dark margin and 2–4 basal purple streaks. Coastal waters in the entire Indo-Pacific excluding Hawaii.

**1588. CTENOGOBIUS CRINIGER** (Cuvier & Valenciennes) 1837
12 cm; D VI; I/9; A I/9; Sc 30–32; tr 11–12. Tail rounded. Second and 3rd dorsal spines sometimes prolonged into filaments. Olive to green above, orange or pearly below. Numerous irregular small blackish spots; a larger spot below 1st dorsal, one below 2nd dorsal and one on peduncle. Fins yellow with rows of dark spots. East Africa to the E. Indies, Philippines, Melanesia, New Hebrides and Queensland.

**1589. CTENOGOBIUS NEBULOSUS** (Forskål) 1775
18 cm; D VI; I/9–10; A I/9–10; Sc 27; tr 10. Pale sandy with rusty spots and
black blotches; dorsals and tail yellow with dark margins and large, rounded
dark spots. Other fins unspotted. Second dorsal spine occasionally produced.
A scavenger of shallow sheltered waters. Most of Indo-Pacific, including the
Red Sea and Queensland; not in Hawaii.

**1590. OPLOPOMUS OPLOPOMUS** (Cuvier & Valenciennes) 1837
8 cm. Light olive green with numerous scattered blue and red dots on body;
some larger dark purple spots on head and 2 longitudinal series of such spots
on body, the last one at base of tail. A large dark spot behind eye and an oblique
purplish bar below eye. First dorsal orange basally, otherwise bright pink with
faint dark dots on the spines. Second dorsal orange yellow with 2 irregular
rows of violet spots and a red margin. Tail orange with a darker longitudinal
stripe along middle rays and a purple stripe along inferior rays. Anal red with 2
longitudinal blue stripes separated by a yellow one and a double row of basal
blue spots. Red Sea and E. Africa to the Seychelles, E. Indies, Philippines,
Carolines and Society islands.

**1591. FUSIGOBIUS NEOPHYTUS** (Günther) 1877                    **Pl. 41**
10 cm. Head longer than broad, lower jaw prominent. Common in tidal pools
throughout the entire Indo-Pacific including Hawaii.

**1592. GNATHOLEPIS ANJERENSIS** Bleeker 1850
8 cm. Lower jaw not projecting, snout blunt. A prominent black bar extending
down from the eye. Strictly marine, very common from shallow water down to
15 m, usually seen sitting on sandy bottom at the base of coral heads. East
Indies, Micronesia and Polynesia to Hawaii.

**1593. QUISQUILIUS EUGENIUS** Jordan & Everman 1903          **Pl. 41**
7 cm. Very common in shallow weedy pools and sometimes occurring in great
numbers. Entire Indo-Pacific including Hawaii.

**1594. QUISQUILIUS AUREOVIRIDIS** Gosline 1903
7 cm. Sc 31. Bright greenish yellow. Generally found in 5 m of water or more.
Hawaii only.

Family ELEOTRIDAE **Gudgeons, Sleepers**
A large group of small to moderate-sized fishes which differ from the gobies in
not having the ventral fins united. Many live in brackish or fresh water, often
many miles from the sea. Some of the marine forms have the habit of hovering
in dense schools above coral heads and of darting into the coral for cover when
alarmed. Nevertheless, they are mostly bottom dwelling and solitary. Only a
selection of the more widespread and better known species can be treated here.

**1595. ASTERROPTERYX SEMIPUNCTATUS** Rüppell 1828
Star-finned Gudgeon
5 cm; D VI; I/9–11; A I/8–10; Sc 24; tr 8. Second dorsal spine much prolonged;
tail rounded, paired fins rather long; general appearance and shape not unlike
an Apogonid. Bright olive green with scattered blue dots and 2 irregular longitudinal series of black spots. Basal half of 1st dorsal black, distal part hyaline.
Second dorsal dark brown with blue dots, tail greenish, anal dark brown.
Common in shallow water on dead coral, rubble and silt. Throughout the entire
Indo-Pacific including Hawaii.

**1596. PTERELEOTRIS MICROLEPIS** (Bleeker) 1856
Long-finned Gudgeon
12 cm; D VI; I/27; A I/27; P 23; Sc 100+. Second dorsal and anal highly elevated. Tail emarginate. Green with several large blue spots on lower head and behind eye. A blue mark at pectoral axil. Twelve to fifteen narrow dull pink angled cross-bars with apices directed backwards; 4–5 narrow dull pink horizontal lines on peduncle. First dorsal pink with 2 longitudinal blue bands, 2nd dorsal and anal pinkish, tail green. East Africa and Seychelles to E. Indies and Melanesia.

**1597. PTERELEOTRIS TRICOLOR** Smith 1956 **Pl. 41**
12 cm. Rather rare; coral reefs in the W. Indian Ocean.

**1598. EVIOTA GYMNOCEPHALA** Weber 1913
Naked-headed Gudgeon
25 mm; Sc 25; tr 7. Yellowish with a series of 8 dark round spots along lower part of body; a larger round black spot above last of series on peduncle. Some smaller dark blotches on head and nape. Anal dusky. Andaman islands, E. Indies, Philippines and Melanesia, on coral reefs.

**1599. EVIOTA VERNA** Smith 1958
25 mm. Green, throat and breast blue, spotted or barred with red or brown. Some specimens with bright orange cheeks and an orange bar across pectoral base. Dorsal fins pink with small red dots on spines and rays; tail greenish with irregular transverse rows of red dots, anal red with a blue margin; pectorals greenish, ventrals bluish. Western Indian Ocean.

**1600. EVIOTA EPIPHANES** Jenkins 1903
25 mm. Each scale with a dark crescent. The smallest of Hawaiian Gobioid fishes. Very common in coral from 1.50 m to about 10 m where it can be obtained in numbers by breaking up coral heads. Hawaii only.

**1601. ELEOTRIODES STRIGATUS** (Broussonet) 1782 **Pl. 37**
15 cm. A handsome fish generally seen in small groups on sandy patches among coral. East Africa and Seychelles to the E. Indies, Philippines, Melanesia, Fiji and Tahiti.

**1602. ELEOTRIODES MURALIS** (Cuvier & Valenciennes) 1837
Lined Gudgeon
12 cm; D VI; I/12; A I/12. Pale green with blue-edged pale pink longitudinal bands. Dorsal pale green with several wavy pink bands and a large black spot behind the tip of the 3rd spine. Coral reefs from India and Ceylon to the E. Indies, Philippines, Japan, Palau islands, Australia and Fiji.

**1603. ELEOTRIODES SEXGUTTATUS** (Cuvier & Valenciennes) 1837
Blue-cheeked Gudgeon
14 cm. Body light green, head pinkish, cheeks pale bluish with 6 round blue spots. Body with 2 indistinct longitudinal pink lines from pectoral base to base of tail, connected by 7–8 pinkish cross-bars. A longitudinal series of 7–8 round blue spots behind pectoral axil; a vertical blue bar on pectoral base. First dorsal plain yellow with membranes deeply indented between spines. Second dorsal yellow with 3 longitudinal red stripes. Tail greenish with pink rays and a red bar along upper and lower margins. Anal yellow with red margin and blue submarginal line. Sandy areas among coral from E. Africa and the Seychelles to Ceylon, E. Indies, Philippines, Melanesia and Samoa.

**1604. ELEOTRIODES HELSDINGENI** Bleeker 1858     **Pl. 41**
15 cm. Rare; known from the E. Indies and from Delagoa Bay (Mozambique).

**1605. ELEOTRIODES LONGIPINNIS** (Lay & Bennett) 1839
Ocellated Gudgeon
18 cm. Greenish above, pearly pink below. Upper part of body with 4 longitudinal orange bands crossed by 8–9 dark orange saddles. A longitudinal row of
equally spaced orange ocelli ringed with red, white and blue along middle of
sides. Four red bands on head. First dorsal hyaline with faint pink oblique
lines; 2nd dorsal with last rays longer than 1st: hyaline with a yellow margin
and 3 rows of blue spots. Tail sharply pointed, hyaline with numerous blue
dots. Anal with last rays longest, hyaline with a red longitudinal stripe and
yellow margin. Coral reefs in the E. Indies, Philippines, Ryukyu islands,
Melanesia and Fiji.

**1606. PARIOGLOSSUS RAINFORDI** McCulloch 1921
Cobra-fish
5 cm; D V; I/16; A I/16. Light green with a bluish black spot at tail base.
Usually a brown band along each side, sometimes indistinct. A brown spot
behind eye, several pale blue spots on cheek and operculum. First dorsal
pinkish, 2nd dorsal yellow with dark violet base and broad pink margin. Anal
bright yellow edged with pink. Tail rounded, yellow with middle rays pink and
2 oblique darker bars; outer margins white. North Queensland, often in logs,
in the empty tunnels of other marine creatures.

**1607. HETERELEOTRIS ZONATUS** (Fowler) 1934
5 cm. Nostrils tubular; tail and fins rounded. Ground colour variable: light
yellowish brown, ochre, or pinkish with a black band from eye to lower part of
pectoral base and one between the eyes, across top of head. A broad black
vertical band below spinous dorsal, edged fore and aft with white. First dorsal
same as ground colour, but dusky anteriorly; 2nd dorsal paler with dusky
submarginal band and white margin; tail dusky with white margin, other fins
pale yellowish. Rocky areas on the E. African coast.

**1608. POGONOCULIUS ZEBRA** Fowler 1938     **Pl. 37**
10 cm. Sandy areas among coral, rare; Aldabra and the Seychelles to the E.
Indies, Philippines and S. Japan.

Suborder **Cottoidei** (= Cataphracti)

### Mail-cheeked Fishes

A varied group of small to moderate-sized carnivorous fishes characterised by
the presence of a bony stay across the cheek, between the suborbital bones and
the preoperculum. In most species this stay is part of a more complete armature
which encases the head and sometimes the body, but may be reduced to a few
bony ridges on the head, or concealed by thick skin. Mostly large-mouthed,
predatory, bottom dwelling, sedentary and solitary fishes found in all seas.
Generally marine, many have grotesque shapes and brilliant colours which

assist them to blend with the background, thus concealing them alike from predators and from potential prey. Many have poisonous spines capable of inflicting extremely painful, occasionally fatal wounds and they should all be handled with the greatest care. Despite their repulsive appearance, most of the larger species are excellent eating, but few are taken in sufficient numbers to be economically important.

Family PLATYCEPHALIDAE
**Flatheads, River Gurnards (S. Africa), Vumbama (Swahili)**
Very depressed, large-mouthed, moderate-sized fishes which spend most of their time buried in the sand or mud of the bottom with just the eyes exposed, ready to snap at any unwary fish of suitable size that may come within range. They blend well with the background, and even their pupils are obscured by a grey flap on the iris. Elongate, depressed anteriorly, cylindrical and tapering posteriorly. Head very depressed, armed with bony ridges and sharp spines. Scales small, ctenoid. Two dorsal fins, the 1st preceded by a small isolated spine. Ventrals widely separated. Lower pectoral rays free at tips. Gill openings wide. Mouth very large, with villous teeth, lower jaw protruding. Usually found in estuaries or on sand on the continental shelf, they are not true coral fishes. Excellent eating; a few species are trawled in some numbers in Australia and are economically important. Some 30 species in the tropical Indo-Pacific, one in W. Africa.

**1609. PLATYCEPHALUS INDICUS** (Linnaeus) 1758
Bar-tailed Flathead                                     Fig., p. 26
100 cm; D I; VII/i; 13; A i/12; P 18–19; L 1 62–69; tr 12/24. Spines on head low and weak; 2 bony ridges on cheek; 2 preopercular spines; no tentacle above eye. Brown spotted with reddish brown above, white below. Paired fins spotted; dorsals pale, faintly spotted. Tail yellow with white-edged dark bars through middle and oblique bars across lobes. Shallow estuarine waters from the Red Sea, E. Africa, Madagascar and the Seychelles to the E. Indies, Philippines, China, Japan, Melanesia and Australia.

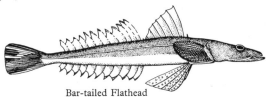
Bar-tailed Flathead

**1610. PLATYCEPHALUS CROCODILUS** Tilesius 1812
50 cm. Bony ridges and spines of head well developed; 2 preopercular spines. Scales smaller than in 1609 (L 1 85). Brown to olive grey with faint cross-bars in young and numerous round dark spots in adults. Fins dark, faintly spotted. Shallow estuarine waters from S. and E. Africa to India, the E. Indies, Philippines and S. Japan.

**1611. CYMBACEPHALUS NEMATOPHTHALMUS** (Günther) 1860
Rock Flathead
35 cm; D I, VII–VIII/i, 10–11; A I/10; P 19–20; L 1 54–55. Ridges and spines
of head strongly developed; 4 spines above eyes, 4–5 spines at top of operculum,
1–3 weak spines between eyes and 2 small spines on preopercular edge. A large
branched tentacle and several simple flaps above each eye and a deep pit behind
each eye. Brownish above with 7 dark saddles and fine pale reticulations, white
below. Fins spotted and mottled with brown and white; dorsal and tail with fine
blackish streaks, anal tips blackish. Among rocks and weeds in shallow water.
East Indies, Philippines, Melanesia and Australia.

**1612. SUGGRUNDUS HARRISII** (McCulloch) 1914
23 cm; D IX; 12; A 11–12; P 20–25; L 1 53. Eyes large, elliptical. Anterior
third of lateral line with indistinct prostrate spines. Light brown above, whitish
below; dorsal spines and rays dotted with brown; anal whitish; paired fins with
brown spots, tail with large, distinct blackish spots. Seldom seen, but taken in
numbers by the prawn trawlers along the Queensland coast.

**1613. INEGOCIA PARILIS** (McCulloch) 1914
Black-freckled Flathead
30 cm; D I, VII–VIII; 11; A 11; P 20–21; L 1 54. Ridges of head well developed,
ending in spines; ridge above eye with an anterior spine and 4–6 small posterior
spines; ridge above operculum with 4–6 strong spines; ridge between the eyes
double; 2 spines below the eye; preoperculum with 2 spines, the upper one much
longer. First 2–3 scales of lateral line with a spine. Dark brown above with 6–7
darker saddles and numerous black freckles; whitish below. Fins mottled with
brown and white forming indistinct cross-bars, but posterior $\frac{2}{3}$ of 1st dorsal
dark brown and distal part of anal dusky. New Guinea and Queensland.

**1614. COCIELLA QUOYI** (Bleeker) 1857
Quoy's Flathead
23 cm; D I, VIII; 11; A 11; L 1 48; tr 8/12. Ridges prominent and spiny.
Ridge above eye with 1 anterior spine and 4–5 posterior spines; ridge above
operculum with 6 strong spines, and 4 spines between eyes; 2 preopercular
spines. Pinkish marbled with brown above, pale below. Tail with 4 transverse
rows of dark spots; ventrals with broad bands, 2nd dorsal and pectorals with
rows of small dots. Shallow coastal waters in the E. Indies, Philippines, and
Melanesia.

Family PERISTEDIIDAE
**Armoured Sea-robins, Crocodilefish**
Curious, degenerate, bottom-dwelling fishes of deep water, found in all seas, but
very seldom seen. Elongated fishes with a large depressed head encased in bony,
spiny armour; body armoured with spiny, bony plates. Two lowest pectoral
rays free, used as feelers. Ventrals widely separated. Mouth small, inferior,
without teeth. Lower jaw with barbels and other dermal appendages. Each
preorbital bone produced into a prominent projection.

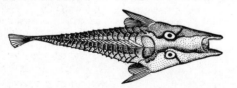
Crocodilefish

## Family TRIGLIDAE **Gurnards**

A fairly large family of small deep water bottom-dwelling fishes found in all warm seas. Elongate, armoured with large scales or bony plates. Head large, completely armoured and spiny. Lower pectoral rays free, used as feelers. Mouth small, terminal or inferior, teeth small. Excellent eating; a few species are of economic importance in S. Africa and Australia.

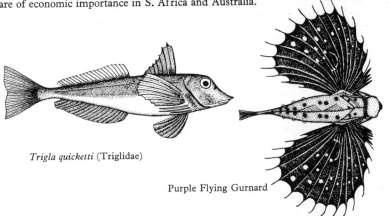

*Trigla quicketti* (Triglidae)

Purple Flying Gurnard

## Family DACTYLOPTERIDAE (= CEPHALACANTHIDAE) **Flying Gurnards**

A very small family of heavily armoured fishes with very large pectoral fins represented in most warm seas. Their systematic position is uncertain: although they resemble the gurnards and are placed next to them by most authors, the bony structure of the head is considered primitive by others who place them in a separate order (Dactyloperiformes).

Elongate and subangular in section. Head blunt in front, completely encased in very heavy bony armour, armed with very stiff spines and keels. A bony ridge across cheek. Body scales scute-like, sharply keeled, especially postero-ventrally. Lateral line absent. Dorsal fin divided, the 2 anterior spines isolated from each other and from the following spines, the 1st on nape, very elongated and carrying little membrane. Anal fin short, without spines. Pectorals very large, wing-like, upper rays shorter, forming a small, separate fin. Ventrals thoracic, consisting of 1 spine and 5 rays. Mouth small, slightly inferior; teeth, granular.

Flying gurnards spend much of their time on the bottom in shallow coastal waters, using their gorgeous pectoral fins for display and courtship. Occasionally they rise out of the water and indulge in short clumsy glides.

### 1615. DACTYLOPTENA ORIENTALIS (Cuvier & Valenciennes) 1829

Purple Flying Gurnard; Lolo-'oau (Hawaii)

40 cm; D I; I; V–VI/6–8; A 6–7; P 30–33; V I/5; Sc 43–48; tr 20–21. Greenish blue with many dark spots with orange edges on head and back; pectorals similarly marked, but brighter. Four yellow cross-bands on tail. Dorsal with a yellow band; ventrals golden yellow; juveniles with 1 large white-ringed black eye spot on pectoral. Entire Indo-Pacific, from S. Africa to Japan, Hawaii, the Tuamotu islands and Queensland.

**1616. DACTYLOPTENA PAPILIO** Ogilby 1910
Rufous Flying Gurnard
18 cm. Slaty blue with round brick red spots. Pectorals slaty blue with brick red spots, rings and reticulations; a large basal black rounded patch with several bright blue spots; margin bright yellow with bright blue markings and a narrow bright blue edge from 13th to 20th ray; free tips of rays red. Known only from Queensland, where it is occasionally caught by the prawn-trawlers.

Family TETRAROGIDAE
Small sluggish fishes with a single very long dorsal fin and a short anal fin. Gill membranes completely free from isthmus; mouth large, oblique, teeth feeble. Ventral fins thoracic, small. Scales absent, lateral line usually present. All are feeble swimmers which depend for survival on concealment and on the possession of poisonous spines. Some 25 species have been described, mostly from the tropical Indo-Pacific, several from deep water.

**1617. TETRAROGE BARBATA** (Cuvier & Valenciennes) 1829
Bearded Roguefish
10 cm; D XIII/8; A III/5–6. A pair of fleshy barbels on chin; a sharp preorbital spine reaching behind eye, 3–5 preopercular spines. Dorsal origin above eye, 2nd and 3rd spines elevated, forming a crest. Colour variable, blackish, brownish, reddish or olive, sometimes marbled or mottled. Tail with transverse bars, other fins except dorsal, darker distally, with a white margin. Shallow weedy waters. East Indies, Philippines and Melanesia.

**1618. TETRAROGE LEUCOGASTER** (Richardson) 1848
White-bellied Roguefish
5 cm. A bony arch above eye and 2–3 cirri on upper part of eye; 2 preorbital and 5 preopercular spines. Dorsal origin above eye, 1st dorsal spines not elevated, membrane incised between spines and a deep notch between spinous and soft dorsal. Brown or purplish mottled with darker above, pale below. A large dark basal spot on 5th–8th dorsal spines. Dorsals and pectorals barred or mottled with brown. Weedy places in shallow water. East Africa and the Seychelles to the E. Indies, Philippines, China, Melanesia and Australia.

**1619. GYMNAPISTES DRACAENA** (Cuvier & Valenciennes) 1829
8 cm; D XI–XII/7–8; A III/5–6. Dorsal originates above eye. Grey brown; a dark blotch between 3rd and 8th dorsal spines. Soft dorsal black posteriorly, pectorals, outer half of ventrals and anal black. Tail pale yellowish with brown dots. Ceylon and India.

**1620. GYMNAPISTES NIGER** (Cuvier & Valenciennes) 1829
Black Smooth Stingfish
7 cm. Dorsal origin above posterior third of eye; first 3–4 dorsal spines more widely spaced than remainder. Brownish black above, whitish pink below, mottled with reddish brown. Tail reddish or yellowish with a broad blackish submarginal band; all fins with a white border. Weedy areas in shallow water, often in river mouths. India, Ceylon, Andaman islands and Philippines.

**1621. AMBLYAPISTUS CRISTAGALLI** (Günther) 1860

Cockatoo Waspfish

8 cm; D XVII/7; A III/5. Scales present, but small, embedded in the skin. One blunt preorbital spine, 4 preopercular spines. Dorsal origin above front of eye; 2nd–5th dorsal spines elevated into a crest much higher than rest of fin, membrane not excised between spines and rays. Dorsal attached to tail fin. Reddish brown with dark spots; fins brown with narrow white margins, dorsal and tail with black spots. Philippines and Melanesia.

**1622. AMBLYAPISTUS BINOTATUS** (Peters) 1855

20 cm. Dorsal crest very pronounced; dorsal membranes excised between middle spines and rays. Olive grey with irregular blackish spots on sides and with a large white spot on each side, behind pectoral base and above lateral line. Western Indian Ocean, among weeds.

**1623. AMBLYAPISTUS TAENIONOTUS** (Cuvier & Valenciennes) 1829

13 cm. Very similar in appearance to 1622, but lacks silvery white spot on sides. Indian Ocean, among weeds.

**1624. PARACENTROPOGON LONGISPINIS**

(Cuvier & Valenciennes) 1829

8 cm. Dorsal crest lacking, membrane very deeply incised between all spines and rays. Olive, brown or reddish, densely speckled with blackish; a conspicuous rectangular whitish patch on side above lateral line. A black blotch between 5th and 8th dorsal spines; dorsal and pectorals with numerous irregular dark cross-bars. Indian Ocean.

**1625. SNYDERINA GUENTHERI** (Boulenger) 1899

23 cm. Dorsal, anal and tail pointed; 1st dorsal spine very short, other dorsal spines and rays of equal length. Olive brown; body and fins densely dotted with white. Rare, Persian Gulf and Gulf of Aden.

**1626. TAENIONOTUS TRIACANTHUS** Lacépède 1802     **Pl. 43**

10 cm. Very variable in colour; lies motionless or drifts slowly among the weeds, looking exactly like a dead leaf; when alarmed it sinks into the weedy growth of the bottom, becoming quite invisible. Known from scattered localities throughout the Indo-Pacific, including Kenya, Mozambique, the Seychelles and Hawaii.

Family SCORPAENIDAE

**Stingfish, Scorpionfish, Waspfish, Firefish, Lionfish, Dragonfish**

A large family of small to moderate carnivorous fishes found in all seas, but mostly around rocks and reefs in the tropics, some being known from deep water only. Head armoured and spiny, scales and lateral line normal, fin spines well developed, gill membranes free from isthmus, dermal flaps, cirri and tentacles often present; mouth large. All Scorpaenids have poisonous spines capable of inflicting extremely painful wounds; the brightly coloured and spectacular *Pterois, Pteropterus* and *Brachirus* are especially dangerous and even small specimens of these genera should always be handled with extreme care. Scorpaenids are sluggish and solitary, lying motionless and almost invisible, ready to pounce on any small fish that may come within range. Little is known of their biology, but some species are believed to be viviparous. The larger species are excellent eating, despite their repulsive appearance.

### 1627. PTEROPTERUS ANTENNATUS (Bloch) 1787          Pl. 42
Turkeyfish; Butterfly-cod
20 cm; D XII/11–12; A III/6–7; P XVII; Sc 53–55. Dorsal spines extremely poisonous. Shallow water among coral throughout the entire Indo-Pacific excluding Hawaii and Queensland.

### 1628. PTEROPTERUS MOMBASAE Smith 1957
20 cm. Similar to 1627, but head more massive, fins shorter, membranes attached to dorsal spines wider; also similar to 1630, but pectoral membranes undivided. A large white ring in front of and slightly above pectoral origin is probably diagnostic. A rare species known only from the Kenya coast.

### 1629. PTEROPTERUS RADIATUS (Cuvier & Valenciennes) 1829
Pl. 42
25 cm. Pectoral and dorsal spines extremely elongated; probably the most graceful of the butterfly-cods; a beautiful aquarium subject, but should be handled with extreme care. Shallow coral reefs from the Red Sea, E. Africa and the Seychelles to the Andamans, Malaya, Micronesia, Fiji and the Society islands.

### 1630. PTEROIS VOLITANS (Linnaeus) 1758          Pl. 42
=PTEROIS MILES (Bennett) 1828
Red Firefish; Scorpion-cod; Dragonfish; Lionfish; Laffe volante (Seychelles)
35 cm; D XIII/10–11; A III/6–7; P XIV; Sc 80–105. The largest, commonest and best known of the Scorpionfish; should be handled with extreme care. Pectoral membranes divided to the base. Common on shallow coral reefs throughout the entire Indo-Pacific excluding Hawaii.

### 1631. PTEROIS RUSSELLI Bennett 1831
=PTEROIS LUNULATA Schlegel 1842
Russell's Fire-fish
30 cm. Very similar to 1630, but tentacle above eye much smaller or absent soft dorsal, tail and anal pale pinkish without dark spots. Spines very dangerous. Coral reefs from E. Africa and the Seychelles to India, Ceylon, the E. Indies, Philippines, Japan and Queensland; much rarer than 1630.

### 1632. PTEROIS SPHEX Jordan & Everman 1903          Pl. 42
Hawaiian Fire-fish
25 cm. Paler than previous species, tentacle above eye reduced or absent pectoral membranes divided to base; as in other species, spines very dangerous. Hawaii only.

### 1633. PTEROIS MACRURUS (Alcock) 1896
30 cm. Very similar to 1630 and possibly a synonym thereof. Supposed to have larger scales and a lower fin count. Deep water in the Indian Ocean.

**634. BRACHIRUS ZEBRA** (Cuvier & Valenciennes) 1829 **Pl. 42**
**=DENDROCHIRUS ZEBRA**
Dwarf Lionfish
20 cm; D XIII/10–11; A III/6–7; Sc 45–54. Pectoral membranes undivided, pectoral spines and rays free at tips only. Spines dangerous. Coral reefs throughout most of the Indo-Pacific, but not in Hawaii.

**635. BRACHIRUS BRACHYPTERUS** (Cuvier & Valenciennes) 1829
**=DENDROCHIRUS BRACHYPTERUS** **Pl. 42**
17 cm; XIII/9; A III/5; L 1 33; tr 7/14. Pectoral membranes undivided, rays and spines free at tips only. Spines dangerous. Rarer than 1634; coral reefs throughout the Indo-Pacific including Hawaii but not Queensland.

**636. BRACHIRUS BIOCELLATUS** (Fowler) 1928
7 cm. A very long barbel from preorbital; 2 dark ocelli on soft dorsal. Four broad dark transverse bands on pectorals; ventrals dark, anal dark basally. Rare, Philippines.

**637. APISTOPS CALOUNDRA** (De Vis) 1886
Short-spined Waspfish
16 cm; D XIV/9; A III/7; L 1 25. Dorsal spines connected by slightly incised membrane; pectorals undivided, reaching tips of rays. A large white-edged black spot between 9th and 12th dorsal spines. Brownish above, pale below; cheeks with dark mottling, body with indistinct longitudinal dark bands; tail with 3 dark transverse bands. Muddy areas in Queensland and New Guinea.

**638. SCORPAENODES GUAMENSIS** (Quoy & Gaimard) 1824
Guam Scorpionfish
10 cm; D XIII/8–9; A III/4–6; L 1 22–26; tr 5/11–12. Eyes project slightly above dorsal profile. Spiny ridges on head, but no grooves across top of head. Three opercular spines. Dark reddish to dark brown with 3–5 darker irregular cross-bands and some dark spots. A white bar across peduncle; fins barred and mottled, a red spot on operculum. Usually under rocks and corals in shallow water; entire Indo-Pacific including Hawaii and Queensland.

ALLIED SPECIES:

**639. SCORPAENODES PARVIPINNIS** Garrett 15 cm. Generally red, with shorter pectorals than 1638. Hawaii only, where it is one of the commonest shallow water Scorpaenids.

**640. S. CORALLINUS** Smith 10 cm. Head rather smooth, pectorals fairly short; reddish mottled and irregularly spotted with whitish; tail and fins pale with dark spots on rays. Western Indian Ocean.

**641. S. VARIPINNIS** Smith 5 cm. A brilliantly coloured small fish; highly variegated in shades of red, yellow, lavender, white and black. A large black spot on rear part of spinous dorsal and a white-ringed black ocellus on ventral fins. Western Indian Ocean.

**642. S. SCABRA** (Ramsay & Ogilby) 9 cm. Three small spines above each eye, 2 opercular and 3 preopercular spines. Brown with 3–4 irregular, indistinct cross-bands; fins barred and spotted, paler terminally. Micronesia, Solomon islands and Fiji to Tahiti.

**1643. SCORPAENOPSIS GIBBOSA** (Bloch & Schneider) 1801 **Pl. 43**
False Stonefish
30 cm; D XII/8–10; A III/5–6; Sc 38–48; tr 7–9/16–18. Colour and markings very variable; numerous small dermal appendages. Coral and weed-covered rocks throughout the entire Indo-Pacific.

**1644. SCORPAENOPSIS CACOPSIS** Jenkins 1901 **Pl. 43**
Nohu, Omakaha
50 cm. Usually in 6 m or more of water; large specimens excellent eating. Hawaii only.

ALLIED SPECIES:
**1645. SCORPAENOPSIS ROSEA** (Day) 15 cm. Eyes elevated, with groove below. A broad tentacle above eye and others on snout, angle of mouth and under chin. Small cirri on fins. Variable, but generally rosy with 1–2 irregular grey bands and much spotting and mottling on body and fins. India and Ceylon.
**1646. S. NOVAE-GUINEAE** (C. & V.) 11 cm. Eyes prominent, tentacles well developed. Pectorals and ventrals reach vent. Pinkish rose clouded and marbled with brown. 2–3 broad oblique blackish bands. A dark basal band followed by a pale transverse band and 2 black stripes on tail; anal and dorsal with dark bands. India, Ceylon, E. Indies, Philippines, New Guinea and Solomon islands.

**1647. DENDROSCORPAENA CIRRHOSA** (Thunberg) 1793 **Pl. 43**
Hairy Stingfish; Poisson Armé (Seychelles)
25 cm; D XI–XII/9–10; A III/5; Sc 50–60. Variable. Weed-covered rocks and coral from the Red Sea, E. and S. Africa, the Seychelles and Ceylon to the E. Indies, Philippines, Japan and S.-E. to the Society islands.

**1648. NOTESTHES ROBUSTA** (Günther) 1860
Bullrout
27 cm; D XV/9; A III/5; L 1 85. Brownish olive, head reddish; heavily mottled and spotted with black, especially on back. Dorsal reddish with blackish spots and vermiculations and black tips to the spines. Basal half of tail bright red with small dark dots on the membrane, distal half heavily mottled with black, margin narrowly and irregularly whitish. Other fins with numerous dark spots. Capable of inflicting exceedingly painful wounds with its many strong spines; symptoms of severe shock can result from the sting of this species. Shallow muddy water and estuaries in Queensland and New Guinea.

**1649. SCORPAENA ALBOBRUNNEA** Günther 1874 **Pl. 43**
45 mm; D XII/10; A III/5; L 1 42–52; tr 7/12–13. Shallow coral reefs in Micronesia, the Bismarck islands, Fiji and Polynesia.

ALLIED SPECIES:
**1650. SCORPAENA CONIORTA** Jenkins A small species known from Hawaii only, where it is quite common in shallow inshore waters; the only species of the genus with normal scales below the strut across the cheek. Body and fins with numerous small black spots.
**1651. S. BALLIEUI** Sauvage 10 cm. Last dorsal ray attached to the back by a membrane; dermal flaps, cirri and colour variable; usually a large black blotch on spinous dorsal. The commonest inshore Scorpaenid in Hawaii.
**1652. S. MOSSAMBICA** Peters 12 cm. Only 4 branched rays in pectorals; tentacles above eye longer than eye diameter. Variable, but usually with several broad irregular dark bands on body, tail and fins. Tidal pools on the east coast of Africa.

**1653. S. ZANZIBARENSIS** Playfair 19 cm. Brown, variously mottled. Dorsal mottled, without black blotch. Tail with 2 light vertical bands. Anal with 3 dark longitudinal bands, pectorals with dark spots on rays. Known from scattered localities (Zanzibar, Fiji, Polynesia).

**1654. S. ASPERELLA** Bennett 11 cm. Tentacles above eye poorly developed. 6–7 dark stripes radiating from pupil, through iris. Brown to olive, much paler below, spotted and mottled with reddish; a large black blotch on posterior dorsal spines; tail and fins pale yellowish, heavily spotted and barred with reddish brown. Micronesia, Fiji and Polynesia as far as Borabora.

**1655. S. HAPLODACTYLUS** Bleeker 10 cm. Tentacle above eye short. Reddish with darker bands and mottling; fins banded, tail with a dark margin, a dark basal band and a dark median band. South and E. Africa to the E. Indies.

## 1656. PARASCORPAENA PICTA (Cuvier & Valenciennes) 1829 **Pl. 43**
Painted Stingfish
16 cm; D XII/10; A III/5; L 1 45; tr 7–8/16. Coral reefs from E. Africa and the Seychelles to the E. Indies, Philippines and New Guinea.

## 1657. PARASCORPAENA AURITA (Rüppell) 1838     **Pl. 43**
10 cm. Very variable in colour; tentacles above eye usually well developed, cirri small and dense. Weedy tidal pools in the W. Indian Ocean. Also recorded from the Red Sea and from the Solomon islands.

ALLIED SPECIES:
**1658. PARASCORPAENA ARMATA** (Sauvage) 12 cm. Interorbital concave, a deep groove below eye, 2 opercular spines. Pinkish brown with darker blotches and yellowish white spots. Head with black spots, fins yellowish brown with darker spots. India, Ceylon.

## 1659. SEBASTAPISTES BYNOENSIS (Richardson) 1845
Marbled Coral Cod; Marbled Scorpionfish (Queensland)
15 cm; D XII/10; A III/5; very spiny and capable of inflicting painful wounds despite its small size. Light yellowish brown with irregular dark markings on body and red spots on snout and lips. Tail with a dark basal band and a dark median band. Dorsal irregularly mottled with brown; anal blotched with brown and bordered with red; pectorals with 2 broad brown bands and red margin, ventrals red. Coral reefs in the E. Indies, Melanesia, Queensland and in Polynesia.

## 1660. OLIGOSCORPAENA BANDANENSIS (Bleeker) 1851
10 cm; D XII/9–10; A III/5–6; L 1 36. No tentacle above eye. Greenish above, golden below, mottled and banded with brown. Fins transversely banded with brown and rose. East Indies, Philippines, Marianas, Solomons, Samoa and Queensland.

## 1661. HYPODYTES CARINATUS (Bloch & Schneider) 1801
Ocellated Waspfish
17 cm; D XV/9; A III/7. Smoother than most Scorpaenids. A strong preopercular spine and 2 pairs of short barbels under the chin. Tail truncate. Lilac above, with darker lines and blotches, whitish on belly; head darker than back, with a short black bar at end of interorbital groove. Spinous dorsal hyaline with lilac markings and with 2 small black spots; a large black ocellus with broad white edge between 9th and 11th spines, sometimes larger; soft dorsal and tail white, spotted with lilac and with a wide submarginal lilac band. Anal white with median lilac band, pectorals and ventrals whitish. Queensland, W. Australia and India, in rather deep water.

## Family APLOACTIDAE **Velvetfish**
A small family of small shallow water tropical fishes which have the body
covered by minute dermal processes (villi) of velvety texture. First 3–4 dorsal
spines inserted well forward and detached from remainder of fin. The anal
spines may be weak or absent, the ventrals are reduced to less than 4 rays.

### 1662. ADVENTOR ELONGATUS (Whitley) 1952
Sandpaper-fish
10 cm; D III; X/10; A 11; P 14; V I/2. Brownish grey, lighter below; fins
darker than body, dorsals and tail mottled. Muddy river mouths in New Guinea
and Queensland.

Sandpaper-fish

### 1663. APLOACTIS MILESII Richardson 1850
15 cm; D XIV/14; A II/10; P 10; V I/2. First 4 dorsal spines very elevated,
forming a high crest, not separated from rest of fin. Several large tubercular
knobs on head; lateral line represented by 12 large papillae. Body and head
entirely covered by dense velvety villi. Dusky brown. Fiji and Australia.

### 1664. ANICULEROSA TAPROBANENSIS Whitley 1933
Ceylon Velvetfish
5 cm; D IV/19; A 10; P 13; V 4. Head with prominent preorbital processes;
cheeks and operculum with blunt ridges and spines. Eyes rather small. Tail
rounded, ventrals reduced. Eleven to thirteen large tubercles on lateral line.
Head, body and even fins covered with soft villi. Ceylon.

## Family CARACANTHIDAE
Very small, sluggish, almost rounded fishes found among coral heads in the
Indo-Pacific. Scales lacking, replaced by very small velvety dermal processes
(villi). Anal fin with 2 spines, pectorals with lower rays simple and thickened.
Ventrals rudimentary. Mouth small, terminal. Only 3 or 4 species are known.

### 1665. CARACANTHUS UNIPINNUS (Gray) 1831                **Pl. 43**
Penny Velvetfish
4 cm; D VII–VIII/11–14; A II/11–13. Usually motionless among coral branches
very difficult to see, but so sluggish that it can be caught with ease with one's
hands, once detected. Very shallow water and tidal pools throughout the Indo-
Pacific including Hawaii, but not in Queensland.

### 1666. CARACANTHUS MACULATUS (Gray) 1831
Red-spotted Velvetfish
4 cm. Very similar to 1665, but decorated with numerous bright red or orange
spots. Distribution and habits as above.

**1667. CARACANTHUS ZEYLONICUS** (Day) 1869
Ceylon Velvetfish
6 cm. A slight notch separating spinous from soft dorsal; 5 blunt spines on
preoperculum. Bluish above, brownish below; several series of indistinct
yellowish spots on back and sides, separated by dark reticulations. Ceylon, India,
Madagascar, E. Africa and Natal.

Family SYNANCEIIDAE **Stonefish, Devilfish, Goblinfish**
Small to moderate-sized fishes which spend most of their lives concealed in mud,
sand, weeds, or amongst rocks and coral. All have very efficient poisonous
spines; some, such as the true stonefishes, are among the most dreaded of
marine creatures. They possess bulbous venom glands at the base of the grooved
dorsal spines and are able to inject an exceedingly painful neurotoxin the effects
of which can be fatal. Grotesque, repulsive fishes with large heads and mouths;
the head is armed with raised ridges and deep cavities. There are no scales and
most species are covered by numerous warts, tentacles and cirri which make
them almost invisible when lying among weeds or coral. A single continuous
dorsal fin; pectorals large, sometimes with 1 or 2 lower rays free and finger-like.
Anal with 2–3 spines; ventrals consisting of 1 spine and 3–5 rays. Gill membranes attached to isthmus. Some 25 species are known, all from the tropical
Indo-Pacific.

**1668. MINOUS VERSICOLOR** Ogilby 1911
Plum-striped Stinger
11 cm; D VIII–IX/12–13; A 10–11; P 11+i; V I/5. A deep interorbital groove
between raised supraorbital bones. A strong keeled spine at preopercular
angle and 5 smaller projections below it. Chin with small cirri and a pair of
larger barbels farther back. Anterior part of body covered by small tubercles.
Dorsal membranes deeply incised behind first 2 dorsal spines. Light brown with
irregular purplish longitudinal bands on body; dorsal fin with irregular diagonal
purplish bands, tail with 3–4 irregular transverse bands. Muddy shallow waters,
often near river mouths; Queensland and Melanesia.

Plum-striped Stinger

**1669. MINOUS MONODACTYLUS** (Bloch & Schneider) 1801
Grey Goblinfish
12 cm; D IX–XI/9–12; A 9–11. Operculum spiny; anal spines weak; dorsal
membranes very deeply incised, spines almost free. Pectoral with basal ray
free. Grey brown to pinkish brown, variously mottled and spotted. Dorsal
with black margin, pectoral blackish with free ray white; tail with 3 vertical
dark bars. Mauritius and Ceylon to the E. Indies.

258        STINGERS, GHOULS

**1670. MINOUS TRACHYCEPHALUS** (Bleeker) 1854
12 cm; D XI/12; A II/10. Head spiny, 2 barbels under chin; dorsal membranes
not as deeply incised as in 1669. Lowest pectoral ray free. Body and fins brownish, mottled and variegated with irregular pale lines; dorsal tips darker. Rather
deep water in Natal, the E. Indies and the Philippines.

**1671. INIMICUS DIDACTYLUS** (Pallas) 1769
Demon Stinger
17 cm; D III; XIII–XIV/8–9; A II/10. Two lowest pectoral rays free; first 3
dorsal spines forming a separate crest; skin smooth and naked. Head depressed,
deeply concave in profile, with a raised knob on snout and eyes raised above
dorsal profile; head without spines. Head, lateral line, fin spines and rays
fringed with dermal appendages. Colour very variable, from brown to brick
red, variously spotted, blotched and banded with brown and white, or unmarked.
River mouths and mangrove swamps. East Indies, Malaya, Philippines, Japan
and Melanesia to the New Hebrides.

**1672. INIMICUS BARBATUS** (De Vis) 1884
Bearded Ghoul
22 cm; D III; XIII–XIV/8–9; A II/11–12. Structurally very similar to 1671;
dermal appendages more numerous and better developed. Very variable in
colour: black or brown, paler below; fins blackish, tail often with a broad pale
transverse band and pectoral sometimes similarly marked; usually a white
mark in front of each eye. Estuarine waters in Queensland.

**1673. INIMICUS FILAMENTOSUS** (Cuvier & Valenciennes) 1829
15 cm. Very similar to 1671 and 1672, but confined to the W. Indian Ocean.

*Inimicus filamentosus*

**1674. EROSA EROSA** (Cuvier & Valenciennes) 1829
Monkey Fish
12 cm; D XVII/7; A III/6. Body short and thick, naked, armed with many
dermal appendages. Head large with deep grooves; mouth large, nearly vertical.
Eyes small. Two strong preorbital spines and 5 blunt preopercular spines.
Dorsal fin continuous, membranes less deeply incised than in previous species.
Pectoral without free rays. Eleven pores on lateral line. Brown, rosy on shoulders.
A large pale patch, rosy above, yellow below, under pectorals. Soft dorsal
purple with a yellow anterior spot. Known from rather deep water in Japan and
Queensland.

**1675. CHORIDACTYLUS MULTIBARBIS** Richardson 1848
Orange-banded Goblinfish
10 cm; D XIII/9; A II/8. Head large, blunt; eye small, orbits prominent; mouth large, horizontal. A fleshy tentacle above eye and several under chin. Ventrals large, 3 lower pectoral rays free. Dorsal continuous, spinous portion less elevated than soft part; tips of spines with numerous small tentacles. Brown with a yellow mark on shoulder and 2–3 vertical orange bands; base of anal and ventrals with white dots; fins blackish, dorsal and tail with a pale band, pectorals with orange margin. East Africa, the Seychelles, India, Ceylon, Indonesia, the Philippines and China.

**1676. PELOROPSIS FRONDOSA** (Günther) 1891
Leafy Sea Goblin
25 cm; D XI; I/9; A III/5. Body with small cycloid scales; head and belly compressed. Third dorsal spine longest. Numerous large, simple and branched tentacles on head, body and fins. Red mottled with brown; a black spot on soft dorsal. Among coral and weeds in shallow water on the Ceylon pearl banks.

**1677. SYNANCEJA HORRIDA** (Linnaeus) 1766
Stonefish
60 cm (exceptional, usually does not exceed 30 cm); D XIII/6–7; A III/6; P 15–16. Brownish fawn above, paler below, irregularly mottled and reticulated, often spotted and speckled with brown or red. Inside of mouth white to pale yellow. Lies motionless and almost invisible in shallow water on mud banks, in estuaries on rocks, coral, or in sand, looking like an eroded piece of rock or coral. If touched it will immediately raise its deadly dorsal spines. Wounds from the spines are excruciatingly painful and can result in death, or gangrene and the loss of a limb. Stout foot-wear should always be worn when walking on coral reefs or in shallow water or on sandy or muddy areas. Strange looking pieces of rock or coral should always be poked with a stick, never touched with the hand. East Indies, Philippines, China, India and Australia.

**1678. SYNANCEJA TRACHYNIS** Richardson 1842
Estuarine Stonefish
32 cm; D XIII/6–7; A III/5–6; P 16. Very similar to 1677 and possibly a synonym. Head and body covered in wart-like tubercles. Very dangerous: see remarks under 1677, which apply equally to this species. Melanesia and Queensland.

**1679. SYNANCEICHTHYS VERRUCOSA** (Bloch & Schneider) 1801
Reef Stonefish; Laffe (Seychelles)                              **Pl. 43**
30 cm; D XIII/6–7; A III/5–6; P 18–19. Warts smaller than in 1678, otherwise very similar. Very dangerous: see remarks under 1677, which apply equally to this species. Usually lies motionless and almost invisible in shallow water among coral rubble. Entire Indo-Pacific, from the Red Sea and E. Africa to Tahiti, but not in Hawaii, nor in Queensland.

## Order **ECHENEIFORMES** (=Discocephali)

Curious fishes with the 1st dorsal fin modified into a sucking disc. The dorsal spines are divided and flattened to form movable vanes which are set inside a fleshy ring on top of the head. When the ring is applied to a broad surface such as the belly of a large fish or the bottom of a boat and the vanes are slightly rotated, a partial vacuum is created, causing strong suction. These fishes attach themselves to sharks and other large fishes, feeding on debris and excreta dropped by the host and in some cases on crustacean parasites of the host. One species (*Remora albescens* Temminck & Schlegel) is known to attach itself inside the gill chamber of Giant Mantas. Generally pelagic, but the young of one or two species attach themselves to quite small fishes such as parrot-fishes and snappers and may be seen close inshore, in shallow water. A single family of less than a dozen species, found in all warm seas.

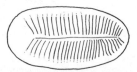

Sucking disc of Remora

### Family ECHENEIDAE **Remoras, Suckerfish, Sharksuckers**
Elongate, cylindrical or somewhat compressed. Head depressed with an oval sucker from snout to nape. Scales minute. Lateral line continuous, straight and mid-lateral. One dorsal fin, opposite to the anal. Tail emarginate to rounded. Pectorals and ventrals small. Mouth large, lower jaw protruding.

### 1680. ECHENEIS NAUCRATES Linnaeus 1758
Slender Suckerfish, Remora, Pilot-fish (N. Queensland)
90 cm; septs in disc 21–28; D 32–41; A 32–38. Tail nearly wedge-shaped. Pectorals pointed. Dark brown with a pale-edged broad blackish mid-lateral band from mouth through eye to base of tail. Fins blackish brown, a pale anterior patch on dorsal and anal. Outer rays of tail white. Coastal waters, usually associated with big sharks. Common in all warm seas.

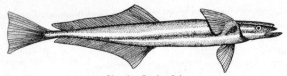

Slender Suckerfish

### 1681. REMORA REMORA (Linnaeus) 1758
Brown Remora, Short Suckerfish
45 cm; septs in disc 16–20; D 22–25; A 23–25. Tail emarginate. Pectorals short and rounded. Uniform dusky brown to almost black. Coastal waters, usually associated with large sharks, marlin or turtles. All warm seas.

## Order **TETRODONTIFORMES** (= Plectognathi)

A varied group of fishes characterised by the reduction of the opercular bones, the very small lateral gill-openings, small mouths and rudimentary or obsolete ventral fins. Mostly sluggish, solitary fishes of tropical waters, which rely for protection on spines, bony armour and on being distasteful or poisonous. The Order comprises three suborders and eleven families.

### Suborder **Balistoidei**

Deep and compressed fishes with normal teeth and a separate spinous dorsal fin, consisting of 1–6 spines; the first is usually much longer than the others and can be locked in an erect position thanks to the special structure of the bones. Ventral fins reduced to a single spine in the Triacanthidae, lacking in the other families.

### Family TRIACANTHIDAE **Triple-spines, Horn-fishes, Tripod-fishes**

A small family of warm water fishes which are less specialised than the other Balistoidei, having retained much of the spinous dorsal fin. Small fishes with strongly compressed body and slender caudal peduncle. Scales very small, not overlapping, rough to the touch. A single lateral line with several anterior branches. First dorsal consisting of 5 spines, the 1st much longer and stouter than the others, capable of being locked in an upright position. Anal spines lacking, pectorals small; ventrals reduced to a single stout spine which can be locked in position in the same way as the 1st dorsal spine. Gill-opening a narrow slit in front of pectoral base. A few species in the Indo-Pacific and one in the Atlantic, several known from deep water.

### 1682. PSEUDOTRIACANTHUS STRIGILIFER (Cantor) 1849

18 cm; D V; 22; A 15–16. Snout produced, upper profile concave; scales larger than in most species. Silvery with wide irregular yellow lines and blotches. Spinous dorsal without black spot. India, Ceylon, Indonesia, Philippines, China and Melanesia.

### 1683. TRIACANTHUS INDICUS Regan 1903

Tripod-fish
21 cm; D V; 24–25; A 18–20. Tail deeply forked. Silvery brown, darker above. First dorsal blackish anteriorly, sometimes a dark blotch below middle of soft dorsal base. India, E. Indies to Melanesia.

Tripod-fish

**1684. TRIACANTHUS BREVIROSTRIS** Temminck & Schlegel 1850
Short-nosed Tripod-fish
24 cm; D V; 22–25; A 16–20. Snout not produced, upper profile straight.
Scales very small. Silvery with a black spot on 1st dorsal and a dark blotch
above the eye. Ceylon to Indonesia, the Philippines, China, Japan and Melanesia.

**1685. TRIACANTHUS BIACULEATUS** (Bloch) 1786
Hollow-snouted Tripod-fish; Black-finned Triple-spine (Australia) 17 cm;
D V; 22–25; A 16–19. Snout produced, upper profile concave. Pale greenish,
whitish below. Most of spinous dorsal black, margin of 1st membrane yellow.
Soft dorsal and anal greyish, yellowish distally; pectorals and tail yellow; iris
brownish red. In the living fish the 1st dorsal spine is produced into a very long,
slender, brittle filament which is almost invariably lost after death. Sandy
beaches from Ceylon and India to the E. Indies, Philippines, China, Melanesia
and Queensland.

Family ALUTERIDAE (including MONACANTHIDAE)
**Filefish, Leatherjackets**
Small to moderate sized, sluggish, herbivorous fishes which differ from the
Triacanthidae in having a single dorsal spine and in lacking ventral fins. Oval to
nearly orbicular, highly compressed. Scales minute, usually with a small spine,
rough to the touch. Lateral line obscure. Two dorsal fins, the 1st consisting of a
single spine which can be locked in an erect position by a rudimentary 2nd
spine. Anal without spines, pectorals small; ventrals absent. Not generally
eaten, some species being considered poisonous. About 50 species; found in all
tropical and temperate waters, but mostly in the tropical Indo-Pacific.

**1686. ACREICHTHYS HAJAM** (Bleeker) 1852
Bristle-tailed Leatherjacket
6 cm; D I; 27–29; A 25–27. Dorsal spine inserted above eye, with 2 rows of
barbs along anterior edge and 2 rows of larger barbs along posterior edge.
Pelvic flap small; tip of pelvic bone exposed and armed with a movable barbed
spine. Tail rounded. A patch of stiff bristles on each side of peduncle and some
small scattered dermal filaments. Brown mottled with black; an irregular white
band from above pectoral tip to above vent. Two dark transverse bands on tail.
East Indies and Melanesia. See 1690.

**1687. LAPUTA CINGALENSIS** Fraser-Brunner 1941
Ceylon Leatherjacket
7 cm; D I; 28; A 28. Dorsal spine slender, armed with 2 rows of slender barbs
fore and aft. Pelvic spine movable, barbed. Grey with 4 longitudinal dark bands,
2 inner ones passing through eye. Tail with 2 dark cross-bands. Coastal waters of
Ceylon.

**1688. PERVAGOR MELANOCEPHALUS** (Bleeker) 1853    **Pl. 44**
Lace-finned Leatherjacket
12 cm; D I; 30–33; A 26–30. Barbed movable pelvic spine present. Common in
weedy areas among coral throughout the Indo-Pacific including Hawaii and
Queensland.

**1689. PERVAGOR SPILOSOMA** (Lay & Bennett) 1839          **Pl. 44**
12 cm. Hawaiian islands only; not recorded from Johnston Island. Very abundant in some years, scarce in others.

**1690. PERVAGOR TOMENTOSUS** (Linnaeus) 1758
Matted Leatherjacket
12 cm; D I; 26–29; A 25–27. Males with patch of long slender spines on either side of caudal peduncle. Brown, spotted and mottled with black; a pale band along anterior part of body. Tail with 2 dark cross-bands. Ceylon and India to the E. Indies, Philippines, China, Palau islands, Melanesia, Fiji and Australia. Possibly a senior synonym of 1686.

**1691. PARAMONACANTHUS OBLONGUS**
(Temminck & Schlegel) 1850
Hair-finned Leatherjacket
16 cm; D I; 25–28; A 25–29. Dorsal spine barbed along posterior edge only. Soft dorsal and anal elevated anteriorly, 2nd dorsal ray produced into a long free filament. Tail rounded with outer rays prolonged as free filaments. Brownish with irregular darker blotches and 3 distinct longitudinal dark bands. Japan to Melanesia and Queensland.

**1692. PARAMONACANTHUS CHOIROCEPHALUS** (Bleeker) 1852
Pig-faced Leatherjacket
D I; 28; A 28–30. Dorsal spine with rough anterior surface and 2 rows of barbs behind. Movable pelvic spine present. Tail rounded, upper ray often prolonged as a long slender free filament. Body with numerous small fleshy tentacles. Grey with large irregular black blotches. Dorsal with 2 dark bands. India, Ceylon and E. Indies.

**1693. PARAMONACANTHUS BARNARDI** Fraser-Brunner 1941
10 cm; D I; 25–27; A25–27. Pale greenish grey with irregular darker blotches and numerous small dark dots all over. Tail bluntly pointed, dark greenish grey with indistinct paler mottling. Common among weeds in shallow water along the east coast of Africa.

**1694. CHAETODERMA PENICILLIGERA** (Cuvier) 1817          **Pl. 44**
Prickly Leatherjacket
25 _m; D 26; A 24. Dorsal spine replaced by a stout branched tentacle. The specimen figured was a rather small juvenile photographed in Singapore; larger individuals tend to be less knobbly and more regular in shape. Usually found in shallow turbid water, among weeds, where the numerous branched tentacles render it almost invisible. Queensland, W. Australia, Samoa, Melanesia and the E. Indies.

**1695. MONACANTHUS MYLII** (Bory de Saint Vincent) 1822          **Pl. 44**
Centreboard Leatherjacket
25 cm; D I; 30–32; A 29–31. Old individuals have 2 short rows of barbs on each side of the caudal peduncle. The pelvic flap is greatly enlarged, extending beyond the end of the pelvic spine. Among weeds in shallow water. Indonesia and New Guinea. See 1696.

**1696. MONACANTHUS CHINENSIS** (Osbeck) 1765
Fan-bellied Leatherjacket
27 cm; D I; 29; A 29. Very similar to 1695 and possibly a senior synonym.
Dark markings apparently less distinct, barbs on peduncle smaller. Very common
in shallow weedy water in Australia, Melanesia, Polynesia, Indonesia, the
Philippines, Ryukyu islands and China.

**1697. PSEUDALUTERIUS NASICORNIS**
(Temmick & Schlegel) 1850
Rhinoceros Leatherjacket
17 cm; D I; 43–48; A 41–46. Very elongate with dorsal spine inserted well
before eye; peduncle slender, tail emarginate in adult. No pelvic flap, spine
absent. Brown with 2 darker longitudinal bands. Small white spots on belly, tail
black. Philippines, Melanesia and Japan to Mauritius and E. Africa.

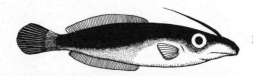

Rhinoceros Leatherjacket

**1698. ALUTERA MONOCEROS** (Linnaeus) 1758
Unicorn Leatherjacket; Loulu (Hawaii)
75 cm; D I; 45–48; A 47–53. Elongated, but profile of head blunt. Dorsal spine
short, inserted above eye. Body very compressed. Pelvic flap and spine lacking.
Skin velvety to the touch. Tail truncate. Olive brown with yellowish fins. All
warm seas.

**1699. OSBECKIA SCRIPTA** (Forster) 1771
Scribbled Leatherjacket; O'ili lepa, Ohua (Hawaii); Chien Catounou (Seychelles)
100 cm; D I; 43–50; A 46–52. Gill opening under eye; dorsal spine very weak,
often lost with age, inserted above eye. Pelvic flap and spine lacking. Tail long,
wedge-shaped. Skin velvety. Buff or olive with small black spots and short,
irregular blue lines. Flesh poisonous. Shallow weedy water, where it may often
be seen nibbling at the weeds, standing on its head. All warm seas.

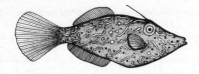

Scribbled Leatherjacket

**1700. BRACHALUTERES TROSSULUS** (Richardson) 1848
Pigmy Leatherjacket
8 cm; D I; 24–28; A 22–26. Body orbicular; pelvic flap large, but spine absent.
Dorsal spine slender, unarmed, inserted above eye. Tail rounded. Olive with
rows of brown spots; lower surface decorated with pale spots and irregular
pale lines. Shallow coastal waters. Melanesia and E. Indies.

**1701. PARALUTERES PRIONURUS** (Bleeker) 1851
Black-saddled Leatherjacket
8 cm; D; 25; A 24. Dorsal spine not fully erectile, connected to the back by
a flap of skin. Tail rounded. Pelvic flap and spine absent. A patch of stiff bristles
and 2 pairs of strong barbs on each side of caudal peduncle. Three wide black
saddles on back; numerous dark dots on head and anterior part of body. East
Africa to the E. Indies and Melanesia.

**1702. SCOBINICHTHYS GRANULATUS** (Shaw) 1790
Rough Leatherjacket
25 cm; D I; 28–30; A 26–29. Dorsal spine inserted above eye, with small barbs
along front edge, 2 rows of larger barbs on rear edge. Pelvic flap and spine
well developed. Tail rounded. Greenish with small dark dots; dark blotches
behind pectorals and blue lines below soft dorsal base, above anal base and on
pelvic flap. East Indies to Melanesia and Queensland.

**1703. AMANSES SCOPAS** (Cuvier) 1829
Brush-sided Leatherjacket
18 cm; D I; 26–29; A 23–25. Dorsal spine strong, long, unarmed, inserted
above eye. Tail rounded, pelvic flap moderate with immovable tip of pelvic
bone protruding. A patch of 5–10 very long bristles on each side in males,
shorter and erect in females. Body and fins uniform brownish black. East
Africa and Seychelles to the E. Indies, Melanesia and Polynesia.

**1704. AMANSES CAROLAE** Jordan & McGregor 1898
30 cm. Easily recognised by the presence of 4 spines directed forwards on each
side of the caudal peduncle and by the pale ring round the mouth. Hawaii to
the Sokorro islands off the coast of Mexico.

**1705. AMANSES FRONTICINCTUS** (Günther) 1866
23 cm; D I; 32–35; A 29–32. Second dorsal ray prolonged in the young. Greenish grey, yellowish below. Several faint, irregular dark longitudinal bands from
behind head to base of tail; a blackish stripe between the eyes. In weeds along
the east coast of Africa.

**1706. AMANSES PARDALIS** (Rüppell) 1835                    **Pl. 44**
18 cm; D I; 32–36; A 29–32. Pelvic spine immovable, with 5 short barbs on
each side. Markings variable. Treated as a juvenile form of 1707 by some
authors. Entire Indo-Pacific, including the Red Sea, Hawaii and Queensland.

**1707. CANTHERINES SANDWICHIENSIS**
(Quoy & Gaimard) 1824                                       **Pl 44**
38 cm; D I; 32–36; A 29–32. Dorsal spine unarmed; pelvic spine immovable.
Males with 2 pairs of small spines on each side of caudal peduncle. Variable,
spots light greenish and indistinct in some specimens. East Africa, the Seychelles
and Mauritius to the E. Indies, Philippines, Melanesia, Hawaiian, Society and
Marquesas islands. See 1706.

**1708. CANTHERINES HOWENSIS** (Ogilby) 1889               **Pl. 44**
32 cm; D I; 38; A 33. Rather rare. Known from the Solomon islands, Fiji,
Lord Howe Island and Tahiti.

**1709. STEPHANOLEPIS DIASPROS** Fraser-Brunner 1940
Reticulated Leatherjacket
23 cm; D I; 32; A 32. Dorsal spine stout and curved, with 2 posterior rows of
barbs. Tail rounded in females, somewhat angular in the males. A triangular
patch of spines on each side of caudal peduncle. Dark with fine pale reticulations.
India and Ceylon.

**1710. OXYMONACANTHUS LONGIROSTRIS**
(Bloch & Schneider) 1801                                          **Pl. 44**
Beaked Leatherjacket
8 cm; D I; 31–32; A 28–31. Dorsal spine with small barbs fore and aft. Pelvic
bone projecting and supporting a small pelvic membrane. Usually seen in small
parties of half a dozen or so, standing on their heads nibbling among coral
branches. East Africa, Seychelles and Mauritius to the E. Indies, Philippines,
Melanesia, Queensland, Guam, Fiji and Samoa.

Family ANACANTHIDAE **Tape-fish**
A family consisting of'a single rather aberrant species.

**1711. ANACANTHUS BARBATUS** (Gray) 1836
**=PSILOCEPHALUS BARBATUS**
Beardie, Tape-fish
30 cm; D I; 49; A 57. Body compressed and extremely elongate. A long fleshy
wide barbel on the chin. Spinous dorsal reduced to a single weak spine. Pelvic
flap and spine absent. Males with a narrow skinny flap from throat to vent.
Dark brown, tail with 6 dark transverse bands often broken into spots. Common
on coral reefs, mudbanks and near mangroves. Said to be able to leap a foot or
so when caught and laid on the beach. Ceylon, India, E. Indies, Philippines,
Australia.

Tape-fish

Family BALISTIDAE
**Triggerfishes, Bourses (Seychelles & Mauritius), Humuhumu (Hawaii)**
Curious brightly coloured herbivorous fishes found on coral reefs and in weedy
shallows. Very similar in shape and habits to the Aluteridae and Triacanthidae,
but they differ in having large rough scute-like scales and a 1st dorsal fin consisting of 3 spines. The 1st spine can be locked in an erect position by the 2nd
spine, but the whole fin is normally depressed into a dorsal groove when the

erect

Trigger mechanism of Balistidae
(Adapted from Smith 1949)

depressed

fish is swimming. The flesh of most triggerfishes is poisonous, but *Abalistes stellaris* is eaten in the Seychelles and *Pseudobalistes flavimarginatus* is regularly sold in the fish market in Suva (Fiji). On the E. African coast most triggerfishes are skinned as soon as they are caught and the flesh is then used for bait: they are not considered edible. Mostly shallow water inshore fishes, but several species may be found many hundreds of miles offshore sheltering among the roots and branches of drifting tree-stumps or among masses of floating sea weeds. Some 30 species are known and the family is represented in all warm seas.

**1712. XANTHICHTHYS RINGENS** (Linnaeus) 1758        **Pl. 46**
Brown-lined Triggerfish
30 cm; D III; 27–29; A 27–29; sc 37–38; tr 18. The 3 or more grooves on the head are diagnostic. Pelvic spine small, movable. Coral reefs from S. and E. Africa to the E. Indies, Melanesia, Polynesia, Hawaii, Easter Island and Clarion Island, off the Pacific coast of Mexico.

**1713. CANTHIDERMIS ROTUNDATUS** (Proce) 1822        **Pl. 45**
White-spotted Triggerfish
55 cm; D III; 26–29; A 24–26; Sc 42–57; tr 28–31. Tail trilobed and white spots more distinct in old adults. Uncommon. Coral reefs in Melanesia and Queensland. See 1714.

**1714. CANTHIDERMIS MACULATUS** (Bloch) 1786
42 cm. Very similar to 1713, but dorsal and anal fins angular. All warm seas including Hawaii.

**1715. ODONUS NIGER** (Rüppell) 1840        **Pl. 46**
Red-toothed Triggerfish
50 cm; D III; 33–36; A 30; Sc 30–35; tr 17. Variable: dark brown, blue, purple or green. May always be recognised by the strongly lunate tail, elevated fins, red teeth and the black stripe resembling a large mouth. All warm seas, but apparently not recorded from Hawaii.

**1716. ABALISTES STELLARIS** (Bloch & Schneider) 1801        **Pl. 45**
Starred Triggerfish; Bourse Nanco (Seychelles)
60 cm; D III; 26–27; A 24–26; Sc 42–46; tr 24–26. A groove before eye. Rows of tubercles or small spines on caudal peduncle. Eaten in the Seychelles. Coral reefs from the Red Sea and E. Africa to the Philippines, Melanesia, Fiji and Australia.

**1717. BALISTOIDES NIGER** (Bonnaterre) 1788        **Pl. 46**
=**B. CONSPICILLUM** (Bloch & Schneider) 1801
White-blotched Triggerfish
50 cm; D III; 25–27; A 20–22; Sc 44–54; tr 27–31. A most spectacular fish regarded as a great prize by aquarists. Widespread among shallow coral reefs, but nowhere common. East Africa, the Seychelles and Madagascar to the E. Indies, Philippines, Japan, Carolines, New Guinea, Solomons, Fiji and Queens-land.

**1718. BALISTOIDES VIRIDESCENS** (Bloch & Schneider) 1801 **Pl. 45**
60 cm; D III; 24–26; A 23–24; Sc 29–34; tr 17–18. Colour variable: fins may
be yellow, orange or reddish. Coral reefs from the Red Sea, E. Africa and the
Seychelles to the Philippines, New Guinea and Caroline islands.

**1719. HEMIBALISTES CHRYSOPTERUS**
(Bloch & Schneider) 1801                                          **Pl. 45**
30 cm; D III; 26–28; A 23–25; Sc 43–47; tr 23–26. Six to eight rows of small
spines on each side of peduncle; pelvic spine movable. Coral reefs throughout
the entire Indo-Pacific excluding Hawaii.

**1720. HEMIBALISTES BURSA** (Bloch & Schneider) 1801
22 cm; D III; 28–30; A 25–27; tr 25. Fins low; tail truncate; a groove before
eye. Several enlarged round plates behind gill-opening. Light fawn; an orange
brown V at rear of head, the anterior arm beginning below eye. A narrow straight
bluish white line from upper lip to vent. Fins and tail hyaline, light brownish.
Widespread but uncommon. Entire Indo-Pacific including Hawaii, but apparently not in Queensland.

**1721. SUFFLAMEN CAPISTRATUS** (Shaw) 1804                        **Pl. 45**
Masked Triggerfish, Bridled Triggerfish
50 cm; D III; 29–31; A 26–28; Sc 55–65; tr 34. Scales on peduncle and base
of tail armed with a rather prominent tubercle. Coral reefs in the entire Indo-
Pacific.

**1722. MELICHTHYS BUNIVA** (Lacépède) 1803                        **Pl. 46**
Black Triggerfish; Humuhumu-'ele 'ele (Hawaii)
50 cm; D III; 31–33; A 28–30; Sc 53–62; tr 26. A groove before eye; 7–8 raised
spiny ridges on caudal peduncle. Third dorsal spine minute. Coral reefs in the
E. Indies, Melanesia, Micronesia and Polynesia including Hawaii and the
Tuamotu islands.

**1723. MELICHTHYS VIDUA** (Richardson) 1844                       **Pl. 46**
White-tailed Triggerfish; Humuhumu-uli (Hawaii)
37 cm; D III; 34–35; A 30–32; Sc 60; tr 32. No spiny ridges on peduncle; 3rd
dorsal spine minute. Coral reefs throughout the entire Indo-Pacific.

**1724. PSEUDOBALISTES FUSCUS** (Bloch & Schneider) 1801  **Pl. 45**
Brown Triggerfish
50 cm; D III; 24–27; A 22–26; Sc 45–55; tr 27–31. Colour and markings
variable; vermiculations and spots may be brown, blue or green. Coral reefs
throughout the entire Indo-Pacific.

**1725. PSEUDOBALISTES FLAVIMARGINATUS** (Rüppell) 1828
                                                                  **Pl. 45**
58 cm; D III; 26–27; A 22–24; Sc 30–35; tr 19–21. Four to six rows of small
spines on posterior body. Eaten in Fiji. Coastal waters in most of the Indo-
Pacific, from the Red Sea to Japan and Tahiti, but not in Hawaii and Queensland.

**1726. BALISTES VETULA** Linnaeus 1758
Queen Triggerfish; Oldwife
50 cm; D III; 30–32; A 28–30; tr 36. Caudal peduncle smooth; anterior rays
of vertical fins and outer caudal rays strongly produced. Pinkish orange with

black lines radiating from the eyes and broader blue lines across lower part of head; 3 vertical blue bands on caudal peduncle; tail and fins pinkish bordered and lined with blue. Tropical Indian Ocean and Atlantic.

**1727. BALISTAPUS UNDULATUS** (Mungo Park) 1797          **Pl. 45**
Red-lined Triggerfish
35 cm; III; 25–27; A 22–24; Sc 40–50; tr 23–26. Caudal peduncle with 6 large spines in 2 rows. Colour variable; specimens from the Pacific tend to have a green tail with orange rays, while Indian Ocean specimens usually have a bright orange tail as figured. A common species, often seen standing on its head nibbling at the coral. Entire Indo-Pacific excluding Hawaii.

**1728. RHINECANTHUS ACULEATUS** (Linnaeus) 1758          **Pl. 46**
White-barred Triggerfish; Humuhumu-nukunuku-a-pua'a (Hawaii)
30 cm; D III; 24–25; A 21–23; Sc 38–41; tr 22–24. Three rows of spines on caudal peduncle. Entire Indo-Pacific, extremely common everywhere; often in very shallow tidal pools, but always difficult to dislodge as it wedges itself in cracks and crevices with locked dorsal spines.

**1729. RHINECANTHUS ECHARPE** (Anon.) 1789          **Pl. 46**
=**BALISTES RECTANGULUS** Bloch & Schneider 1801
Wedge-tailed Triggerfish
23 cm; D III; 22–25; A 20–22; Sc 42–45; tr 24–28. Three to five rows of re-curved spines on peduncle. Coral reefs throughout the entire Indo-Pacific; not as common as 1728.

**1730. RHINECANTHUS VERRUCOSUS** (Linnaeus) 1758          **Pl. 46**
Black-bellied Triggerfish
22 cm; D III; 24–26; A 21–22; Sc 42–43; tr 24. Two and a half to three and a half rows of recurved spines on each side of peduncle. Coral reefs from India and Mauritius to the Philippines, China, the E. Indies, New Guinea, the Palau Solomon and Society islands. Uncommon. *Balistes assasi* Forskål 1775, described from Arabia, is probably a synonym.

Suborder **Ostracioidei** (=Ostracodermi)

Family OSTRACIIDAE (=OSTRACIONTIDAE, including ARACANIDAE)
**Boxfishes, Cowfishes, Turret-fishes; Coffres (Seychelles)**
Small degenerate herbivorous fishes of shallow water and coral reefs in all tropical seas. Scales replaced by bony plates fused together to form a hard carapace which encloses the head and body. The carapace is open behind to allow free movement to the caudal peduncle in most genera; genera in which the carapace ends before the insertion of the dorsal and anal fins, such as *Aracana* and *Strophiurichthys* are placed in a separate family (Aracanidae) by some authors.
    Fins small, fin spines absent, mouth shaped like a small blunt beak, gill opening a small slit before pectoral base. Curious slow moving fishes which are reputed to be poisonous and to release toxic substances into the water when placed in an aquarium. Beautiful and quaint aquarium subjects, but for the above reason, they should not be kept with other species.

**1731. STROPHIURICHTHYS ROBUSTUS** Fraser-Brunner 1941
Robust Boxfish
25 cm; D 10; A 10. Base of dorsal and anal free of carapace; carapace with a
median ventral ridge. Yellowish brown with dark spots on back and upper
sides. Found at depths of down to 300 m and recorded from scattered localities
such as S. Africa, the Solomon islands and Queensland.

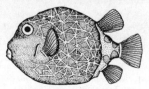

Robust Boxfish

**1732. ARACANA ACULEATA** (Houttuyn) 1782
10 cm. Dorsal and anal fins free, ventral keel well developed. Rare, known from
deep water in Japan and Hawaii.

**1733. TETRASOMUS CONCATENATUS** (Bloch) 1795
30 cm; D 9; A 9–10. Carapace triangular in section, enclosing dorsal and anal
fins; ventral keel absent. Yellow with vivid blue lines and spots. South and E.
Africa to the Seychelles, E. Indies and Japan.

*Tetrasomus concatenatus*

**1734. TETRASOMUS GIBBOSUS** (Linnaeus) 1758
30 cm; D 9; A 9. Similar to 1733 in shape, but with a sharp triangular spine
on middle of dorsal ridge. Olive brown with 3 indistinct dark bands on lower
surface; each bony plate with a central blue spot. Recorded from most of the
Indo-Pacific including the Red Sea and Queensland, but apparently absent from
Polynesia and Hawaii.

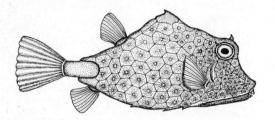

*T. gibbosus*

**1735. RHINESOMUS REIPUBLICAE** (Ogilby) 1913
Turretfish
15 cm; D 9; A 9. Carapace triangular; a spine above each eye, 2 spines on dorsal
ridge and 3 backward directed spines along each lateral ridge. All spines lost
with age. Uniform brown. Shallow coastal waters in Melanesia and Queensland.

**1736. OSTRACION SOLORENSIS** Bleeker 1856
Reticulated Boxfish
11 cm; D 9; A 9. Carapace quadrangular in section, without spines. Back and
upper sides dark with alternate black and pale blue stripes, the latter interrupted.
Males with dark-ringed bluish ocelli on sides; females with dark spots on snout
and pale reticulations on sides. Fins pale yellow, tail with a few dark spots.
East Indies, Melanesia; also recorded from Johnston Island.

**1737. OSTRACION TUBERCULATUM** Linnaeus 1758          **Pl. 47**
=**O. CUBICUM** Linnaeus 1758 (juvenile, **Pl. 47**)
Blue-spotted Boxfish; Coffre (Seychelles)
45 cm; D 9–10; A 9–10. One of the commonest species of the family; found in
the entire Indo-Pacific excluding Hawaii. The very attractive juveniles, looking
like slowly revolving yellow dice, may often be seen in shallow rock pools.

**1738. OSTRACION LENTIGINOSUM**
Bloch & Schneider 1801                                   **Pl. 47** (♀)
=**O. SEBAE** Bleeker 1851 (♂)
=**O. PUNCTATUS** Bleeker 1865 (♀)
22 cm; D 8–10; A 9. Female as illustrated. Male with plain snout, ocellated
blue spots on sides and some red between the eyes and along the dorso-lateral
ridge. Coral reefs from E. Africa and the Seychelles to the E. Indies, Philippines,
Melanesia, Hawaii and the Society islands.

**1739. RHYNCHOSTRACION NASUS** (Bloch) 1785           **Pl. 47**
Small-nosed Boxfish
20 cm; D 9; A 9. Shape of carapace as in *Ostracion*, but with a fifth ridge along
back. Colour variable, juveniles orange. Most of Indo-Pacific, but not in Hawaii.

**1740. RHYNCHOSTRACION RHINORHYNCHUS** (Bleeker) 1852
Horn-nosed Boxfish
27 cm. Fifth (dorsal) ridge present, but poorly defined, without spines. A very
large lump on snout, leaving only slight concavity before eyes. Numerous brown
dots on back and tail and sometimes on sides. Ventral surface unmarked. India
and Ceylon to the E. Indies and Philippines.

**1741. ACANTHOSTRACION PENTACANTHUS** (Bleeker) 1857
Spiny-backed Cowfish
15 cm. A spine in front of the eye and a larger one along dorsal ridge, before
insertion of fin; latero-ventral ridges terminating in a short spine. Irregularly
marked with blackish and blue. East Indies to Australia and Hawaii. See 1744.

**1742. LACTORIA CORNUTA** (Linnaeus) 1758            **Pl. 47**
Long-horned Cowfish
50 cm; D 9; A 8–9. Tail increases in length with age, becoming as long as body.
A curious slow-moving fish of shallow weedy waters. Entire Indo-Pacific
excluding Hawaii.

**1743. LACTORIA DIAPHANA** (Bloch & Schneider) 1801
25 cm; D 9; A 9. Anterior and posterior spines shorter than in foregoing
species; a small spine on each dorso-lateral ridge. The young are almost transparent. Shallow coastal waters and estuaries. Recorded from Hawaii, Australia
and S. Africa.

**1744. LACTORIA FORNASINI** (Bianconi) 1846
Described from Mozambique and since recorded from S. Africa, the Seychelles,
Ceylon and Hawaii. Apparently very similar to 1741 and probably a senior
synonym.

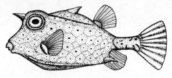

*Lactoria fornasini*

## Suborder **Tetrodontoidei**

A fairly large group of warm water fishes found in all seas. Teeth fused to form
a bony beak. Body without scales. Fin spines and ventral fins absent. Pelvic
bones not protruding through body wall. Gill opening a lateral slit. Flesh
poisonous. Most species capable of inflating the body.

### Family DIODONTIDAE **Porcupinefish, Balloonfish, Spiny Puffers**
Rounded spiny fishes of all warm seas. They differ from other puffers in having
the dental plates of the beak undivided and in being covered by fixed or erectile
spines. They are able, when alarmed, to puff themselves up into a round ball
with water or air, thus causing the spines to stand erect. Lateral line absent.
Nostrils separate and borne on a tubular papilla or confluent and each appearing
as a bifid tentacle. Usually in shallow water, among weeds or coral. Some 15
species have been described.

**1745. DICOTYLICHTHYS PUNCTULATUS** Kaup 1899
Three-bar Porcupinefish
42 cm; D 12; A 12. Nostrils carried on a fleshy bifid tentacle. Spines on head
2-rooted, erectile; other spines 3-rooted, fixed. Caudal peduncle spineless.
Three short vertical black bars on sides and numerous small round black spots
on body. Coastal waters from S. and E. Africa to the E. Indies and Melanesia.

**1746. CYCLICHTHYS ECHINATUS** (Gray) 1854
Fringed Porcupinefish
25 cm; D 12; A 11. Each nostril tubular with 2 openings. All spines 3-rooted,
immovable. Caudal peduncle spineless. Most spines provided with a flap of
skin at base. Sides of head and body with round black spots as large as pupil.
Coastal waters in all warm seas.

**1747. CYCLICHTHYS ORBICULARIS** (Bloch) 1785
20 cm; D 12; A 12. Very similar to 1746, but with a few large black spots on
back and sides. The commonest porcupinefish in S. Africa, where it is often
washed up on the beach. Throughout the tropical Indo-Pacific and Atlantic;
not so far recorded from Hawaii and Queensland.

**1748. LOPHODIODON CALORI** (Bianconi) 1855
50 cm; D 12; A 12. Spines on head with 2 roots, erectile; remaining spines
3-rooted, fixed. Two spines on each side of tail; a filament above each eye.
Whitish with 4 very irregular black saddles; eye and fins yellow, unspotted.
South and E. Africa to the Seychelles and E. Indies.

**1749. CHILOMYCTERUS AFFINIS** Günther 1870
O'opu-hue
50 cm. All spines short, broad-based, triangular and immovable. Four narrow
brown saddles. Hawaii, uncommon.

**1750. DIODON MACULIFER** Kaup 1855
Long-spined Porcupinefish
25 cm; D 12; A 12. Each nostril tubular with 2 openings. All spines 2-rooted
and movable; caudal peduncle spineless. Dark above, with irregular blackish
spots. Belly and fins unspotted. All warm seas.

**1751. DIODON HYSTRIX** Linnaeus 1758                              **Pl. 48**
Spotted Porcupinefish; Penvis (S. Africa); O'opu-kawa (Hawaii)
90 cm; D 12; A 12. Spines and nostrils as above; spines on head shorter than
on body. The largest and commonest of the porcupinefishes; they frequently
blow themselves up with air which for some reason they are unable to expel
and are often washed up inflated on the beach. All warm seas including the
Atlantic.

**1752. DIODON HOLACANTHUS** Linnaeus 1758
50 cm. Probably the juvenile of 1751. Head and body with small black dots.
A blackish collar around the throat and usually several large yellow-edged
patches on back. All warm seas.

**1753. DIODON JACULIFERUS** Cuvier & Valenciennes 1818          **Pl. 48**
25 cm; D 12; A 12. Each nostril a raised flap with an anterior and a posterior
opening. All spines fixed, with 3 roots, except 2 long ones behind each pectoral.
Most of the Indo-Pacific, excluding Hawaii; very common in Queensland.


Family CANTHIGASTERIDAE **Tobies, Sharp-nosed Puffers**
Small brightly coloured, slow-moving, solitary puffers of coral reefs. They are
capable of slight inflation only and differ from related families in having single
inconspicuous nostrils and very short gill-openings. Short and robust, slightly
compressed with a relatively sharp, long snout. Skin rough, without scales.
Lateral line absent; fin spines and ventral fins absent; tail truncate. Teeth of
both jaws fused into 2 separate plates divided by a median suture, forming a
parrot-like beak. Very variable and difficult to identify; capable of startling
colour changes when excited or alarmed. A single genus and a dozen species are
recognised, all from the tropical Indo-Pacific. Very popular aquarium subjects.

**1754. CANTHIGASTER CINCTUS** (Richardson) 1848        **Pl. 47**
Black-saddled Puffer
20 cm; D 9–10; A 8–9. As illustrated, but juveniles may have orange spots with
blue centres on pale parts. *C. valentini* (Bleeker) 1853 is almost certainly a
synonym. Coral reefs in the entire Indo-Pacific including Hawaii and Queensland.

**1755. CANTHIGASTER STRIOLATUS** (Quoy & Gaimard)
12 cm. Back and sides with fine undulating longitudinal pale and dark lines.
Tail with fine vertical undulating lines; a blue-ringed black ocellus at base of
dorsal; lower sides and head spotted with bright blue. Philippines and E.
Indies to the Solomons and New Hebrides.

**1756. CANTHIGASTER AMBOINENSIS** (Bleeker) 1865
25 cm; D 11–12; A 11. Dark olive with numerous mixed round black and light
spots. Fine blue lines radiating from eye and around snout; tail spotted. South
and E. Africa to the Seychelles, E. Indies, Philippines and Hawaii.

**1757. CANTHIGASTER SOLANDRI** Seale
12 cm. Uniform pale pinkish brown; head with blue lines; body and tail spotted
with bright blue; an oblique blue line at base of dorsal. Micronesia.

**1758. CANTHIGASTER RIVULATUS** Schlegel 1850
=**C. BITAENIATUS** Jenkins 1901
12 cm; A 10; D 10. A few spines on belly and back. Juvenile grey on snout and
back, vermiculated with black and spotted with scattered bluish dots and lines;
sides paler with 2 blackish longitudinal bands from base of tail, meeting in
front of pectoral base, which has a black spot. Adults with a broad blackish band
from chin to vent and sides reticulated with black. *C. bitaeniatus* is the juvenile
and *C. caudofasciatus* Günther 1870, described from the Indian Ocean, is almost
certainly a synonym. An uncommon fish, found down to about 80 m; known
from Natal, E. Africa and the Seychelles as *C. caudofasciatus* and from Japan
to Hawaii as *C. rivulatus*.

**1759. CANTHIGASTER BENNETTI** (Bleeker) 1854        **Pl. 47**
Bennett's Puffer
6 cm; D 9; A 8. A very common attractive little fish of tidal pools and coral
reefs. Entire Indo-Pacific excluding Hawaii.

**1760. CANTHIGASTER MARGARITATUS** (Rüppell) 1828        **Pl. 47**
Ocellated Puffer
15 cm; D 9–10; A 9–10. Similar to 1759, but larger, darker and with a spotted
tail. Common in tidal pools and coral reefs throughout most of the Indo-Pacific,
but not in Hawaii and Queensland.

**1761. CANTHIGASTER JACTATOR** Jenkins 1901        **Pl. 47**
8 cm; D 9; A 9. Coral reefs in Hawaii, where it is the commonest member of
the family.

**1762. CANTHIGASTER JANTHINOPTERUS** (Bleeker) 1860
8 cm. Very similar to 1761, but light spots smaller and more numerous; tail
darker. Uncommon. East Africa and the Seychelles to the E. Indies, Philippines,
Carolines and New Hebrides.

Family LAGOCEPHALIDAE
**Pufferfish; Toados (Australia); Blaasop (S. Africa); Tobies; Globefish**
Moderate to rather large fishes which differ from other families of puffers in the
structure of the skull and in the arrangement of the nostrils. Subcylindrical in
section; skin naked or armed with small blunt spines. Lateral line present,
branched on head, sometimes double. Fin spines and ventral fins absent. Gill-
opening a rather long slit in front of pectoral base. Teeth fused into a beak with a
median suture. Two nostrils on each side, flush with the skin, or on either side
of a raised tube. Weak swimming, slow moving, solitary fishes of shallow coastal
waters which blow themselves up like balloons when alarmed. Flesh extremely
toxic, although some species are eaten in Japan and elsewhere after special
preparation. They occur in all tropical seas and some 25 species have been
described.

**1763. GASTROPHYSUS SCELERATUS** (Gmelin) 1788        **Pl. 48**
Giant Toadfish, Silver-cheeked Toadfish; Piton (Seychelles)
75 cm; D 11–12; A 10–11. A very poisonous fish. Coastal waters from S. and E.
Africa to the E. Indies, Philippines, Japan, Melanesia, Australia and Polynesia
as far as Tahiti.

**1764. GASTROPHYSUS LUNARIS** (Bloch & Schneider) 1801
Green Toadfish
30 cm; D 11–12; A 11–14. Back in front of dorsal and entire belly covered by
small spines. Dark green above, becoming yellow on sides and white on belly.
Fins greenish yellow. Red Sea and Indian Ocean to the E. Indies, Philippines,
Japan and Melanesia. Flesh poisonous.

**1765. GASTROPHYSUS SPADICEUS** (Richardson) 1844
Brown-backed Toadfish
30 cm; D 12; A 10–12. Distribution of spines as in 1764, but absent from a large
area in front of dorsal fin. Colours as in 1764, but back usually darker. Flesh
poisonous. Distribution as in 1764, possibly only a variety of it.

**1766. GASTROPHYSUS PLEUROSTICTUS** (Günther) 1871
Banded Toado
15 cm; D 12; A 8. Greyish olive, lighter on sides, whitish on belly. Four dark
saddles which fade on lower sides. Eye black, surrounded by a patch of golden
brown or bright red. Fins pale to yellow or orange. A few dark spots on peduncle
and posterior sides. Common in estuaries in Queensland and N. Australia.

**1767. GASTROPHYSUS HAMILTONI** (Gray & Richardson) 1843
Common Toado
13 cm; D 9; A 6. Brown above, whitish below; numerous close set round black
spots on back and upper sides; cheeks with dark vertical bands and sides with
large dark blotches. Very common in shallow coastal waters in Australia,
Melanesia, Polynesia and New Zealand.

**1768. LAGOCEPHALUS INERMIS** (Schlegel) 1847
50 cm; D 12; A 11–12. Body smooth, but skin of belly granular. Greenish
above, silvery on sides and below. No spots nor markings. Flesh poisonous.
South and E. Africa to the C. Indo-Pacific.

**1769. LAGOCEPHALUS LAGOCEPHALUS** (Linnaeus) 1758
Blue Toby
60 cm; D 12; A 11–12. Spines present on belly only. Back and fins bright blue-green, sides and belly silvery white. Flesh poisonous. Primarily pelagic, but occasionally found in estuaries. Indian and Atlantic Oceans; also known from Hawaii.

**1770. TAKIFUGU OBLONGUS** (Bloch) 1786
36 cm; D 12–13; A 10–12. Two lateral lines, the lower along ventral profile, not joining upper. Tail truncate, fins angular. Back and anterior part of belly with 2-rooted spines. Brownish olive above with pale spots; lower sides and belly yellowish, dark colour of back extending to sides as irregular vertical bands. Poisonous. Known from most of the Indo-Pacific including Hawaii.

**1771. AMBLYRHYNCHOTES HYPSELOGENEION**
(Bleeker) 1852                                                        **Pl. 48**
Bar-cheeked Toadfish
18 cm; D 8–9; A 7–8. Rather strong dermal spines present on back and belly, on cheeks and in a narrow transverse band behind pectoral base. Poisonous. Most of the Indo-Pacific including the Red Sea and Hawaii, but not in Queensland.

**1772. AMBLYRHYNCHOTES SPINOSISSIMUS** (Regan) 1908
12 cm; D 8; A 6–7. Tail truncate, fins rounded. Dirty olive above, whitish on sides and below; a large indistinct dark spot behind and slightly above eye. Spiny all over, except caudal peduncle and snout. Uncommon; S. and E. Africa to the E. Indies.

Family TETRODONTIDAE (=TETRAODONTIDAE)
**Puffers, Toadfish, Blowfish, Globefish**
A fairly large family of small to moderate-sized puffers which differ from the Lagocephalidae mainly in the structure of the nostrils. Short and robust fishes with smooth skins or short embedded spines. Lateral line always present, single or double. Fins and teeth as in the Lagocephalidae. Flesh poisonous. A single nostril on each side of snout, opening variously shaped. Found in shallow coastal waters in all warm seas; a number of species enter estuaries and rivers, some living permanently in fresh water, often hundreds of miles from the sea.

**1773. CHELONODON PATOCA** (Hamilton-Buchanan) 1822
Marbled Toado
37 cm; D 9–11; A 8–10. Nostril a pit with a narrow anterior flap and a broad posterior flap. Two lateral lines; lower rather short, joined by upper lateral line above anal base. Back and belly spiny. Brown above, with large round milky spots, lower sides yellowish and belly whitish. Two or three indistinct broad dark saddles. South and E. Africa to India, the E. Indies, Philippines, China, Melanesia and Australia. Flesh poisonous.

**1774. AROTHRON IMMACULATUS** (Bloch & Schneider) 1801
Narrow-lined Toadfish
30 cm; D 9–10; A8–10. Each nostril ending in a bifid tentacle. Skin more or less prickly except on snout and posterior peduncle. Brown above, white below. Seven to nine longitudinal dark lines, one or two meeting in front of pectoral base; juveniles more heavily lined, with lines radiating from eye. Fins yellow, tail with a black margin. Coral reefs throughout most of the Indo-Pacific and Red Sea, but not in Hawaii. Flesh poisonous.

**1775. AROTHRON MAPPA** (Lesson) 1826
Scribbled Toadfish
32 cm; D 11; A 11. Nostrils as above; lateral line bent, single; spines as in 1774. Snout, back, sides, bases of fins and entire tail with dense, very irregular dark reticulations; belly with large round white spots. Poisonous. East Indies, Philippines, Melanesia, Queensland and Polynesia as far as the Society islands.

**1776. AROTHRON NIGROPUNCTATUS** (Bloch & Schneider) 1801
Black-spotted Toadfish
25 cm; D 9–10; A 9–10. Nostrils as in 1774; lateral line as in 1775. Spines variable, quite large and covering most of body in some specimens. Brownish or greenish above, paler on sides and below. Some irregularly scattered black spots. Fins unmarked; area surrounding mouth and vent blackish. Very poisonous. Entire Indo-Pacific excluding Hawaii.

**1777. AROTHRON CITRINELLUS** (Günther) 1870          **Pl. 48**
Yellow Toadfish
25 cm. Structure and distribution as for 1776; probably only a variety. Very poisonous.

**1778. AROTHRON STEIGERI** (Castelnau) 1878
10 cm. Nostrils as in 1774. Spines rather large. Dark slaty blue above, white below; back with irregularly spaced round black spots; a large dark spot at pectoral base. Queensland, originally described from the Brisbane river, and since recorded from New Guinea.

**1779. AROTHRON STELLATUS** (Bloch & Schneider) 1801          **Pl. 48**
Starry Toadfish
90 cm; D 10–11; A 10–12. Nostrils as in 1774. Lateral line as in 1775. Spines small, covering most of body. Very poisonous. Coastal waters from E. Africa and the Seychelles to the E. Indies, Melanesia and Queensland.

**1780. AROTHRON AREOSTATICUS** (Jenyns) 1842
20 cm; D 10–11; A 10–11. Nostrils as in 1774; lateral line as in 1775 and spines as above. Green or orange with numerous black spots on back and upper sides; belly with broad oblique black bands inclined down and forward. East Africa and the Seychelles to the E. Indies, Philippines, Japan and Melanesia. Poisonous.

*Arothron areostaticus*

**1781. AROTHRON HISPIDUS** (Linnaeus) 1758 **Pl. 48**
Broad-barred Toadfish; O'opu-hue, Makimaki, Keke (Hawaii)
50 cm; D 10; A 10–11. Nostrils as in 1774; lateral line as in 1775. Spines small.
Poisonous. One of the commonest and most wide-ranging species; entire
Indo-Pacific, including Hawaii and Queensland.

**1782. AROTHRON RETICULARIS** (Bloch & Schneider) 1801 **Pl. 48**
Reticulated Toadfish
42 cm; D 10–11; A 10–11. Nostrils as in 1774; lateral line as in 1775. Spines
continued to base of tail. Development of bands very variable; cheeks and
sometimes belly unmarked in juveniles. Very poisonous. India and Ceylon to
the E. Indies, Philippines, Melanesia, Fiji and Queensland.

**1783. AROTHRON MELEAGRIS** (Bloch & Schneider) 1801
30 cm. A rather short, squat fish. Entire body and fins very dark slaty grey
with dense, regularly spaced white dots. Poisonous. East Africa and Seychelles
to the E. Indies, Philippines, Hawaii and Tuamotu islands.

Family MOLIDAE **Ocean Sunfishes**
The family consists of 3 species of peculiar oceanic fishes which occur in all
seas. The body is compressed, truncate behind, without tail, looking very much
like a head without a body. The mouth is small and the teeth are fused into a
bony beak. Dorsal and anal fins high, ventrals lacking. The sunfishes are large
harmless creatures which spend their time drifting with the current at the
surface feeding on small planktonic animals. The largest species is the Ocean
Sunfish, *Mola mola* (Linnaeus) 1758, which attains 3 m in length and half a
ton in weight.

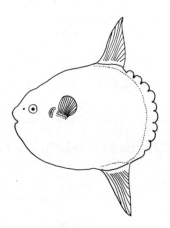

Ocean Sunfish

## Order **XENOPTERYGII**

This order comprises the single family Gobiesocidae.

Family GOBIESOCIDAE **Clingfishes**
Small rather degenerate and highly specialised fishes which occur in all temperate waters. Mainly marine, though a few species occur in fresh water. All the species lack fin spines and are scaleless; as they grow they develop a very powerful sucking disc on the ventral surface which is derived from skin folds on the belly and not from the ventral fins. They are very weak swimmers which spend most of their time clinging to rocks and other submerged objects and they are able to resist very strong currents and wave action.

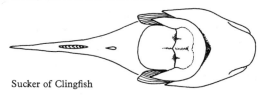

Sucker of Clingfish

**1784. LEPADICHTHYS FRENATUS** Waite 1904
Bridled Clingfish
5 cm; D 15–17; A 12–15. Pinkish yellow with a scarlet stripe from upper lip through eye to upper margin of operculum; fins hyaline. Queensland and Lord Howe Island.

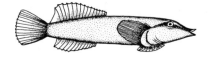

Bridled Clingfish

## Order **BATRACHOIDIFORMES** (= Haplodoci)

Family BATRACHOIDIDAE **Frogfishes**
Curious, robust, bottom-dwelling fishes with large mouths and broad depressed heads. They are closely related to the blennies and form a connecting link between those fishes and the anglerfishes. Scales absent, or concealed by thick mucus. Head and lateral line (one or more) decorated with frilly dermal appendages. Two dorsal fins, 1st armed with 3 short spines, tail rounded; ventrals inserted before pectorals. Mouth large, teeth strong.

Frogfishes are found on shallow muddy or weedy bottoms in all warm seas, some ascending rivers. They usually bury themselves in the mud, just leaving the head and mouth exposed, or conceal themselves among the weeds. When taken out of the water, or when breeding, they emit loud croaking noises. The eggs are few and large, attached to rocks, or laid in crevices and generally guarded by the males. The young look very much like tadpoles and have a

ventral sucking disc which is lost with age. The dorsal spines are poisonous and
some species have perforated opercular spines with basal poison sacks. Although
not as dangerous as stonefishes, they should be handled with care.

### 1785. PSEUDOBATRACHUS DUBIUS (Shaw) 1790
Estuarine Frogfish
30 cm; D III; 19–20; A 15–16. Body naked. Three obscure lateral lines, pores
without dermal appendages. Pectoral with a large axillary pore; head tentacles
short; 2 opercular spines and 2 subopercular spines (upper lost with age). Dark
brown with paler mottling above, dirty whitish below. Fins brown, dorsal and
anal with indistinct whitish bands, sometimes with white tips to rays. Estuaries
in New Guinea and Queensland.

### 1786. HALOPHRYNE DIEMENSIS (Le Sueur) 1824
Banded Frogfish
23 cm; D III; 19–20; A 16–17. Body naked; 3 lateral lines, each pore decorated
with a dermal appendage. Head tentacles branched. Two opercular spines and 2
subopercular spines, the lower lost with age. Purplish to black above, pearly
below. Posterior body with 4 paler cross-bands. In some individuals there is
some orange or red on the back, dorsal fin and head. Tail lilac with pale transverse bands. Paired fins violet-grey, sometimes with 2 purple cross-bands.
Shallow coastal waters from India and Ceylon to the E. Indies, Melanesia and
Queensland.

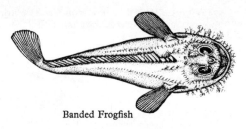

Banded Frogfish

## Order LOPHIIFORMES (=Pediculati)

### Anglerfishes, Monkfishes

Specialised, degenerate bottom-dwelling fishes. Shape variable, sometimes very
depressed, sometimes almost globular. Scales and lateral line absent; spinous
dorsal reduced, with 3–4 spines on head, the 1st of which is modified into a
fishing lure. Ventrals small when present; pectorals with a broad, elbowed
muscular base which enables the·fish to crawl on the bottom. Gill opening
small, placed in or behind the pectoral axil. Mouth very large. A few species
occur in shallow water, but the majority are deep sea creatures which lie motionless on the bottom, waving the 1st dorsal spine which carries at its tip a bulb,
a frilly flap, or even a luminous organ and acts as a lure for smaller fishes which
are engulfed by the enormous mouth. Anglerfishes are generally able to swallow
fishes considerably larger than themselves. The males of some species are small
degenerate creatures which live parasitically on the female.

## Suborder **Ceratioidei**

### Deep-sea Anglerfishes

Deep sea forms which differ from other anglerfishes in lacking ventral fins. Only the females have fishing lures, most of the males being parasitic. The following families are recognised; Melanocetidae, Ceratiidae, Diceratiidae, Centrophrynidae and Oneirodidae.

## Suborder **Lophioidei**

### Family LOPHIIDAE **Monkfish, Goosefish**

Very repulsive large-mouthed fishes of deep waters found in all temperate and tropical seas. They are the largest and least specialised of the anglerfishes and differ from the deep-sea anglers in the possession of small ventral fins. One of the best known species is the European *Lophius piscatorius*.

## Suborder **Antennarioidei**

Consists of 2 families of very different looking fishes. Both have shorter bodies than the monkfishes and well developed pectoral and ventral fins with elbow-like joints.

### Family ANTENNARIIDAE **Fishing Frogfishes**

Small flabby anglerfishes of shallow coastal waters and of tidal pools in the tropics; some species are pelagic and drift at the surface among floating masses of sea-weed. They are very sluggish and move by waddling on the bottom, but most of the time they sit motionless, waving their fishing pole and waiting to devour any small creature that they may be able to attract.

Compressed, oval, loose-skinned and sack-like. Scales absent, lateral line reduced to a few pores. The spinous dorsal fin consists of 4 spines, the 1st of which carries the fishing lure (illicium).

### 1787. HISTRIO HISTRIO (Linnaeus) 1758                    Pl. 48
Sargassum Fish
12 çm; D I, I, I/12–14; A 7–8. Skin without prickles, but with numerous weed-like appendages. Colour and markings very variable. Usually in clumps of floating sargassum weed. All tropical waters, including the Atlantic.

### 1788. GOLEM CRYPTACANTHUS (Weber) 1913
Rodless Anglerfish
8 cm; D 12–14; A 7–8. Skin smooth, without dermal appendages. Dorsal spines and illicium buried under skin. Dorsal and anal connected to the base of the tail by a membrane. Greenish with regularly spaced dark green spots on body and fins; head with irregular brown patches with red centres. Coastal waters in the E. Indies and Melanesia.

### 1789. TRIANTENNATUS ZEBRINUS (Schultz) 1957
17 cm; D I, I, I/12; A 7. Skin prickly; bait on illicium consisting of 3 fleshy tentacles. Pale brown with numerous dark zebra-like stripes breaking into spots on belly. Coastal waters in Melanesia and the E. Indies.

**1790. ANTENNATUS BIGIBBUS** (Lacépède) 1802
Reticulated Anglerfish
20 cm; D I, I, I/12; A 7. Skin prickly. Stem of illicium slender, bait a long simple filament. Head and anterior part of back plain red or orange; rest of fish covered with dark brown reticulations. Dorsal reticulated; tail and anal with a dark transverse band. Entire Indo-Pacific including Hawaii, but not in Queensland.

**1791. ANTENNARIUS OLIGOSPILOS** Bleeker 1857     **Pl. 48**
16 cm; D I, I, I/11; A 7. Colour variable, but larger spots fairly constant. Coral reefs and tidal pools from S. and E. Africa to the E. Indies.

**1792. ANTENNARIUS CHIRONEMUS** Lacépède 1802
Black Anglerfish
25 cm; D I, I, I/11–12; A 6–7. Skin prickly. Illicium very long, bait a long ribbon with some filaments attached to base. There are 2 colour phases: it may be black with whitish tips to the fins, or pale reddish brown with scattered dark spots and mottlings and a few paler ocellated spots. East Indies and Melanesia.

**1793. ANTENNARIUS HISPIDUS** (Bloch & Schneider) 1801
Zebra Anglerfish
20 cm; D I, I, I/12–13; A 7. Skin prickly. Bait of illicium a cluster of short reddish tentacles. Pinkish brown with irregular narrow blackish lines on body and radiating from eye. Chin, breast and belly with longish white dermal filaments. Dorsal with heavy broad oblique blackish bars. Tail and anal yellow with transverse rows of blackish spots. South and E. Africa to India, the E. Indies, Philippines, Melanesia and Polynesia as far as the Society islands.

**1794. ANTENNARIUS NUMMIFER** (Cuvier) 1817
Ocellated Anglerfish
16 cm; D I, I, I/13; A 7. Skin prickly; bait a tuft of filaments. Pale greyish brown mottled with darker brown. A large yellow-ringed black ocellus at base of dorsal fin. Fins yellowish with darker bands and a few black spots. The Red Sea and E. Africa to India, the E. Indies, Philippines, Melanesia and Queensland.

**1795. ANTENNARIUS DOREHENSIS** Bleeker 1859
White-spotted Anglerfish
7 cm; D I, I, I/12; A 7–8. Skin prickly. Bait a tuft of filaments. Black with small white spots all over. East Indies, the Philippines and Melanesia.

**1796. ANTENNARIUS STRIATUS** (Shaw & Nodder) 1794
Striped Angler
17 cm; D I, I, I/12. Illicium trifid. Brownish or yellowish with blackish streaks radiating from the eye and irregularly covering entire body and fins, breaking into spots on tail and belly. Known from the E. Indies, S. Africa and Queensland, where it is very common.

**1797. ANTENNARIUS MOLUCCENSIS** Bleeker 1855
30 cm; D I, I, I/13–14. Illicium long and slender, bait a bunch of short filaments. Uniform dark brown or blackish with scattered white or pinkish spots. Paired fins with a white margin. Occasionally pale brown, yellowish or red with darker spots and blotches. Known from the E. Indies, Queensland, Polynesia and Hawaii.

**798. ANTENNARIUS DROMBUS** Jordan & Everman 1903
o cm; D I, I, I/12; A 7–8. A particularly rounded lumplike species with heavy
ayers of flesh. Illicium short, the bait a rounded mass of short filaments. Many
branched tentacles on head and body, especially conspicuous on chin. Colour
nd markings very variable: plain, spotted or mottled; tail with 4 dark cross-
bands in most specimens. Hawaii.

Family OGCOCEPHALIDAE
**Handfish, Batfish, Rattlefish**
Strange, extremely flattened fishes which superficially resemble the rays. Head
very broad, depressed; mouth small, inferior. Gill openings very small, placed
bove and behind pectoral axils. Scales absent, but upper surface of head and
body covered by bony plates. Body short and slender. Spinous dorsal reduced to
a short fishing pole (illicium) which can be retracted into a special cavity on the
forehead when not in use. Soft dorsal and anal short, ventrals placed well
orward, pectorals well developed, with a strong elbowed base. Bottom-dwelling
fishes of warm seas, mostly from deep water. Some 35 species are recognised,
he majority from American waters.

*Malthopsis triangularis*, a Handfish

# References

**Allen, G. R.** 1972 Anemonefishes T.F.H. Publications, Hong Kong

**Bleeker, P.** 1877 Atlas Ichthyologique des Indes-Orientales Neerlandaise Amsterdam.

**Burgess, W. & Axelrod, H. R.** 1971 Pacific Marine Fishes (Book 1 T.F.H. Publications, Hong Kong.

**Fowler, H. W.** 1928 The Fishes of Oceania *Mem. Bishop Mus.* 10 (Honolulu) and Supplements, 1931, 1934, 1949.

— 1959 Fishes of Fiji Government of Fiji, Suva.

**Fowler, H. W. & Bean, B. A.** 1929 Fishes of the Philippines and Adjacent Seas *Bull. U.S. nat. Mus.* No. 100 (Washington).

**Gosline, W. A. & Brock, V. E.** 1960 Handbook of Hawaiian Fishes University of Hawaii Press (Honolulu).

**Herre, A. W.** 1953 Check List of Philippine Fishes Research Report 20 U.S. Dept. of the Interior.

**Klunzinger, C. B.** 1884 Die Fische des Rothen Meeres Stuttgart.

**Marshall, T. C.** 1964 Fishes of the Great Barrier Reef Angus & Robertson, Sidney.

**Munro, I. S. R.** 1955 The Marine and Fresh Water Fishes of Ceylon Dept. of External Affairs, Canberra.

— 1967 The Fishes of New Guinea Dept. of Agriculture, Port Moresby.

**Playfair, R. L. & Gunther, A. C. L. G.** 1866 The Fishes of Zanzibar London.

**Schultz, L. P.** 1953 Fishes of the Marshall and Marianas islands Vol. 1 *U.S. nat. Bull.* 202 (Washington).

**Smith, J. L. B.** 1949 The Sea Fishes of Southern Africa Central News Agency, South Africa.

— 1963 The Fishes of Seychelles Rhodes University, Grahamstown.

**Tinker, S. W.** 1944 Hawaiian Fishes Tongg Publishing Co. Honolulu.

**Weber, M. & Beaufort, L. F. de** 1936 The Fishes of the Indo-Australian Archipelago London.

# Index to Scientific Names

Figures in **bold** type refer to the species number of each fish. Plate numbers are given in *italic* type, thus '*Pl. 23*'. Page references are in normal type, thus 'p. 267'.

# Index to Common Names

Figures in **bold** type refer to the species number of each fish. Page references are in normal type.